Logic
for Problem
Solving

THE COMPUTER SCIENCE LIBRARY

Artificial Intelligence Series
NILS J. NILSSON, *Editor*

ARTIFICIAL INTELLIGENCE SERIES

7

Logic for Problem Solving

Robert Kowalski

Imperial College of Science and Technology
University of London

NORTH-HOLLAND

NEW YORK · AMSTERDAM · OXFORD

Elsevier Science Publishing Co., Inc.
52 Vanderbilt Avenue, New York, New York 10017

Sole Distributors Outside USA and Canada:
Elsevier Science Publishers B. V.
P.O. Box 211, 1000 AE Amsterdam, The Netherlands

Library of Congress Cataloging in Publication Data

Kowalski, Robert.
    Logic for problem solving.
    (Artificial intelligence series) (The Computer science library)
    Bibliography: p.
    Includes index.
    1. Problem solving. 2. Electronic digital computers—Programming.
    3. Logic, Symbolic and mathematical. 1. Title.
QA63.K68   519.7   79-22659
ISBN 0-444-00365-7 (hbk.)
ISBN 0-444-00368-1 (pbk.)

To

my parents

Table of Contents

Table of Contents

Table of Contents

Table of Contents

This book investigates the application of logic to problem-solving and computer programming. It assumes no previous knowledge of these fields, and may be appropriate therefore as an introduction to

> logic,
> the theory of problem-solving, and
> computer programming.

Logic

Logic is an important tool in the analysis and presentation of arguments. It investigates whether assumptions imply conclusions, independently of their truth or falsity and independently of their subject matter. This book aims to apply the traditional methods of logic to contemporary theories of problem-solving and computer programming.

As an introduction to logic, the book differs from others in its use of the clausal form of logic. This has several advantages. Clausal form is simpler than the standard form of logic but is just as powerful. It is simple enough to be introduced directly, without the usual preliminary study of propositional logic, and it bears greater resemblance than standard form to other formalisms used in data processing and computer programming.

This book is not concerned with the mathematics of logic but with its applications. For an interesting and more thorough discussion of the relationships between logic and language the reader is advised to consult the books by Quine [1941] and Hodges [1977].

Problem-solving

The clausal form of logic can be used to elucidate and compare models of problem-solving developed in cognitive psychology and artificial intelligence. This book investigates the heuristic search, problem-reduction and program execution models of problem-solving and argues that logical inference provides a model which is both simpler and more powerful.

The interpretation of logical inference as problem-solving builds upon the distinction between bottom-up reasoning, forward from assumptions to conclusions, and top-down reasoning, backwards from goals to subgoals.

The problem-solving interpretation of inference is primarily the top-down interpretation. Bottom-up inference is the manner in which solutions are generally presented and justified, whereas top-down inference is the manner in which solutions are most often discovered. Bottom-up inference is the synthesis of new information from old; top-down inference is the analysis of goals into subgoals.

This book covers similar ground to the problem-solving sections of the books by Nilsson [1971], Winston [1977] and Bundy et al [1978]. Where those books use production systems, LISP or LOGO as the unifying formalism, ours uses the clausal form of logic.

Computer programming

Employed as a language for communicating with computers, logic is higher-level and more human-oriented than other formalisms specifically developed for computers. In contrast with conventional computing methodology, which employs different formalisms for expressing programs, specifications, databases, queries and integrity constraints, logic provides a single uniform language for all of these tasks. We shall investigate the use of logic for databases, but concentrate on its use as a programming language.

The meaning of programs expressed in conventional languages is defined in terms of the behaviour they invoke within the computer. The meaning of programs expressed in logic, on the other hand, can be defined in machine-independent, human-oriented terms. As a consequence, logic programs are easier to construct, easier to understand, easier to improve, and easier to adapt to other purposes.

The same methods of top-down inference which give logic a problem-solving interpretation can be used to execute logic programs efficiently by means of computers. Top-down inference unifies problem-solving and computer programming. Moreover, it provides many of the facilities for intelligent program execution, such as non-determinism, parallelism, and procedure call by pattern-matching, which are under development for more conventional programming languages today. An efficient programming language, called PROLOG [Colmerauer et al 1972], [Roussel 1975], [Bruynooghe 1976], [Warren, Pereira and Pereira 1977] and [Clark and McCabe 1979], based on the clausal form of logic, has been used for applications in artificial intelligence, databases and engineering.

Mechanical theorem-proving

The use of the clausal form of logic and its associated systems of inference is based upon investigations into the mechanical proof of theorems by means of computers. The resolution rule of Robinson [1965a] and the model-elimination proof procedure of Loveland [1968, 1969] have been the main antecedents of the inference systems investigated in this book. Their inference methods in turn are based upon earlier researches by Herbrand [1930] and Prawitz [1960].

Preface

Although the inference methods in this book were originally designed for use by computers, they can also be used by human beings. The problem-solving strategies developed for efficient mechanical theorem-proving are similar to those investigated by researchers concerned with computer simulation of human problem-solving. In particular we have attempted to present a view of logic which reconciles the machine-oriented view of resolution with the heuristic proof-procedures of Bledsoe [1971, 1977] and his colleagues.

This book can be regarded as a text in the field of mechanical theorem-proving, similar to those by Chang and Lee [1973], Loveland [1978] and Robinson [1979]. It is less formal, however, and makes no attempt to give a broad coverage of the field.

Organisation of the book

The book is organised into three parts. The first part, Chapters 1 and 2, deals with the machine-independent semantics of the clausal form of logic and the use of clausal form for representing information; the second part, Chapters 3 to 8, deals with inference systems for clausal form; and the third , Chapters 9 to 13, investigates extensions of clausal form as well as more powerful problem-solving methods.

The first part of the book emphasises that logic, unlike most other formalisms, can be understood without understanding its behaviour. Examples are given of the use of logic for describing programs and databases, and clausal form is compared with semantic networks for representing the meanings of natural language sentences.

The second part of the book introduces inference methods for clausal form in stages of increasing complexity. Chapters 3 to 6 deal with inference methods for Horn clauses, which are simplified sentences, mainly of the form

$$A \quad \text{if} \quad B_1 \text{ and } B_2 \text{ and } \ldots \text{ and } B_m.$$

Top-down and bottom-up inference are introduced in Chapter 3 as generalisations of top-down and bottom-up parsing procedures for context-free grammars. Chapter 4 deals with the problem-solving interpretation of top-down inference, whereas Chapter 5 deals with its programming language interpretation. Chapter 6 describes the application of Horn clause logic to plan-formation problems. Inference methods for non-Horn clause problems and their problem-solving interpretation are investigated in Chapters 7 and 8.

Chapter 9 deals with global problem-solving methods for clausal form, whereas the remaining chapters investigate various extensions of clausal form. Although clausal form is as powerful as the standard form of logic, it is sometimes less natural. The standard form of logic and its relationship to clausal form are investigated in Chapter 10. Definitions using "if-and-only-if" are treated separately in Chapter 11. In Chapter 12 we consider an extension of logic which combines the use and mention of sentences in a manner similar to that of natural language. The final chapter deals with the dynamics of changing information systems, paying special attention to the role of contradiction in determining the direction of change. This combines the problem-solving interpretation of logic with the classical use of logic in the analysis of human knowledge and belief.

Level of the book

This book is an extension of lecture notes prepared in March 1974 [Kowalski 1974b] for an advanced course on the Foundations of Computer Science held at the Mathematics Centre in Amsterdam. Short courses on the same material were given by the author in Edinburgh, Milan, Rome and Stockholm, between 1973 and 1975. Since 1975, parts of the book have been used for introductory courses in logic and in problem-solving given to computing students at Imperial College. A complete course covering all the material in the book was given at the University of Syracuse in 1978.

The book is written at an informal level and contains almost no proofs. It assumes no previous background in logic, problem-solving or computer science, and may be suitable,therefore, for students at the first year undergraduate level. Many of the exercises, however, are of a more advanced level. Moreover, some of the discussion in Chapter 5, comparing logic with conventional programming languages, may not be completely intelliigible to readers without previous programming experience.

Acknowledgements

Much of the material in this book has been influenced by the work of my colleagues Keith Clark, Alain Colmerauer, Pat Hayes, Maarten van Emden and David Warren. I am grateful to them and to Frank Brown, Alan Bundy, Tony Hoare, Wilfred Hodges, Chris Hogger, Jan Nilsson, George Pollard, Ray Reiter, Richard Waldinger and George Winterstein, for the valuable comments they have made on earlier drafts of the book, and to Karen King, Frank McCabe, Kevin Mitchell and Chris Moss, for helping to produced the camera-ready copy. I am also happy to acknowledge the support of the Science Reseach Council.

I am especially indebted to my wife, Danusia, and children, Dania, Tania and Janina, for their patience and encouragement.

CHAPTER 1

Introduction

Logic studies the relationship of implication between assumptions and conclusions. It tells us, for example, that the assumptions

> Bob likes logic. and
> Bob likes anyone who likes logic.

imply the conclusion

> Bob likes himself.

but not the conclusion

> Bob only likes people who like logic.

Logic is concerned not with the truth, falsity or acceptability of individual sentences, but with the relationships between them. If a conclusion is implied by true or otherwise acceptable assumptions, then logic leads us to accept the conclusion. But if an unacceptable or false conclusion is implied by given assumptions, then logic advises us to reject at least one of the assumptions. Thus, if I reject the conclusion that Bob likes himself then I am logically compelled to abandon either the assumption that Bob likes logic or the assumption that Bob likes anyone who likes logic.

To demonstrate that assumptions imply a conclusion, it is helpful to construct a proof consisting of inference steps. For the proof to be convincing, the individual inference steps need to be direct and obvious and should fit together correctly. For this purpose, it is necessary that the sentences be unambiguous and it is useful if the grammar of the sentences is as simple as possible. The requirement that the language of proofs be both unambiguous and grammatically simple motivates the use of a symbolic language rather than a natural language such as English.

The symbolic language of the clausal form of logic, used in the first nine chapters of this book, is exceedingly simple. The simplest sentences are <u>atomic</u> <u>sentences</u> which name relationships between individuals:

> Bob <u>likes</u> logic.
>
> , John <u>likes</u> Mary.
>
> John <u>is</u> 2 <u>years older than</u> Mary.

(The underlined words are part of the names of relationships. Those not underlined are names of individuals.) More complex sentences express that atomic conditions imply atomic conclusions:

> Mary <u>likes</u> John if John <u>likes</u> Mary.
>
> Bob <u>likes</u> x if x <u>likes</u> logic.

Here x is a variable which names any individual. Sentences can have several joint conditions or several alternative conclusions:

> Mary <u>likes</u> John or Mary <u>likes</u> Bob if Mary <u>likes</u> x.
> (Mary likes John or Bob if she likes anything at all).
>
> x <u>likes</u> Bob if x <u>is a student of</u> Bob and x <u>likes</u> logic.

Sentences are also called <u>clauses</u>. In general, every clause expresses that a number (possibly zero) of joint conditions imply a number (possibly zero) of alternative conclusions. Conditions and conclusions express relationships among individuals. The individuals may be fixed and named by words such as

> Bob, John, logic or 2

called (somewhat confusingly, perhaps) <u>constant</u> <u>symbols</u>, or they may be arbitrary and named by <u>variables</u> such as

> u, v, w, x, y, z.

The use of <u>function</u> <u>symbols</u> to construct more complex names such as

> dad(John)   (i.e. John's dad)
>
> fraction(3,4)   (i.e. the fraction 3/4)

will be considered later.

This informal outline of the clausal form of logic will be elaborated and slightly modified in the next section of this chapter. But the great simplicity of clausal form compared with natural languages should already be apparent. It is surprising therefore that clausal form has much of the expressive power of natural language. In the last four chapters of the book we shall investigate some of the shortcomings of clausal form and propose ways of overcoming them.

The <u>family</u> <u>relationships</u> <u>example</u> <u>and</u> <u>clausal</u> <u>form</u>

It is convenient to express the <u>atomic</u> <u>formulae</u> which serve as the conditions and conclusions of clauses in a simplified, if somewhat less natural, form. The name of the relation is written in front of the atomic formula, followed by the sequence of names of individuals to which the relation applies. Thus we write Father(Zeus,Ares) instead of Zeus <u>is</u> <u>father</u> <u>of</u> Ares and Fairy-Princess(Harmonia) instead of Harmonia <u>is</u> <u>a</u> <u>fairy</u> <u>princess</u>. Here, strictly speaking, "Fairy-princess" names a property of individuals rather than a relation among individuals. However, in order to simplify the terminology, we shall include properties (also called <u>predicates</u>) when we speak of relations.

Moreover,to mix terminology thoroughly we shall refer to names of relations as <u>predicate</u> <u>symbols</u>.

We use the arrow <—, read "if", to indicate implication, writing, for example,

> Female(x) <— Mother(x,y)

to express that

> x is female if x is mother of y.

To simplify notation and the inference rules later on, it is convenient to regard all clauses as implications, even if they have no conditions or conclusions. Thus we write

> Father(Zeus,Ares) <—

instead of

> .Father(Zeus,Ares).

Implications without conclusions are denials. The clause

> <— Female(Zeus)

expresses that Zeus is not female.

The following clauses describe some of the properties and family relationships of the Greek gods.

F1   Father(Zeus,Ares) <—

F2   Mother(Hera,Ares) <—

F3   Father(Ares,Harmonia) <—

F4   Mother(Aphrodite,Harmonia) <—

F5   Father(Cadmus,Semele) <—

F6   Mother(Harmonia,Semele) <—

F7   Father(Zeus,Dionysus) <—

F8   Mother(Semele,Dionysus) <—

F9   God(Zeus) <—

F10   God(Hera) <—

F11   God(Ares) <—

F12   God(Aphrodite) <—

F13   Fairy-Princess(Harmonia) <—

The intended meaning of the clauses should be obvious. The following clauses constrain, and therefore help to clarify, their meaning.

F14   Female(x) <— Mother(x,y)

F15   Male(x) <— Father(x,y)

F16   Parent(x,y) <— Mother(x,y)

F17   Parent(x,y) <— Father(x,y)

These clauses state that, for all x and y,

        x is female if x is mother of y,

        x is male   if x is father of y,

        x is parent of y if x is mother of y, and

        x is parent of y if x is father of y.

Variables in different clauses are distinct even if they have the same name. Thus the variable x in clause F14 has no connection with the variable x in F15. The name of a variable has significance only within the context of the clause in which it occurs. Two clauses which differ only in the names of the variables they contain are equivalent and are said to be variants of one another.

In the clausal form, all the conditions of a clause are conjoined together (i.e. connected by "and"), whereas all the conclusions are disjoined (i.e. connected by "or"). Hence the connectives "and" and "or" can safely be replaced by commas. Commas between conditions, therefore, are read as "and" and between conclusions are read as "or". Thus

F18   Grandparent(x,y) <— Parent(x,z), Parent(z,y)

F19   Male(x), Female(x) <— Human(x)

where x, y and z are variables, state that for all x, y and z

        x is grandparent of y if x is parent of z and
                            z is parent of y,

        x is male or x is female if x is human.

If several conclusions are implied by the same conditions then separate clauses are needed for each conclusion. Similarly if the same conclusion is implied by alternative conditions then separate clauses are needed for each condition. For example, the sentence

        Female(x) and Parent(x,y) <— Mother(x,y)

which can be expressed directly in the standard form of logic (defined in Chapter 10) can be expressed equivalently by the clauses

$$\text{Female}(x) \; \leftarrow \; \text{Mother}(x,y)$$

$$\text{Parent}(x,y) \; \leftarrow \; \text{Mother}(x,y).$$

The two clauses are implicitly connected by "and": i.e. x is female if x is the mother of y and x is the parent of y if x is the mother of y. Similarly, the sentence

$$\text{Parent}(x,y) \; \leftarrow \; \text{Mother}(x,y) \; \underline{\text{or}} \; \text{Father}(x,y)$$

can be expressed by the clauses

$$\text{Parent}(x,y) \; \leftarrow \; \text{Mother}(x,y)$$

$$\text{Parent}(x,y) \; \leftarrow \; \text{Father}(x,y)$$

x is parent of y if x is mother of y and
x is parent of y if x is father y.

Predicate symbols can name relationships among more than two individuals. For example, the atomic formula

$$\text{Parents}(x,y,z)$$

could be used to express that

x is the father of z and y is the mother of z

i.e. $\text{Parents}(x,y,z) \; \leftarrow \; \text{Father}(x,z), \; \text{Mother}(y,z).$

A more precise definition of clausal form

We shall define the syntax (grammar) of clausal form more precisely and at the same time indicate its correspondence with English.

A clause is an expression of the form

$$B_1, \ldots, B_m \; \leftarrow \; A_1, \ldots, A_n$$

where $B_1, \ldots, B_m, A_1, \ldots, A_n$ are atomic formulae, $n \geq 0$ and $m \geq 0$. The atomic formulae $A_1, \ldots, A_n$ are the joint conditions of the clause and $B_1, \ldots, B_m$ are the alternative conclusions. If the clause contains the variables $x_1, \ldots, x_k$ then interpret it as stating that

for all $x_1, \ldots, x_k$
B_1 or ... or B_m if A_1 and ... and A_n.

If $n = 0$ then interpret it as stating unconditionally that

for all $x_1, \ldots, x_k$
B_1 or ... or B_m.

If m = 0 then interpret it as stating that

> for all $x_1,\ldots,x_k$
> it is not the case that
> A_1 and ... and A_n.

If l = n = 0 then write it as □ and interpret it as a sentence which is always false.

An <u>atom</u> (or <u>atomic formula</u>) is an expression of the form

$$P(t_1,\ldots,t_m)$$

where P is an m-place predicate symbol, $t_1,\ldots,t_m$ are terms and $m \geq 1$. Interpret the atom as asserting that the relation called P holds among the individuals called $t_1,\ldots,t_m$.

A <u>term</u> is a variable, a constant symbol or an expression of the form

$$f(t_1,\ldots,t_m)$$

where f is an m-place function symbol, $t_1,\ldots,t_m$ are terms and $m \geq 1$.

The sets of <u>predicate symbols</u>, <u>function symbols</u>, <u>constant symbols</u> and <u>variables</u> are any mutually disjoint sets. By convention, we reserve the lower case letters

$$u,v,w,x,y,z,$$

with or without adornments, for variables. The types of other kinds of symbols can be identified by the positions they occupy in clauses.

The arrow of clausal form ← is written in the opposite direction to that normally used in the standard form of logic. Where we write

B ← A   (B if A)

it is more usual to write

A → B   (if A then B).

The difference, however, is only superficial. We use the notation B ← A in order to draw attention to the conclusion of the clause.

The various places of a predicate symbol or function symbol are also called its <u>arguments</u>. In the atom $P(t_1,\ldots,t_m)$, the first argument is t_1 and the last argument is t_m.

Composite terms are needed in order to refer to infinitely many individuals using only finitely many clauses. For example, the non-negative integers can be represented by the terms

$$0, \; s(0), \; s(s(0)), \quad \ldots, \; \underbrace{s(s(\ldots s(0)\ldots))}_{n \text{ times}}, \; \ldots$$

where Ø is a constant symbol and s is a 1-place function symbol (s stands
for "successor"). The term s(t) names the number which is one larger then
the number named by the term t. It is the <u>successor</u> of t in the
succession of integers. The clauses

Num1   Numb(Ø) <—

Num2   Numb(s(x)) <— Numb(x)

state that

    Ø is a number and

    s(x) is a number if x is.

<u>Top-down</u> <u>and</u> <u>bottom-up</u> <u>presentation</u> <u>of</u> <u>definitions</u>

The definition of clausal form has been presented in a top-down
manner. The first definition explains the goal concept of clause in terms
of the concept of atomic formula, (which has not yet been defined). It
becomes the new goal concept, which in the next definition is reduced to
the two subgoal concepts of predicate symbol and term. The concept of
term is defined recursively and reduces eventually to the concepts of
constant symbol, variable and function symbol. Thus the original concept
finally reduces to the four concepts of predicate symbol, constant
symbol, variable and function symbol. It does not matter what objects
these symbols are, provided they can be distinguished from one another
and do not get confused with the "reserved" symbols:

        <— , (and)

We assume therefore that the reserved symbols are not contained within
the other symbols.

The top-down presentation of definitions has the advantage of always
being well-motivated. Its disadvantage is that, since goal concepts are
defined in terms of subgoal concepts which are not yet defined,
definitions cannot be completely understood as they are presented.

The bottom-up presentation of definitions is the opposite. It begins
with concepts which are undefined, either because they are "primitive"
and undefinable or else because they are already well understood. Then it
defines new concepts in terms of ones already given. The definitions
terminate when the goal concept has been defined. Definitions can be
understood as soon as they are given, but the motivation cannot be
appreciated until all the definitions have been completed.

The distinction between top-down and bottom-up applies not only to the
presentation of definitions, but also to the presentation and discovery
of proofs and to the writing of computer programs. Proofs can be
presented in the traditional, bottom-up, mathematical manner; reasoning
forward from what is given, deriving new conclusions from previous ones
and terminating when the goal has been derived. Alternatively, proofs can
be presented in a top-down manner which reflects the process of their
discovery; reasoning backward from the goal, by reducing goals to

subgoals and terminating when all the subgoals are recognised as
solvable.

Computer programs also can be written bottom-up, starting with
primitive programs already understood by the computer and writing new
programs in terms of old ones. At each stage the programs can be executed
by the computer and can be tested. If the low-level programs already
written cannot be put together into suitable higher-level programs, then
they have to be rewritten. Experience teaches that it is better to write
programs top-down, writing the highest-level programs first in terms of
unwritten lower-level ones. The lower-level programs are written later
and are guaranteed to fit together properly. Moreover, the lower-level
programs later can be changed and improved without affecting the rest of
the program.

Together with the utility of using symbolic logic to represent
information, the distinction between top-down and bottom-up reasoning is
one of the major themes of this book. It is the distinction between
analysis (top-down) and synthesis (bottom-up), between teleology (top-
down) and determinism (bottom-up). Moreover, the use of top-down
inference in preference to bottom-up inference reconciles the classical,
logical view of reasoning as it ought to be performed with the
psychological view of reasoning as it is performed by human beings in
practice.

Top-down reasoning relates the human problem-solving strategy of
reducing goals to subgoals to the method of executing computer programs
by replacing procedure calls with procedure bodies. It unifies the study
of logic with both the study of human problem-solving and the study of
computer programming.

Semantics of clausal form

Syntax deals with the grammar of sentences. Historically, it also
deals with inference rules and proofs. Semantics, on the other hand,
deals with meaning. The translation of clauses into English gives only an
informal guide to their semantics.

In natural languages we speak casually of words and sentences as
having meanings. In symbolic logic we are more careful. Any meaning that
might be associated with a predicate symbol, constant symbol, function
symbol or sentence is relative to the collection of sentences which
express all the relevant assumptions. In the family relationships
example, for instance, if F1-19 express all the assumptions, then there
is nothing to rule out an interpretation in which the assertion

F   Mother(Zeus,Ares) <—

holds. Such a possibility is consistent with the stated assumptions
F1-19, which alone determine any meaning that might be associated with
the symbols

        "Mother", "Father", "Zeus", etc.

To rule out the possibility F we need some additional assumption such as

F20   <— Male(x), Female(x).

F is consistent with F1-19 but inconsistent with F1-20.

Given a set of clauses which express all the assumptions concerning a problem-domain, to understand any individual symbol or clause it is necessary to determine what is logically implied by the assumptions. The meaning of a predicate symbol, such as "Mother", might be identified with the collection of all sentences which contain the predicate symbol and are logically implied by the assumptions. Thus the meaning of "Mother" in F1-20 includes the denial

F*   <— Mother(Zeus,Ares)

but the meaning of "Mother" in F1-19 does not.

It follows that it is unnecessary to talk about meaning at all. All talk about meaning can be reexpressed in terms of logical implication. To define the semantics of the clausal form of logic, therefore, it suffices to define the notion of logical implication.

In the clausal form of logic, to determine that a set of assumptions imply a conclusion we deny that the conclusion holds and show that the denial of the conclusion is inconsistent with the assumptions. The semantics of clausal form, therefore, reduces to the notion of inconsistency. To determine, for example, that the consequence F* is part of the meaning of motherhood as determined by the clauses F1-20, we show that the denial of F*, namely the assertion F, is inconsistent with F1-20. The reduction of semantics to the notion of inconsistency may seem unnatural, but it has significant computational advantages.

The inconsistency of a set of clauses can be demonstrated "semantically" by showing that no interpretation of the set of clauses makes them all true, or it can be demonstrated "syntactically" by constructing a proof consisting of inference steps. This book is about the syntactic, proof-theoretic method of demonstrating inconsistency. But, because clauses can be understood informally by translating them into English or more formally by considering the interpretations in which they are true, we shall delay the investigation of inference rules and proofs until Chapter 3.

The semantics of symbolic logic, based upon the notion of interpretation, is independent of the inference rules used to manipulate expressions in the language. This distinguishes logic from the vast majority of formalisms employed in computing and artificial intelligence. Programs expressed in normal programming languages need to be understood in terms of the behaviour they evoke inside a computer. The burden of communication falls upon the programmer, who needs to express information in machine-oriented terms. However, when programs are expressed in symbolic logic, they can be understood in terms of their human-oriented, natural language equivalents. The burden of communication then falls upon the machine, which needs to perform mechanical operations (equivalent to inference steps) to determine whether the information expressed in a program logically implies the existence of a solution to a given problem. The machine needs to be a problem-solver. The tasks of constructing proofs, executing programs and solving problems become identical. Moreover, similar problem-solving strategies apply, whether they are applied by human-beings to problems posed in natural language or by machines to problems posed in symbolic logic.

Before presenting the precise, semantic definitions of inconsistency and interpretation, we shall illustrate by examples some of the expressive capabilities of clausal form and some of the characteristics of its semantics.

The fallible Greek example

To show that the assumptions

G1   Human(Turing) <—

G2   Human(Socrates) <—

G3   Greek(Socrates) <—

G4   Fallible(x) <— Human(x)

imply the conclusion that there is a fallible Greek, we deny the conclusion

G5   <— Fallible(u), Greek(u)

and show that the resulting set of clauses is inconsistent. Moreover, the demonstration of inconsistency can be analysed to determine the reason for the inconsistency of G5 with G1-4, namely the substitution

u = Socrates

which identifies an individual that is both fallible and Greek. In this way the clause G5 can be regarded as expressing the problem of finding an individual u which is a fallible Greek. The substitution, u = Socrates, which can be extracted from the proof, can be regarded as a solution to the problem.

The example of the fallible Greek was first introduced to explain the behaviour of programs written in the programming language PLANNER [Hewitt 1969]. Our intention here is just the opposite: to show that information expressed in logic can be understood without understanding the behaviour it evokes inside a machine.

The factorial example

The fallible Greek example is not typical of programs written in conventional programming languages. However, the factorial example is.

The factorial of 0 is 1.
The factorial of x+1 is x+1 times the factorial of x.

The simplest formulation of the definition uses function symbols:

         fact(x)   names   the factorial of x,
         times(x,y)   the product of x and y,
         s(x)   x+1.

A 2-place predicate symbol expresses equality. Equal(x,y) holds when x "is" y.

         Equal(fact(0), 1) <-

         Equal(fact(s(x)), times(s(x), fact(x))) <-

To complete the definition, additional definitions are needed to characterise "times" and "Equal". The following clauses are typical of the ones which are necessary for equality.

(1)   Equal(x,x) <-

(2)   Equal(x,y) <- Equal(x,z), Equal(z,y)

(3)   Equal(fact(x), fact(y)) <- Equal(x,y)

To find the factorial of 2, for example, we deny that it exists:

(4)   <- Equal(fact(s(s(0))), w)

But (1) and (4) alone are inconsistent and the substitution

         w = fact(s(s(0)))

can be identified as the reason for inconsistency. Unfortunately, the substitution is not very informative.

    The problem is that the function symbols "fact", "times" and "s" allow numbers to be referred to by many different names. The variable-free terms

         s(s(0)),   s(1),   s(fact(0)),   s(fact(times(0, s(0)))))

all name the same number 2 and are equal to one another. The problem can be solved if individuals are given unique names. In this example it suffices to employ only the constant symbol 0 and the function symbol s. The factorial and multiplication functions can be treated as relations.

         Fact(x,y)   holds when the factorial of x is y.
         Times(x,y,z) holds when x times y is z.

Then the clauses

Fact1   Fact(0, s(0)) <-

Fact2   Fact(s(x), u) <- Fact(x,v), Times(s(x), v, u)

completely define the factorial relationship relative to an appropriate definition of multiplication. The equality relation does not appear and its definition is unnecessary. Assume that a definition of multiplication, including such clauses as

$$Times(\emptyset,x,\emptyset) \leftarrow$$

$$Times(s(\emptyset), y, y) \leftarrow$$

etc.

is provided. To solve the problem of finding the factorial of 2, we deny that it exists.

Fact3 $\leftarrow Fact(s(s(\emptyset)), w)$

The resulting set of clauses Fact1-3 is inconsistent with any definition of Times which implies the assertions

$$Times(s(s(\emptyset)), s(\emptyset), s(s(\emptyset))) \leftarrow$$

$$Times(s(\emptyset), s(\emptyset), s(\emptyset)) \leftarrow .$$

Given a demonstration of inconsistency it is possible to extract the only substitution

$$w = s(s(\emptyset))$$

which solves the problem. In this way the definition of Fact supplemented by a definition of Times serves as a program which can be used by a computer to calculate factorials. The program can be understood without understanding how the computer works.

The universe of discourse and interpretations

In this section and the next we define the semantics of clausal form. These sections are more rigorous than the rest of the chapter and may be safely skimmed through on a first reading.

The two formulations of the factorial definition illustrate a general principle of clausal writing style. To avoid problems associated with individuals having more than one name, constant symbols and function symbols should be used sparingly. If individuals are named by unique variable-free terms, then the universe of discourse of a set of clauses, which intuitively represents the collection of all individuals described by the clauses, can be identified with the collection of all variable-free terms which can be constructed from the constant symbols and function symbols occurring in the set of clauses. A candidate interpretation for a set of clauses can then be regarded as any assignment to each n-place predicate symbol occurring in the set of clauses of an n-place relation over the universe of discourse.

The assumptions G1-4 of the fallible Greek problem are a simple example. They have a small, finite universe of discourse, consisting of the two constant symbols

"Turing" and "Socrates".

To specify a candidate interpretation is to specify a relation over the universe of discourse for each of the three predicate symbols in the set of clauses. Each predicate symbol can be assigned four different interpretations and therefore the set of clauses as a whole has a total of

$$4*4*4 = 64$$

different candidate interpretations.* But only two of them make all of the clauses G1-4 true. One of them makes all of the variable-free atoms

Human(Socrates), Human(Turing),
Fallible(Socrates), Fallible(Turing),
Greek(Socrates), Greek(Turing)

true. The other makes the atoms

Human(Socrates), Human(Turing),
Fallible(Socrates), Fallible(Turing),
Greek(Socrates)

true but   Greek(Turing)

false.

The larger set of clauses G1-5 has the same universe of discourse and the same collection of 64 candidate interpretations. However, none of the 64 interpretations make all five clauses G1-5 simultaneously true. The two interpretations which make G1-4 all true make G5 false. In particular the instance

G'5 $\leftarrow$ Fallible(Socrates), Greek(Socrates)

of G5, in which u = Socrates, is false in both interpretations, because the two conditions

Fallible(Socrates) and Greek(Socrates)

denied by G'5 are true in both interpretations. Since G'5 is false in both interpretations, G5 is false also (because a clause containing variables is true in an interpretation if and only if all its instances are true and is false if one of its instances is false). Therefore G1-5 is inconsistent because there is no interpretation which makes all of its clauses true. By analysing the proof of inconsistency it is possible to identify the individual

u = Socrates

whose existence is inconsistently denied by the clause G5.

The semantic method of showing the inconsistency of a set of clauses, by demonstrating that no interpretation makes all of its clauses true, is a general method which can be used for any set of clauses. Moreover,

----

* The symbol "*" is used throughout this book for multiplication.

the interpretations which need to be considered can always be restricted to those whose domain of individuals consists of the universe of discourse. If the set of clauses contains no constant symbols, then it is necessary to include in the universe of discourse a single, arbitrary constant symbol. In this case <u>the</u> <u>universe</u> <u>of</u> <u>discourse</u> consists of all variable-free terms which can be constructed from the given constant symbol symbol and any function symbols which might occur in the set of clauses.

The inclusion of an arbitrary constant symbol in the universe of discourse, if there is none in the set of clauses, formalises the assumption that at least one individual exists. Because of this assumption, the clause

(1)   Good(x) <−

which expresses that everything is good, implies that at least one thing is good. It is inconsistent with the assumption that nothing is good

(2)   <− Good(y) .

The universe of discourse consists of some single, arbitrary constant symbol, say -◊- . There are only two candidate interpretations - one in which

            Good(-◊-) is true

the other in which

            Good(-◊-) is false.

The first interpretation falsifies (2). The second interpretation falsifies (1). So (1) and (2) are, therefore, simultaneously true in no interpretation and are inconsistent. Notice that the demonstration of inconsistency does not depend on the name of the arbitrary member of the universe of discourse. The argument is the same no matter what constant symbol is used.

The notion of interpretation itself can be simplified. To specify an interpretation it suffices to specify its effect on the truth or falsity of variable-free atomic formulae. An <u>interpretation</u> of a set of clauses, therefore, can be regarded as any assignment of either one of the two <u>truth</u> <u>values</u>

            <u>true</u> or <u>false</u>

to every every variable-free atom which can be constructed from the universe of discourse and the predicate symbols occurring in the set of clauses.

<u>A</u> <u>more</u> <u>precise</u> <u>definition</u> <u>of</u> <u>inconsistency</u>

We are now in a position to present a more precise definition of inconsistency.

> A set of clauses S is <u>inconsistent</u> if and only if it is not consistent. It is consistent if and only if all its clauses are true in some interpretation of S.
>
> A <u>clause</u> <u>is</u> <u>true</u> in an interpretation of a set of clauses S if and only if every variable-free instance of the clause, obtained by replacing variables by terms from the universe of discourse of S, is true in the interpretation. Otherwise the <u>clause</u> <u>is</u> <u>false</u> in the interpretation.
>
> A <u>variable-free</u> <u>clause</u> <u>is</u> <u>true</u> in an interpretation I if and only if whenever all of its conditions are true in I, at least one of its conclusions is true in I. Equivalently, the clause is true in I if and only if at least one of its conditions is false in I or at least one of its conclusions is true in I. Otherwise, the <u>clause</u> <u>is</u> <u>false</u> in I. ·

The precise definition of inconsistency clarifies the semantics of the empty clause, ☐. Since the empty clause has neither conditions nor conclusions it cannot possibly be true in any interpretation. It is the only clause which is self-inconsistent. To demonstrate the inconsistency of a set of clauses it suffices to demonstrate that it logically implies the obviously inconsistent empty clause. The empty set of clauses, however, is consistent. All clauses which belong to it are true in all interpretations, since it contains no clauses which can be false.

The notions of instantiation and substitution are important not only for defining the semantics of clausal form but also for defining the inference rules later on. An <u>instance</u> of a clause is obtained by applying a substitution to the clause. A <u>substitution</u> is an assignment of terms to variables. Only one term is assigned to any given variable. It is convenient to represent a substitution as a collection of independent substitution components:

$$\{x_1 = t_1, \quad x_2 = t_2, \quad ...., \quad x_m = t_m\}$$

Each component $x_i = t_i$ of the substitution assigns a term t_i to a variable x_i. The <u>result</u> of applying a substitution σ to an expression E is a new expression $E\sigma$ which is just like E except that, wherever σ contains a substitution component $x_i = t_i$ and E contains an occurrence of the variable x_i, the new expression contains an occurrence of t_i. The application of σ to E replaces all occurrences of the same variable by the same term. The <u>expression</u> E can be any term, atom, clause or set of clauses. Different variables may be replaced by the same term.

It follows that distinct variables do not necessarily refer to distinct individuals. The assumptions

L1   Likes(Bob,logic) <—

L2   Likes(Bob,x) <— Likes(x,logic)

L3   <— Likes(x,y) , Likes(y,y)
              No one likes anyone who likes himself.

for example, are inconsistent because L1 and L2 are inconsistent with the
instance

← Likes(Bob,Bob), Likes(Bob,Bob)

of L3 in which both x = Bob and y = Bob.

The semantics of alternative conclusions

The precise definition of inconsistency clarifies the semantics of
alternative conclusions. If a clause has several conclusions, then it
should be interpreted as stating that if all its conditions hold then at
least one (but possibly more) of its conclusions hold. This inclusive
interpretation of "or" contrasts with the exclusive interpretation in
which "A or B" is interpreted as expressing that either one or other of A
and B holds, but not both.

The inclusive interpretation of "or" implies, for example, that the
set of assumptions

B1   Animal(x), Mineral(x), Vegetable(x) ←

B2   Animal(x) ← Oyster(x)

B3   Mineral(x) ← Brick(x)

B4   Vegetable(x) ← Cabbage(x)

is consistent with the possibility that something is both an animal and a
vegetable:

B5   Animal(x) ← Bacterium(x)

B6   Vegetable(x) ← Bacterium(x)

B7   Bacterium(𝒪ν) ←

The exclusive sense of "or" can be captured by means of inclusive "or"
and denial. To express, for example, that every human is either male or
female but not both, requires two clauses:

Female(x), Male(x) ← Human(x)

← Female(x), Male(x), Human(x)

Horn clauses

For many applications of logic, it is sufficient to restrict the form
of clauses to those containing at most one conclusion. Clauses containing
at most one conclusion are called Horn clauses, because they were first
investigated by the logician Alfred Horn [1951]. It can be shown, in
fact, (exercise 5 in Chapter 12) that any problem which can be expressed

in logic can be reexpressed by means of Horn clauses.

The majority of formalisms for computer programming bear greater resemblence to Horn clauses than they do to "non-Horn" clauses. In addition, most of the models of problem-solving which have been developed in artificial intelligence can be regarded as models for problems expressed by means of Horn clauses.

Because Horn clauses are such an important subset of clausal form, and because inference methods for Horn clauses have a simple problem-solving and computer programming interpretation, we shall investigate them in detail (in Chapters 3-6) before investigating the full clausal form in general (in Chapters 7-8). It is important to appreciate, however, that although non-Horn clauses might be dispensible in theory they are indispensible in practice. Moreover, the extension of Horn clause problem-solving methods to clausal form in general is a significant extension of the simpler models of problem-solving which are more popular today.

Mushrooms and toadstools

A simple example which can be expressed naturally only by means of non-Horn clauses is one which expresses some typical beliefs concerning mushrooms and toadstools. Suppose I believe

(1)   Every fungus is a mushroom or a toadstool.

(2)   Every boletus is a fungus.

(3)   All toadstools are poisonous. and

(4)   No boletus is a mushroom.

Symbolically,

Fung1   Mushroom(x), Toadstool(x) <— Fungus(x)

Fung2   Fungus(x) <— Boletus(x)

Fung3   Poisonous(x) <— Toadstool(x)

Fung4   <— Boletus(x), Mushroom(x)

then I should also believe at least the more obvious of the logical consequences of my beliefs. In particular I should believe that

               All boleti are poisonous.

Fung5   Poisonous(x) <— Boletus(x)

But every collector of edible fungi knows that few boleti are poisonous and most are quite tasty. If I reject the conclusion Fung5 and maintain my belief in logic then I must reject at least one of my initial assumptions Fung1-4. It is surprising how many people abandon logic instead.

Exercises

1) Using the same vocabulary (i.e. predicate symbols, constants and function symbols) as in F1-19, express the following sentences in clausal form:

    a)   x is a mother of y if
          x is a female and x is a parent of y.

    b)   x is a father of y if
          x is a male parent of y.

    c)   x is human if
          y is a parent of x and y is human.

    d)   An individual is human if
          his (or her) mother is human and
          his (or her) father is human.

    e)   If a person is human
          then his (or her) mother is human or
          his (or her) father is human.

    f)   No one is his (or her) own parent.

2) Given clauses which define the relationships

          Father(x,y)   (x is father of y)
          Mother(x,y)   (x is mother of y)
          Male(x)   (x is male)
          Female(x)   (x is female)
          Parent(x,y)   (x is parent of y)
          Diff(x,y)   (x is different from y)

define the following additional relationships:

          M(x)   (x is a mother)
          F(x)   (x is a father)
          S(x,y)   (x is a son of y)
          D(x,y)   (x is a daughter of y)
          Gf(x,y)   (x is a grandfather of y)
          Sib(x,y)   (x is a sibling of y)

For example the clause

          Aunt(x,y) <- Female(x), Sib(x,z), Parent(z,y)

defines the relationship Aunt(x,y) (x is an aunt of y) in terms of the Female, Sib and Parent relations.

3) Let the intended interpretation of

```
Hc(x)            be      x is a heavenly creature
Wd(x)                    x is worth discussing
Star(x)                  x is a star
Comet(x)                 x is a comet
Planet(x)                x is a planet
Near(x,y)                x is near y
Ht(x)                    x has a tail.
```

a)   Express in clausal form the assumptions:

Every heavenly creature worth discussing is a star, planet
or comet.
Venus is a heavenly creature, which is not a star.
Comets near the sun have tails.
Venus is near the sun but does not have a tail.

b)   What "obvious" missing assumption needs to be added to the
clauses above for them to imply the conclusion

Venus is a planet ?

4) Using only the predicate symbols, Numb, Odd and Even, the function
symbol s, and the constant 0, express in clausal form

a)   the conditions under which a number is even,

b)   the conditions under which a number is odd,

c)   that no number is both odd and even,

d)   that a number is odd if its successor is even,

e)   that a number is even if its successor is odd,

f)   that the successor of a number is odd if the number is
even and that the successor is even if the number is odd.

5) Let the intended interpretation of

```
Parity(x,odd)     be x is odd
Parity(x,even)    be x is even.
```

Let the notion of opposite parities be expressed by the two clauses

```
Opp(odd,even) <—
Opp(even,odd) <—
```

Define the notion of a number being odd or even using only three
additional clauses, two of them variable-free assertions.

6) Inventing your own predicate symbols, express the following
assumptions in clausal form. Use only two constants, one to name my cat,
the other to name me.

Birds like worms.
Cats like fish.
Friends like each other.
My cat is my friend.
My cat eats everything it likes.

What do these assumptions imply that my cat eats?

7) Assume that arcs in a directed graph, e.g.

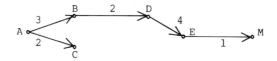

are described by assertions of the form

Distance(r,s,t) <—
(the length of the arch from r to s is t).

Thus the assertion

Distance(A,B,3) <—

describes the arc from A to B. Assume also that the relationship

Plus(x,y,z),

which holds when x+y = z, is already given. Using only one clause,
extend the definition of the relationship Dist(x,y,z) so that it
expresses that there is a path of length z from x to y.

8) Assume that the relationships

Empty (x)   (the list x is empty)
First(x,u)   (the first element of list x is u)
Rest(x,v)   (the rest of the list x following
                      the first element, is the list v)

are already given. Pictorially, the relationship

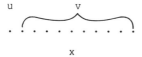

holds when both of the conditions First(x,u) and Rest(x,v) hold.

a)   Define the new relationship

Memb(z,x)   (element z is a member of list x)

in terms of the First and Rest relations. Two clauses are

necessary.

b)   Define the relationship

Sub(x,y)   (all elements of list x
                            are elements of list y)

in terms of the Empty, First, Rest and Memb relations.

c)   Assume

Plus(x,y,z)   (x + y = z)

is given. Define the relationship

Sum(x,w)   (the sum of all elements in
                            the list of numbers x is w)

in terms of the Empty, First, Rest and Plus relations.

9) Using predicate symbols of your own invention, but no function
symbols or constants, express the following sentences in clausal form:

        No dragon who lives in a zoo is happy.
        Any animal who meets kind people is happy.
        People who visit zoos are kind.
        Animals who live in zoos meet the people who visit zoos.

What two missing additional assumptions are needed to justify the
conclusion

        No dragon lives in a zoo. ?

        10) There are four different variable-free atoms which can be
constructed from the vocabulary of clauses L1-3. Consequently there are
16 different interpretations of L1-3.   How many of these interpretations
make both L1 and L2 true? How many make L3 true? How many make all of
L1-3 true?

CHAPTER 2

Representation in Clausal Form

In order to construct a mechanical problem-solving system, it is necessary to express information in an unambiguous language. Moreover, for the system also to serve as a model of human problem-solving, the language needs to resemble the natural languages used by human beings. The language of symbolic logic is both precise enough to be understood and manipulated by computers and natural enough to be regarded as a simplified form of natural language.

In this chapter, we shall compare the clausal form of logic with some of the features of natural language. We shall also compare it with semantic networks for representing natural language meanings and with relational databases for representing information in computers. In order to make the relationship between logic and natural language more apparent, we introduce the infix notation for predicate symbols.

Infix notation

The informal notation used to introduce clausal form at the beginning of the first chapter can be given formal status.

Binary (two-place) predicate symbols can be written between their arguments. Instead of writing atoms in prefix form

$$= (x,y), \quad \leq (x,y), \quad \text{Father}(x,y)$$

we can write them in infix form

$$x = y, \quad x \leq y, \quad x \text{ is the father of } y$$

respectively. The expression "is the father of" is regarded as a single predicate symbol.

Unary (one-place) predicate symbols can be written after their arguments, without the attendant parentheses. Thus we can write

$$x \text{ is good} \leftarrow x \text{ accomplishes } y, \ y \text{ is good}$$

instead of

$$\text{Good}(x) \leftarrow \text{Accomplishes}(x,y), \text{Good}(y).$$

Unary predicate symbols written after their arguments are also regarded as infix notation.

For predicate symbols having more than two arguments, infix notation distributes parts of a predicate symbol between its arguments. Thus we can write

John <u>gave</u> book <u>to</u> Mary <—

instead of

Gave(John, book, Mary) <—

where "<u>gave</u>" and "<u>to</u>" are regarded as the first and second parts of the single predicate symbol "Gave".

Infix notation, though easier to read, increases the possibility of ambiguity. The expression

John is a student <—

in infix notation can be interpreted as either one of the two clauses

Student(John) <—

Isa(John,student) <—

in prefix notation. To eliminate ambiguity, we underline infix predicate symbols and their parts. Thus the atom in the clause

John <u>is a student</u> <—

has one argument, whereas the atom in

John <u>is a</u> student <—

has two arguments. Underlining may be omitted, as in the case of the two binary predicate symbols " = " and " $\leq$ ", when there is no ambiguity.

Infix notation can also be employed for function symbols. We can write

$x + y$, $x * y$, $x!$, $x + 1$, x'<u>s dad</u>

for example, instead of

$+(x,y)$, times(x,y), fact(x), s(x), dad(x).

Infix notation for function symbols and associated conventions for reducing parentheses will be discussed again in Chapter 5.

<u>Variables</u> <u>and</u> <u>types</u> <u>of</u> <u>individuals</u>

The analogue of variables in logic are such words in English as

"something", "anything", "everything",
"nothing", "a thing", "things".

For example,

$\leftarrow$ x is good, x is bad
Nothing is both good and bad.

x is bad $\leftarrow$ x accomplishes y, y is bad
Anything which accomplishes something bad is bad itself.

There are many occasions, however, in which logic uses a variable, but English uses a word which refers to a specific type (or classification) of individual. It is usual in logic to name types by means of one-argument predicate symbols. Thus, the English sentence

All men are animals.

would be expressed by the clause

x is an animal $\leftarrow$ x is a man .

The variable x in the clause is avoided in the English by referring to the type "men". This is even more obvious if the English sentence is paraphrased

Men are animals.

The English words "anyone", "everyone", "anywhere", "somewhere", "anytime", "sometime" refer to individuals of type "human", "place", and "time".

Relative pronouns in English, such as "who", "which" and "where" refer to individuals already mentioned in the same sentence. For example

Anyone who eats animals is a carnivore.
x is a carnivore $\leftarrow$ x is human,
                    x eats y,
                    y is an animal

The restrictive relative clause

who eats animals

adds two extra conditions concerning the individual x mentioned in the main sentence

Anyone is a carnivore.
x is a carnivore $\leftarrow$ x is human

The non-restrictive relative clause, however, in the sentence

John, who eats animals, is a carnivore.
John is a carnivore $\leftarrow$
John eats y $\leftarrow$ y is an animal

adds an extra sentence to the main sentence.

The words "is a" occur so frequently in English that it is natural to treat them as a single unit and to symbolize them by a binary predicate symbol. Thus we write

x <u>is a</u> animal <− x <u>is a</u> human

treating types as individuals rather than as properties of individuals.
The treatment of types as individuals increases expressive power. It
allows us to write clauses which refer to types by means of variables,
for example

x <u>is a</u> y <− x <u>is a</u> z, z <u>is a</u> y

which expresses the <u>transitivity</u> of "is a". Transitivity cannot be
expressed in clausal form if types are treated as properties.

Existence

The English word "some" expresses existence. In the standard form of
logic the existence of individuals can be expressed without giving them a
name. But in the clausal form of logic, existence is expressed by naming
individuals, using constant symbols and function symbols. The sentence

Some men are animals.

for example, can be expressed by means of the clauses

☺ <u>is a</u> man <−

☺ <u>is a</u> animal <−

where the constant symbol   is not used elsewhere to name a different
individual. Notice, however, that the same clauses can also be regarded
as expressing the English sentence

Some animals are men.

The English words "has" and "have" often express existence. The
sentence

Zeus has a parent who loves him.

for example, can be reexpressed as

Some parent of Zeus loves him.

In clausal form, a constant symbol is needed to name the loving
parent. The name doesn't matter provided it is not used elsewhere for a
different individual. If the constant symbol ☺ satisfies this
condition, then the sentence is symbolized by means of the clauses

☺ <u>is a parent of</u> Zeus <−

☺ <u>loves</u> Zeus <−

To express that

> everyone has a parent who loves him

the loving parent needs to be named by a function symbol. The simpler clauses

☺ is a parent of x <— x is a human

☺ loves x <— x is a human

express the stronger assumption that a single individual, who is a parent of everyone, loves everyone. We need to express the more modest assumption that for every human x there is an individual which is a loving parent of x. Different individuals might have different loving parents. The loving parent of x is a function of x and its name needs to be constructed by a function symbol applied to x. Any function symbol can be used, provided it is different from any used elsewhere. If the function symbol "par" satisfies this condition, then the term par(x) names the loving parent of x and the sentence can be expressed by the clauses

par(x) is a parent of x <— x is a human

par(x) loves x <— x is a human.

In a similar manner, the assumptions

> Everyone has a mother.

> Offices have desks.

> Birds have wings.

can be symbolized, using function symbols, by such clauses as

mum(x) is a mother of x <— x is a human

d(x) is a desk <— x is a office

d(x) is in x <— x is a office

w(x) is a wing <— x is a bird

w(x) is part of x <— x is a bird.

Individuals can be named by function symbols having several arguments. The "English" sentence

> For every individual x and every list y
> there exists a list whose first element
> is x and rest is y.

for example, can be expressed by the clauses

cons(x,y) <u>is a</u> list <— y <u>is a</u> list

x <u>is the first of</u> cons(x,y) <— y <u>is a</u> list

y <u>is the rest of</u> cons(x,y) <— y <u>is a</u> list

where the term cons(x,y) names the list

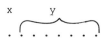

constructed by putting the element x in front of the list y. Although the infix notation for the clauses is easy to read, the prefix notation is more compact:

L(cons(x,y)) <— L(y)

First(x, cons(x,y)) <— L(y)

Rest(y, cons(x,y)) <— L(y).

The existence of an individual which is referred to in the conclusions of a statement needs to be expressed by a constant symbol or function symbol. However, it needs to be expressed by a variable if the individual is referred to in the conditions of the statement but not in the conclusions. For example

One person is a grandparent of another if he has a child who is parent of the other.

x <u>is grandparent of</u> y <— x <u>is human</u>,
                              y <u>is human</u>,
                              x <u>is parent of</u> z,
                              z <u>is parent of</u> y

It is often easier to understand a clause if variables which occur in conditions but not in conclusions are read as expressing existence. For example, the clause

Mary <u>likes</u> John <— Mary <u>likes</u> x

can be read as stating that

if there is anything that Mary likes at all, then Mary likes John.

The clause

x <u>has</u> y <— z <u>gives</u> y <u>to</u> x

expresses that x has y if someone gives y to x.

Negation

Negation can be expressed directly in the standard form of logic. In
the clausal form it can only be expressed indirectly.   The conclusion-
less clauses

>   <— Mother(Zeus,x)
>
>   <— Mother(x,y), Father(x,z)

for example, state that

>   Zeus is not the mother of anyone and
>   no one is both a father and a mother.

It is a feature of clausal form semantics that a negated condition
can be reexpressed as an unnegated conclusion. The sentence

>   Robert is at work if he is not at home.

which can be expressed directly with a negative condition

>   At(Robert,work) <— not-At(Robert,home)

in standard form can be expressed without negation in clausal form by
means of a non-Horn clause

>   At(Robert,work), At(Robert,home) <— .

The sentence

>   not-Happy(John) <— not-Likes(Mary,John)

in standard form can be reexpressed in clausal form

>   Likes(Mary,John) <— Happy(John).

Notice that the different English sentences

>   Every fungus which is not a toadstool is a mushroom.
>   Every fungus which is not a mushroom is a toadstool.
>   Everything which is neither a mushroom nor a
>   toadstool is not a fungus.

all have the same clausal form

>   Toadstool(x), Mushroom(x) <— Fungus(x).

Denial of conclusions which are implications

In clausal form, to show that assumptions imply a conclusion, it is
necessary to deny that the conclusion holds and to demonstrate

inconsistency. A typical conclusion often has the form of an implication:

All boleti are poisonous.

Poisonous(x)   <— Boletus(x)

for example. In general, an _implication_ is a Horn clause with a single conclusion and one or more conditions.   A Horn clause with a conclusion, but no condition, is called an _assertion_.   It is often convenient, however, to use the terminlogy "implication" in the wider sense which includes assertions.

To deny an implication it is necessary to assert the existence of individuals satisfying all of the conditions and to deny that they satisfy the conclusions. In this case, we assert the existence of an individual, say ♈ , which is a boletus and deny that it is poisonous.

Boletus(♈) <—

<— Poisonous(♈)

In Chapter 10, when we investigate the standard form of logic, we shall formulate a systematic procedure for transforming denials of sentences into clausal form. Meanwhile, it suffices to use the rule above for denying conclusions which have the form of implications.

Conditions which are implications

In natural language and in the standard form of logic it is common for a condition to have the form of an implication. For example, the implication

All Bob's students like logic.

which has the structure of a Horn clause

x _likes_ logic <— x _is a student of_ Bob

is the condition of the sentence

(1)   Bob is happy if all his students like logic.

Although the sentence can be expressed directly in the standard form of logic, it needs to be paraphrased before it can be expressed in clausal form. In Chapter 10 we shall present a systematic method for transforming such sentences from standard form into clausal form. Here we can illustrate the method by successively transforming the original sentence (1) in English:

(2)   Not all of Bob's students like logic if Bob is unhappy.

(The unnegated condition and conclusion of (1) become the negated conclusion and negated condition of (2).)

(3)   There is a student of Bob, who doesn't like
                       logic, if Bob is unhappy.

(The conclusion of (2), which is the denial of an implication, is reexpressed by asserting the existence of an individual which satisfies the condition of being a student of Bob but not the conclusion of liking logic.)

(4)   There is a student of Bob, say ☺ ,
                       and ☺ doesn't like logic, if Bob is unhappy.

(The culprit is given a name.)

(5)   ☺ is a student of Bob if Bob is unhappy.
                       ☺ doesn't like logic if Bob is unhappy.

(The two conclusions are expressed by two sentences having the same condition.)

(6)   ☺ is a student of Bob or Bob is happy.
                       Bob is happy if ☺ likes logic.

(The negated condition is reexpressed as an unnegated conclusion and the negated conclusion as an unnegated condition.)

(7)   ☺ is a student of Bob, Bob is happy <—
                       Bob is happy <— ☺ likes logic

    The transformation from English to clausal form can be compressed. In the simple case where the English sentence has the form

              A if B is implied by C.

i.e.   A <— [B <— C]

in the standard form of logic, the corresponding clauses have the form

              A, C <—

              A <— B.

Complications arise when, as in the preceding example, the condition
B <— C

contains variables which need to be replaced by constant symbols or terms involving function symbols.

    Although sentences having conditions which are implications may appear unnatural in clausal form, they have a natural problem-solving interpretation, discussed in Chapters 7 and 8. In Chapter 10 we shall investigate such sentences in greater detail. Until then we shall concentrate on examples which can be expressed by Horn clauses, whose conditions are simple atomic formulae.

Definitions and "if-and-only-if"

It is normal in mathematics and logic to express definitions by means
of "if-and-only-if":

> x is grandparent of y if-and-only-if
> there is a z which is child of x and parent of y.

The expression

> A if-and-only-if B

is interpreted as meaning

> A if B   and   A only-if B.

"A only-if B" is normally interpreted as

> B if A.

This interpretation of "only-if", however, is not the only one.   In
Chapter 11 we shall discuss an alternative interpretation.

The expression "if-and-only-if" can be expressed directly in the
standard form of logic. In the clausal form, however, the two halves need
to be expressed independently. Moreover, the only-if half is often
unnatural. In the case of the only-if half of the grandparent definition

> x is parent of rel(x,y) <— x is grandparent of y

> rel(x,y) is parent of y <— x is grandparent of y

a function symbol is necessary to name the relative of x and y who is a
child of x and a parent of y.

If-and-only-if definitions and sentences having conditions which are
implications are the two main cases in which clausal form is more awkward
than both natural language and the standard form of logic. Until Chapters
10 and 11 we shall avoid complications by using only the if-halves of
definitions, which is adequate for most purposes.

Semantic networks

Many researchers in the field of artificial intelligence use semantic
networks, as an alternative to symbolic logic, to represent information
in computers. Semantic networks are used both as models of human memory
organisation and as representation schemes for the meanings of natural
language sentences.

A <u>semantic</u> <u>network</u> is a graph whose <u>nodes</u> represent individuals and whose <u>directed</u> <u>arcs</u> represent binary relationships. Each individual is represented by only one node. The information in the clauses F1-6 of Chapter 1, for example, can be represented by means of the semantic network.

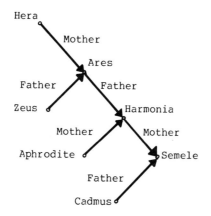

In general, a semantic network can be regarded as equivalent to the set of variable-free assertions represented by its arcs. An arc labelled R directed from node s to node t

represents the assertion

R(s,t) <— .

Simple semantic networks have no provision for representing variables, function symbols, n-ary predicate symbols or clauses having conditions or alternative conclusions. As we shall see later, the restriction to binary relations is not an important limitation, because every n-ary relationship can be reexpressed as the conjunction of n+1 binary relationships. Other restrictions, however, are more serious and have motivated several investigators to propose extensions [Shapiro 1971, 1972], [Hendrix 1975], [Schubert 1977], all of which treat semantic networks as an alternative syntax for symbolic logic. The one described below treats extended semantic networks as a pictorial syntax for clausal form [Deliyanni and Kowalski 1979].

Extended semantic networks

   As in simple semantic networks, nodes represent individuals and arcs
represent binary relationships. However, nodes can be constants,
variables or terms constructed using function symbols. Arcs can
represent conditions as well as conclusions and are grouped into clauses.
Conditions are drawn with two lines and conclusions with one heavy line
as before. Clauses containing more than one atom are delimited by
enclosing them within subnetworks. The extended semantic network

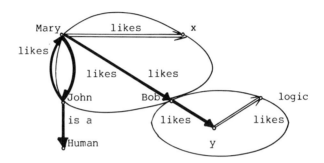

corresponds to the set of clauses

        John likes Mary <—

        John is a human <—

        Mary likes John, Mary likes Bob <— Mary likes x

        Bob likes y <— y likes logic.

   Apart from their pictorial aspect, semantic networks have two other
attractions: They provide a useful scheme for storing information, and
they enforce the discipline of using binary rather than more general n-
ary predicate symbols. The fact that every individual is represented by
a single node means that all information about the individual is directly
accessible from the node. This feature has been exploited in the design
of path-finding problem-solving strategies. In the next two sections,
however, we shall compare the use of binary predicate symbols with that
of more general n-ary predicate symbols.

The representation of information by binary predicate symbols

   Every n-ary relationship can be reexpressed as a conjunction of n+1
binary relationships. For example, the assertion

        John gave book to Mary <—

can be reexpressed in English:

> There is an event e
> which is an <u>act</u> of giving
> by an <u>actor</u> John
> of an <u>object</u> book
> to a <u>recipient</u> Mary.

In clausal form, ignoring the assertion which describes that e is of type "event", the single 3-place relationship can be reformulated as 4 binary relationships.

> e <u>is an act of</u> giving <—

> e <u>has actor</u> John <—

> e <u>has object</u> book <—

> e <u>has recipient</u> Mary <—

The semantic network representation

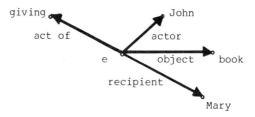

of the clauses is similar to the case structure analysis of natural language employed in linguistics [Fillmore 1968] and artificial intelligence [Quillian 1968], [Schank 1973, 1975], [Simmons 1973].

In general, to replace an n-ary relationship by binary relationships it is necessary to treat the n-ary relationship and its relation as individuals (giving them names such as "e" and "giving" in the preceding example). It is necessary to introduce a binary relationship which expresses that the n-ary relationship belongs to the n-ary relation: in this example, the binary relationship

> e <u>is an act of</u> giving <— .

For every argument of the n-ary relationship, a binary relationship is needed to express that the argument belongs to the n-ary relationship.

We shall refer to the representation of information by general n-ary relationships as the <u>n-ary</u> <u>representation</u> and the corresponding representation by means of binary relations as the <u>binary</u> <u>representation</u>.

Binary relationships can replace n-ary relationships in both conditions and conclusions of clauses. For example, the English sentence

> A person possesses an object
> after it is given to him.

can be expressed in the form

For every event u in which x gives y to z,
there exists a situation, say result(u),
immediately after u, which is a
state of possession by the subject z of the
object y.

The systematic formulation of the sentence in clausal form using
binary predicate symbols ignoring types, produces four Horn clauses all
having the same conditions.

```
result(u) is immediately after  u <- u is an act of giving,
                                     u has actor x,
                                     u has object y,
                                     u has recipient z

result(u) is a state of possession <- u is an act of giving,
                                     u has actor x,
                                     u has object y,
                                     u has recipient z

        result(u) has subject z <- u is an act of giving,
                                     u has actor x,
                                     u has object y,
                                     u has recipient z

        result(u) has object y  <- u is an act of giving,
                                     u has actor x,
                                     u has object y,
                                     u has recipient z
```

In this example, the binary representation is less compact than an n-
ary representation which includes explicit arguments for the act u and
the state result(u).

```
result(u) is immediately after u <-
                      u is an act of giving by x of y to z

result(u) is a state of possession by z of y <-
                      u is an act of giving by x of y to z
```

However, if we assume that every act of giving has an actor, object and
recipient then the original binary representation can be reformulated
more compactly.

```
result(u) is immediately after u   <- u is an act of giving

result(u) is a state of possession <- u is an act of giving

result(u) has subject z <- u has recipient z

result(u) has object y <- u has object y
```

Advantages of the binary representation

   The binary representation is generally more expressive than the n-ary
representation. It makes it easier to add new information and to ignore
information that is unknown.

   In the binary representation, relations and relationships are treated
as individuals. Consequently it is possible to talk about them in such
sentences as

               Mary wants John to give her the book.

               Mary wants e <— .

The corresponding expression in the n-ary representation

               Mary wants (John gave book to Mary) <—

is not a legal sentence of clausal form.

   The ability to talk about relationships in the binary representation
also makes it easier to add new information about a relationship. For
example, having expressed that

               John gave the book to Mary

to add the new information that he did so in Hyde park requires only the
addition of a new assertion

               Hyde park is the location of e <—

in the binary representation. But, in the n-ary representation, it
requires replacing the original assertion which used a 3-place predicate
symbol

               John gave book to Mary <—

by a new one with a 4-place predicate symbol.

               John gave book to Mary in Hyde park <—

   Notice, however, that it is really the treatment of relationships as
individuals which is responsible for the advantages of the binary
representation in the preceding two examples. Both of the sentences

               Mary wants e <—

               Hyde park is the location of e <—

can be expressed in an n-ary representation with an an explicit argument
which names the relationship e.

               e is an act of giving by John of book to Mary <—

The binary representation is also more convenient than the n-ary representations when components of a relationship are unknown. For example, to express that

> the book was given to John

it suffices in the binary representation simply to state what is known and to ignore what is unknown.

> e' is an act of giving <—
> e' has object book <—
> e' has recipient John <—

In the two n-ary representations, on the other hand, it is necessary to give the unknown actor a name.

> ☺ gave book to John <—

or > e' is an act of giving by ☺ of book to John <—

The argument in favour of binary relations is not conclusive. There are many relationships, such as

> x times y is z,
> x received grade y for course z,
> x is the y-th element of sequence z, and
> v is a proof that the assumptions x
> imply the conclusion y
> obtained by the proof procedure u,

for which an n-ary representation is more convenient than the binary representation. The use of general n-ary relations moreover is more common than the use of binary relations in the field of databases.

Databases

A database is a collection of information to be used for a variety of purposes. A typical database might contain a firm's personnel records, details of bank transactions or the police files of convicted criminals. Increasingly, such databases are represented in a form which can be processed by computers. These are used to update the databases, to check the consistency of data, and to answer requests for information.

A single database might be used to obtain information by many users with little computer training. In this case the data need to be represented in a simple form which is independent of its representation inside the computer. Consequently, the database query language must be both simple to learn and easy to use. It is now widely accepted that these requirements can best be satisfied if data are viewed as relations [Codd 1970].

The relational view of data is equivalent to the representation of data by tables: The argument positions of a relation can be regarded as the columns of a table and the relationships which make up the relation are its rows. Thus the 5-column, 3-row table

Birthday club	Name	Office	Dues	Birthdate	Date joined
	Mary	president	10p	4.Mar.77	4.Mar.77
	John	secretary	10p	2.Mar.78	2.Mar.78
	Bob	treasurer	10p	1.Jan.80	1.Jan.80

represents the 5-argument relation which is described by the 3 assertions:

```
Club(Mary, president, 10p, 4.Mar.77, 4.Mar.77) <—
Club(John, secretary, 10p, 2.Mar.78, 2.Mar.78) <—
Club(Bob,  treasurer, 10p, 1.Jan.80, 1.Jan.80) <—
```

The same information can be described by using binary predicate symbols. In this example the binary representation can be simplified because each row of the table can be uniquely identified by the value in its first column. Accordingly, the value in that column is said to be a key of the table. In the binary representation of the table, the key can function as the name of the relationship which it identifies.

```
B1          Member(Mary, birthday club) <—
B2          Member(John, birthday club) <—
B3          Member(Bob,  birthday club) <—
B4          Office(Mary, president) <—
B5          Office(John, secretary) <—
B6          Office(Bob,  treasurer) <—
B7          Dues(Mary, 10p) <—
B8          Dues(John, 10p) <—
B9          Dues(Bob,  10p) <—
B10         Birthdate(Mary,  4.Mar.77) <—
B11         Birthdate(John,  2.Mar.78) <—
B12         Birthdate(Bob,   1.Jan.80) <—
B13         Datejoined(Mary, 4.Mar.77) <—
B14         Datejoined(John, 2.Mar.78) <—
B15         Datejoined(Bob,  1.Jan.80) <—
```

Notice that the binary representation of the table, though more longwinded, is easier to read than the n-ary representation. The names of the columns, which are necessary for understanding the table, are not represented in the n-ary representation, but are represented by binary predicate symbols in the binary representation.

More importantly from a computational point of view, the binary representation can often express general laws which could not be expressed at all in the n-ary representation. In particular, the general laws

```
Dues(x, 10p)      <— Member(x, birthday club)
Datejoined(x,y)   <— Member(x, birthday club),
                     Birthdate(x,y)
```

can replace the specific assertions B7-9 and B13-15 in the binary representation, but cannot be formulated in the n-ary representation at all.

Data query languages

The relational view of data has been used more for data queries than for data description.

Most relational query languages use the symbolism of symbolic logic or relational algebra. Relational calculus query languages [Codd 1972] can be regarded as using a binary representation of relations. Given, for example, the data contained in the Birthday club and the Address tables

Birthday club	Name	Office	Dues	Birthdate	Date joined

Address	Name	Street number	Street	Town

the query   What Birthday club members live
                 on Euclid Avenue?

can be formulated in the binary representation

                    <— Answer(x)
                    Answer(x) <— Member(x, birthday club),
                               Street(x, Euclid Ave)

in a manner similar to that of the relational calculus. It can also be formulated in the n-ary representation

                    <— Answer(x)
                    Answer(x) <— Club(x,y,z,u,v),
                               Address(x, y', Euclid Ave, z')

similar to that of the tabular query-by-example language [Zloof 1975].

The relationship between queries expressed in the clausal form of logic and ones expressed in query-by-example has been investigated by van Emden [1979]. A classification of relational query languages, all based on the standard form of logic, has been made by Pirotte [1978].

Data description

The relational model of data is not concerned with the formalism used to represent data within the computer. It is compatible with any formalism which can be viewed   abstractly in terms of relations. Nevertheless, the use of symbolic logic is especially attractive. It has the advantage that the same formalism can be used both for expressing queries and for defining data. Moreover, when the data can be defined by

means of general laws, the data definitions are indistinguishable from
programs. The sentence

Dues(x, 10p) <— Member(x, birthday club)

for example, can be regarded both as a general law and as a program which
computes the dues paid by members of the birthday club.

Symbolic logic was used before the relational model of databases to
describe both data and queries in question-answering systems. Among the
first systems were those described by Darlington [1969] and Green [1969a,
1969b]. The use of the "Answer" predicate symbol, in particular, was
introduced by Green.   More recent systems have been developed in
Marseille [Colmerauer et al 1972], [Dahl and Sambuc 1976] and Maryland
[Minker et al 1973], [McSkimin and Minker 1977], and by Nicolas and Syre
[1974] and Kellogg, Klahr and Travis [1978].

Integrity constraints

Since data often contain errors, integrity constraints are used to
describe properties which the data need to satisfy in order to be
correct. The clause

y is before z <— Today(z),
Member(x, birthday club),
Birthdate(x,y)

for example, expresses that all members of the birthday club were born
before today. If today were 1.Apr.79

Today(1.Apr.79) <—

then given an appropriate definition of the is before relation, the data

Member(Bob, birthday club) <—
Birthdate(Bob, 1.Jan.80) <—

would be inconsistent with the integrity constraint and should be
rejected by an intelligent database management system.

Using symbolic logic as a formalism for describing information blurs
the conventional distinction between databases and programs. Integrity
constraints for databases are indistinguishable from program properties.
The clause

x ≤ y <— Fact(x,y)

for example, describes a property which needs to be satisfied by a
correct definition of the factorial relation. Like an integrity
constraint, its purpose is not to contribute to the definition of the ≤
and Fact relations but rather to constrain the definitions from having
unacceptable properties.

Integrity constraints can be used for other purposes. They can be used
to reject inconsistent queries

The substitution   x = 304

which can be extracted from the proof answers the query. The answer
extraction can be done automatically by the problem-solving system.

Equality

   Mathematical notation normally uses function symbols and the binary
predicate symbol = (equality) where we have used other predicate symbols.
It is usual to write

$$x*y = z$$ instead of   Times(x,y,z)
$$x! \ = y$$ instead of   Fact(x,y)
$$x \ = father(y)$$ instead of   Father(x,y).

   Similarly, the relational calculus query language uses function
symbols and equality, writing

office(x) = y instead of   Office(x,y)
dues(x) = y instead of   Dues(x,y)
birthdate(x) = y instead of   Birthdate(x,y)
datejoined(x) = y instead of   Datejoined(x,y).

   Functional notation is often more compact than relational notation. It
is simpler, for example, to express

        The date on which a member of the
        birthday club joins the club is the
        same as his birth date.

in the functional notation

        birthdate(x) = datejoined(x) $\leftarrow$ Member$(x,$ birthday club$)$

than in the relational notation

        Birthdate(x,y) $\leftarrow$ Member$(x,$ birthday club$)$, Datejoined(x,y)
        Datejoined(x,y) $\leftarrow$ Member$(x,$ birthday club$)$, Birthdate(x,y).

   Equality is necessary whenever an individual has more than one name.
For example:

        Jove = Jupiter $\leftarrow$.

It is also necessary, even in the relational notation, to express that
one argument of a relation is a function of the others. For example:

        x = y $\leftarrow$ Father(x,z), Father(y,z)

   To show that a set of clauses S containing the equality symbol is
inconsistent, the set of clauses needs to contain the following axioms
characterising the equality relation, for every function symbol f and
every predicate symbol P occurring in S, (including the equality symbol).

What number is less than 1,300
and is the factorial of 5,200 ?

and to transform difficult goals into easier ones. The use of integrity
constraints to aid problem-solving is investigated in Chapter 9.

A departmental database

The PROLOG [Roussel 1975] Horn clause problem-solving system developed
in Marseille has been used for a variety of tasks which combine features
of both databases and programs. It has been used in Marseille for natural
language question answering [Colmerauer et al 1972], [Dahl and Sambuc
1976] and symbolic integration [Bergman and Kanoui 1973], in Edinburgh
for plan-formation [Warren 1974, 1976], geometry theorem-proving [Welham
1976], [Coelho and Pereira 1975], the solution of mechanics problems
expressed in English [Bundy et al 1979] and compiler-writing [Warren,
Pereira and Pereira 1977] and in Budapest for computer-aided design
[Markusz 1977] and drug analysis [Futo, Darvas and Szeredi 1978]. In
London we have implemented part of a database which describes the
activities of our department. The following clauses are typical of those
used to describe the data.

```
x    is occupied with    y    <- x teaches y
x    is occupied with    y    <- x attends y
x    is occupied with    y    <- x is member of committee y
9:30 is the hour of 304  <-
Fri  is the day of  304  <-
3    is the level of 304 <-
145  is the room of  x   <- 3 is the level of x
RAK  teaches  304        <-
145  has capacity 80     <-
65   people attend  304  <-
x    attends  y          <- x is a student in year z,
                            z is the level of y
Problem-solving is the name of 304 <-
```

Here it is assumed that course 304 meets only once a week. If it meets
more often, then composite terms, part(304,1), part(304,2), for example,
might be used to name diferent parts of the course.

Various integrity constraints, such as

```
<- x is the room of y, x has capacity u,
   v people attend  y, u < v
```

can be expressed and tested for consistency with the data. Queries can be
answered by denying that they have an answer, proving inconsistency and
extracting from the proof the information needed to construct the answer.
Thus, to determine the activity with which RAK is occupied at 9:30 on
Fridays it suffices to deny that there is such an activity:

```
<- Answer(x)
Answer(x) <- RAK  is occupied with x,
             9:30 is the hour of x,
             Fri  is the day of  x
```

E1 $x = x \leftarrow$
E2 $P(x_1,\ldots,x_m) \leftarrow P(y_1,\ldots,y_m), \quad x_1=y_1, \quad \ldots, \quad x_m=y_m$
E3 $f(x_1,\ldots,x_m) = f(y_1,\ldots,y_m) \leftarrow x_1=y_1, \quad \ldots, \quad x_m=y_m$

For example, to demonstrate that the assumptions

J1   Jekyl = Hyde $\leftarrow$
J2   father(John) = Hyde $\leftarrow$
J3   Member(father(John), birthday club) $\leftarrow$

imply the conclusion

                Member(Jekyl, birthday club) $\leftarrow$

it is necessary to deny the conclusion

J4 $\leftarrow$ Member(Jekyl, birthday club)

and add the appropriate axioms for the equality relation:

J5 $x = x \leftarrow$
J6   Member$(x_1,x_2) \leftarrow$ Member$(y_1,y_2), \; x_1 = y_1, \; x_2 = y_2$
J7 $x_1 = x_2 \leftarrow y_1 = y_2, \; x_1 = y_1, \; x_2 = y_2$
J8   father$(x) = $ father$(y) \leftarrow x = y$

The resulting set of clauses J1-8 is inconsistent because J1-3 are
"obviously" inconsistent with the instances

                Hyde = Hyde $\leftarrow$
                birthday club = birthday club $\leftarrow$
     Member(Jekyl, birthday club) $\leftarrow$ Member(father(John), birthday club),
                                Jekyl = father(John),
                                birthday club = birthday club
     Jekyl = father(John) $\leftarrow$ Hyde = Hyde, Jekyl = Hyde, father(John) = Hyde

of J5-7. Clause J8 in this example does not contribute to the
inconsistency.

Problem-solving is considerably simplified if individuals have only
one name (distinct variable-free terms naming distinct individuals). Then
the single axiom

E1 $x = x \leftarrow$

expresses the only situation in which two individuals are the same (if
they have the same names). The infinitely-many axioms

D   Diff(s,t) $\leftarrow$

for every pair of distinct variable-free terms s and t, express the only
situations in which individuals are different (if they have different
names). Given a finite set of clauses S the infinitely-many axioms D can
be replaced by finitely many clauses

D1   Diff(a,b) <—
                for every pair of distinct constants a and b in S

D2   Diff(a, f(x_1,...,x_m)) <—
D3   Diff(f(x_1,...,x_m), a) <—
                for every constant a and function symbol f in S.

D4   Diff(f(x_1,...,x_m), g(y_1,...,y_n)) <—
                for every pair of distinct function symbols f and g in S.

D5   Diff(f(x_1,...,x_m), f(y_1,...,y_m)) <— Diff(x_i,y_i)
                for every function symbol f in S and argument i of f.

    Diff(x,y) is the same as not-(x = y). This can be expressed

                Diff(x,y)   if-and-only-if   not-(x = y), i.e.
D*1   Diff(x,y) <— not-(x = y)
D*2   not-(x = y) <— Diff(x,y)

in the "standard form" of logic or

                Diff(x,y), x = y <—
                <— Diff(x,y), x = y

in the clausal form. However, there is another interpretation of

                Diff(x,y)   only-if   not-(x = y)

which is different from D*2, namely

D*   D*1 describes the only condition for which the conclusion
                Diff(x,y) holds.

D* talks about the sentence D*1. It is a sentence of the meta-language,
talking about individuals which are sentences of the object language.
The relationship between the object language, in which one uses
sentences, and the meta-language, in which one talks about sentences, is
investigated in Chapters 11 and 12.

    To simplify matters for the remainder of the book we shall, whenever
possible, refer to individuals by unique names, using the equality and
Diff predicate symbols only in conditions of clauses, except for their
"definitions":

E1   x = x <—   and
D   Diff(s,t) <—
                for all pairs of distinct variable-free terms s and t.

In practice the Diff relation is defined by more efficient means.

Exercises

    1) Express the following sentences in clausal form. Some of them are
ambiguous.

    a)   Everyone likes someone.

    b)   Everyone likes everyone.

    c)   Someone likes everyone.

    d)   No one likes anyone.

    e)   No one likes someone.

    f)   Someone likes no one.

    g)   John and Mary like themselves.

    h)   A teacher is happy if he belongs to no committees. (Paraphrase the sentence first: It is not the case that a teacher is happy and belongs to some committee.)

    i)   Anyone who knows anything about logic likes logic.

2) In each of the following arguments the assumptions imply the conclusion. Express the assumptions and the denial of the conclusion in clausal form, so that the resulting set of clauses is inconsistent. Demonstrate inconsistency by showing that the set of clauses is true in no interpretation.

a) Assumption   There is a single individual who is a loving parent of everyone.

   Conclusion   Everyone has a parent who loves him.

b) Assumptions   All easterners like all westerners.
All westerners like all easterners who like some westerner.

   Conclusion   All westerners like all easterners without exception.

c) Assumptions   Canaries are birds.
All birds have wings.

   Conclusion   Canaries have wings.

d) Assumptions   Anything which accomplishes something good is good itself.
Anything which accomplishes something bad is bad itself.
War accomplishes both peace and suffering.
Peace is good and suffering is bad.

   Conclusion   Some things are both good and bad.

e) Assumptions   x is a member of cons(x,y).
x is a member of cons(u,y) if x is a member of y.

   Conclusion   A is a member of cons(C, cons(A, cons(C, nil))).

f) Assumption   Bob is happy if all his students like logic.

Conclusion   Bob is happy if he has no students.

3) The word "like" in exercise (6) of Chapter 1 disguises two
different meanings. Redo exercise (6) distinguishing between the notions

              x likes to eat y and
              x likes to be with y.

You can do so either by using two completely distinct predicate symbols,
Like$_1$ and Like$_2$, or by using a single three argument predicate symbol,
one of which is the name of an event (eating) or of a state (being with).

4) Express in clausal form the information represented in the
following semantic network and English sentences:

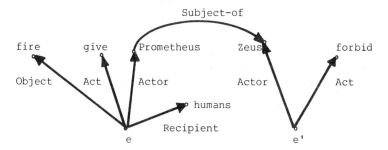

          The object of e' is any act of giving fire to humans.
          If a ruler forbids an act which is performed by one of his
          subjects then there is another event in which the ruler
          punishes the subject.

5) This exercise is based on Schank's [1973, 1975] conceptual analysis
of actions. Let the intended interpretation of

              Act(x,y)   be   x is an act of type y,
              Possess(x,y,u)   x possesses y in state u,
              Actor(x,y)   the actor of act x is y,
              Object(x,y)   the object of act x is y,
              Donor(x,y)   the donor of act x is y,
              Recipient(x,y)   the recipient of act x is y.

Let the terms

              ATRANS   name   the type of all acts of abstract
                                transactions,
              GIVE   the type of all acts of giving,
              TAKE   the type of all acts of taking,
              result(u)   the state immediately after the act u,
              prior(u)   the state immediately prior to the act u.

Express the following sentences in clausal form:

a) In the state immediately after any act of type ATRANS, the recipient of the act possesses the object of the act.

b) In the state immediately prior to any act of the type ATRANS, the donor possesses the object of the act.

c) An act of type ATRANS is an act of giving if the actor is the donor.

d) An act of type ATRANS is an act of taking if the actor is the recipient.

6) Redo exercise (5) using equality and function symbols. Let

act(x)	name	the type of act x,
actor(x)		the actor of x,
object(x)		the object of x,
donor(x)		the donor of x,
recipient(x)		the recipient of x.

7) Let Parents(x,y,z) hold when x is the father and y the mother of z. Formulate a set of clauses whose only variable-free assertions concern the Parents relation but which imply the variable-free assertions F1-8 of Chapter 1.

8) Assume that data is given in the Supplier, Part and Supply tables:

Supplier	Supplier-Number	Name	Status	City

Part	Part-Number	Name	Colour	Weight

Supply	Supplier-Number	Part-Number	Quantity

Formulate the following queries in clausal form. Use both the binary and the n-ary representations, taking advantage of the fact that Supplier-Number is a key of the Supplier table and Part-Number is a key of the Part table. Assume that the relationship

$x < y$ (x is less than y)

is already given.

a)   What are the numbers of suppliers of nuts?

b)   What are the names of suppliers of bolts?

c)   What are the locations of suppliers of nuts and bolts?

d)   What are the names of parts supplied by the supplier named John?

e)   What are the names of suppliers located in London who supply nuts weighing more than one ounce?

f)   What are the names of suppliers of both nuts and bolts?

g)   What are the names of suppliers of nuts or bolts?

CHAPTER 3

Top-down and Bottom-up Horn Clause Proof Procedures

Introduction

   The parsing problem - to show that a string of words forms a sentence
according to given rules of grammar - can be represented in logic as a
problem of demonstrating the inconsistency of a set of Horn clauses.

   Different parsing procedures for determining that a string is a
sentence correspond to different proof procedures for demonstrating
inconsistency. Top-down parsing procedures correspond to goal-directed
proof procedures which work backwards from the conclusion by using
implications to reduce problems to subproblems. The aim is to reduce the
original problem to a set of subproblems each of which has been solved.
Bottom-up parsing procedures correspond to proof procedures which work
forward from the initial set of assumptions, by using implications to
derive conclusions from assumptions.   The aim is to derive assertions
which directly solve each of the initially given problems.

   Top-down and bottom-up proof procedures apply to the solution of any
problem. Top-down inference is the analysis of goals into subgoals;
bottom-up inference is the synthesis of new information from old.   In
this chapter we define top-down and bottom-up inference for Horn clauses
only. Later we shall extend their definition to non-Horn clauses and
investigate systems which combine both directions of inference.

The parsing problem

   The following description of the parsing problem is based on Foster's
description [Foster 1970] of a formulation by Amarel.

   Given a grammar and a string of words such as

          "The slithy toves did gyre"

the problem is to demonstrate that the string is a sentence. This can be
done by filling in the triangle

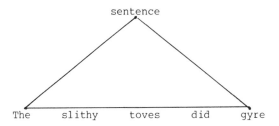

with a parse tree:

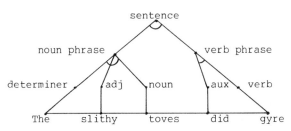

The parse tree is constructed in accordance with a grammar. In this example, the following rules of grammar have been used.

(1) A noun phrase followed by a verb phrase is a sentence.
(2) A determiner followed by an adjective followed by a noun is a noun phrase.
(3) An auxiliary followed by a verb is a verb phrase.
(4) "The" is a determiner.
(5) "slithy" is an adjective.
(6) "toves" is a noun.
(7) "did" is an auxiliary.
(8) "gyre" is a verb.

Different ways of filling in the triangle determine different parsing procedures. Top-down procedures are determined by filling in the triangle from the top downwards. Bottom-up procedures are obtained by filling in the triangle from the bottom upwards.

A top-down procedure might generate all branches in parallel:

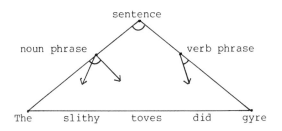

or it might generate one branch at a time, say from left to right.

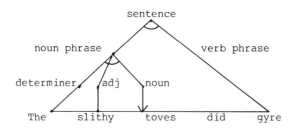

Similarly, a bottom-up procedure might work on all words in the input
string in parallel:

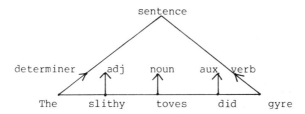

or it might work on one word at a time.

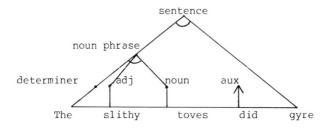

The triangle can be filled in from right to left, bi-directionally
top-down and bottom-up, and even from the middle out. Every systematic
method of filling in the triangle determines a parsing procedure. At this
point, it is important to distinguish mainly between the top-down and
bottom-up procedures.

A predicate logic representation of the parsing problem

There are many ways to represent the parsing problem in logic. The one we describe here has the property that different parsing procedures correspond to different proof procedures for the same representation.

We regard the initial string of words as a graph. A node of the graph occurs between adjacent words of the initial string and also at the beginning and end of the string. We regard words in the string as labels on the arcs connecting adjacent nodes:

The nodes are arbitrarily named 1-6. No ordering is implied by the numbers used to name the nodes.

The rules of grammar can be regarded as statements concerning labelled graphs:

> If there is a path from node x to y labelled "the" then the path from x to y is also labelled "determiner", i.e.
>
> Det(x,y) ← the(x,y).

> If there is a path from x to u labelled "determiner" and a path from u to v labelled "adjective" and a path from v to y labelled "noun" then there is a path from x to y labelled "noun phrase", i.e.
>
> Np(x,y) ← Det(x,u), Adj(u,v), Noun(v,y).

A parse of the initial string of words can be regarded as a graph which is labelled according to rules of grammar and has a path, from the beginning of the string to the end, labelled "sentence":

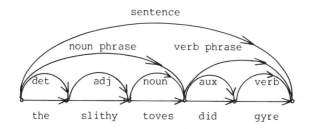

The initial graph is represented by a set of assertions:

Parse 1	the(1,2)	<-
Parse 2	slithy(2,3)	<-
Parse 3	toves(3,4)	<-
Parse 4	did(4,5)	<-
Parse 5	gyre(5,6)	<-

The rules of grammar are represented by clauses containing variables:

Parse 6	Sent(x,y)	<- Np(x,z), Vp(z,y)
Parse 7	Np(x,y)	<- Det(x,u), Adj(u,v), Noun(v,y)
Parse 8	Vp(x,y)	<- Aux(x,z), Verb(z,y)
Parse 9	Det(x,y)	<- the(x,y)
Parse 10	Adj(x,y)	<- slithy(x,y)
Parse 11	Noun(x,y)	<- toves(x,y)
Parse 12	Aux(x,y)	<- did(x,y)
Parse 13	Verb(x,y)	<- gyre(x,y)

These are the only rules of grammar needed to parse the original string of words. In a more realistic formulation of the problem, we have to consider the use of other rules of grammar as well. For example:

Parse 14	Np(x,y)	<- Det(x,z), Noun(z,y)
Parse 15	Np(x,y)	<- Noun(x,y)
Parse 16	Vp(x,y)	<- Verb(x,y)
Parse 17	Det(x,y)	<- a(x,y)
Parse 18	Adj(x,y)	<- brillig(x,y)
Parse 19	Noun(x,y)	<- wabe(x,y)
Parse 20	Verb(x,y)	<- gimble(x,y)

To show that the string of words from 1 to 6 is a sentence we show that the denial of the goal

Parse 21   <- Sent(1,6)

is inconsistent with Parse 1-20.

Bottom-up inference

A bottom-up refutation begins with assertions in the input set of clauses. It uses implications to derive new assertions from old ones, and ends with the derivation of assertions which explictly contradict the denial of the goal.

A graphical representation of the bottom-up refutation of Parse 1-21 is shown below. It resembles the parse tree turned upside-down. Nodes are labelled by assertions. The implication used to derive a new assertion labels the bundle of arcs leading from the old assertions to the new one.

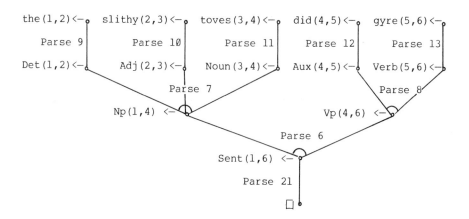

The assertion

$$Np(1,4) \;\leftarrow$$

for example, is obtained from the three assertions

$$\begin{aligned}
Det(1,2) \;&\leftarrow \\
Adj(2,3) \;&\leftarrow \\
Noun(3,4) \;&\leftarrow
\end{aligned}$$

by matching them with the three conditions of the clause

$$Np(x,y) \;\leftarrow\; Det(x,u),\; Adj(u,v),\; Noun(v,y).$$

Matching is accomplished by finding a most general substitution, in this case

$$\{x=1,\; u=2,\; v=3,\; y=4\},$$

which makes the assertions identical to the conditions.

    In general, one step of bottom-up inference matches (in the most general possible manner) a number of assertions with the conditions of a clause and derives a new assertion. The new assertion consists of the conclusion of the clause instantiated by the matching substitution. If the clause is a denial (which has no conclusion) then the derived clause is the empty clause. A more precise definition is given at the end of the chapter.

    Bottom-up inference is a generalisation of instantiation combined with the classical rule of modus ponens:

From   A ←   and   B ← A   derive   B ← .

Instantiation is restricted to the minimum needed to match assertions with conditions, so that modus ponens can be applied.

Top-down inference

A top-down refutation begins with a denial in the input set of clauses. It uses implications and assertions to derive new denials from old ones and ends with the derivation of the empty clause.

A graphical representation of a top-down refutation of Parse 1-21 is given below. Nodes are labelled by denials. An arc is labelled by the input clause which is used to derive the denial at the bottom of the arc. Selected atoms are underlined.

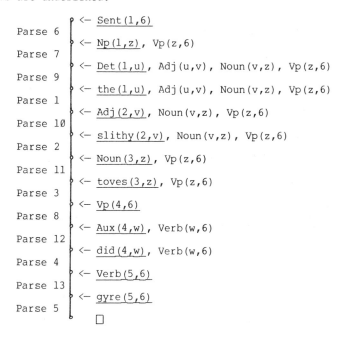

Beginning with the initial denial

        <- Sent(1,6)

top-down inference matches the condition of the denial with the conclusion of the implication

        Sent(x,y) <- Np(x,z), Vp(z,y)

deriving the new denial

        <- Np(1,z), Vp(z,6)

which consists of the conditions of the input clause instantiated by the matching substitution

        {x=1, y=6}.

The inference step formalises the reasoning that

> if there is no sentence from 1 to 6 then there is no z such that there is a noun phrase from 1 to z followed by a verb phrase from z to 6.

The same inference step can also be interpreted from a problem-solving point of view:

> The goal of showing that there is a sentence from 1 to 6 can be solved if a z can be found such that the subgoals of showing there is a noun phrase from 1 to z and a verb phrase from z to 6 can be solved.

In the problem-solving interpretation, the original goal is reduced to two new subgoals.

In general, top-down inference involves matching a selected condition of a denial with the conclusion of an implication and deriving a new denial by replacing the selected condition by the conditions of the implication and applying the matching substitution. If the implication is an assertion, which has no conditions, then the selected condition is simply deleted and the matching substitution is applied. If, in addition, the selected condition is the only condition in the denial then the derived clause is the empty clause. In the problem-solving interpretation, a denial is interpreted as a collection of goals. Top-down inference replaces a selected goal (in the context of a collection of goals) by a set of subgoals. A precise definition of top-down inference is given at the end of the chapter, while the problem-solving interpretation is investigated in the next chapter.

Top-down inference is a generalisation of instantiation combined with modus tollens:

> From not-A and A $\leftarrow$ B derive not-B.

Instantiation is restricted to the minimum needed to apply the modus tollens rule.

Different top-down refutations are determined by selecting different atoms in denials for the application of top-down inference. For example, clause Parse 8 could be applied to the denial

$$\leftarrow Np(1,z), \underline{Vp(z,6)}$$

to derive the new denial

$$\leftarrow Np(1,z), Aux(z,u), Verb(u,6)$$

If there is a refutation for one selection of atoms then there is a refutation for any other selection.

It is also possible (as in bottom-up inference) to select all conditions in a denial simultaneously. The figure below illustrates such a top-down parallel refutation. Below each selected condition is the name of the clause used in the derivation of the next denial.

← Sent(1,6)

    Parse 6

← Np(1,z), Vp(z,6)

    Parse 7 Parse 8

← Det(1,u), Adj(u,v), Noun(v,z), Aux(z,w), Verb(w,6)

    Parse 9   Parse 10 Parse 11   Parse 12 Parse 13

← the(1,u), slithy(u,v), toves(v,z), did(z,w), gyre(w,6)

    Parse 1   Parse 2   Parse 3   Parse 4   Parse 5

□

This formulation of the parsing problem was obtained by Alain Colmerauer with the author by expressing his Q-system [Colmerauer 1973] in logic. It is significant that, whereas the Q-system is a bottom-up parsing procedure, the Horn clause formulation is more abstract and can be used either top-down or bottom-up.

Although the example uses only context-free rules of grammar, it is easy to extend the representation to express context-sensitive grammars and arbitrary rewriting systems [Chomsky 1957].

The family relationships example

The concepts of top-down and bottom-up inference apply to any set of Horn clauses. The clauses which define family relationships, F1-19 of Chapter 1, provide another example.

Given clauses F1-19, the problem of showing that Zeus is a grandparent of Harmonia can be represented as the problem of filling in the triangle

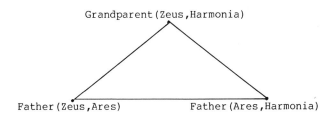

with a derivation tree:

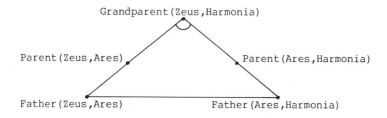

In the clausal form of logic, the problem is to show that the denial

F*   <— Grandparent(Zeus,Harmonia)

is inconsistent with the clauses F1-19. The figures below illustrate bottom-up, top-down, and parallel top-down refutations.

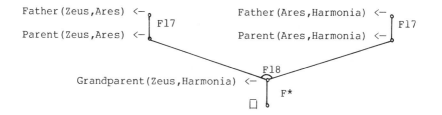

A bottom-up refutation of F* and F1-19

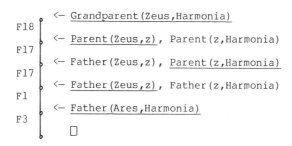

A top-down refutation of F* and F1-19

<- Grandparent(Zeus,Harmonia)
       F18

    <- Parent(Zeus,z), Parent(z,Harmonia)
           F17   F17

    <- Father(Zeus,z), Father(z,Harmonia)
          F1   F3

         □

A parallel top-down refutation of F* and F1-19.

   Because the operation of matching atomic formulae is so general, top-down and bottom-up inference can be used not only to show that Zeus is a grandparent of Harmonia but also to find a grandparent of Harmonia or to find a grandchild of Zeus. This is illustrated in the top-down refutation which shows the inconsistency of F1-19 with F**.

F**   <- Grandparent(u,Harmonia)

The grandparent of Harmonia whose existence contradicts F** can be determined by analysing the matching substitutions used in the refutation. The last step of the refutation matches the variable u from the initial denial with the constant symbol "Zeus", determining that u = Zeus is a grandparent of Harmonia.

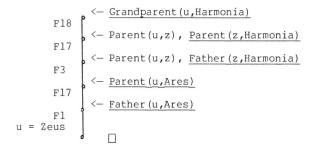

            <- Grandparent(u,Harmonia)
   F18
            <- Parent(u,z), Parent(z,Harmonia)
   F17
            <- Parent(u,z), Father(z,Harmonia)
   F3
            <- Parent(u,Ares)
   F17
            <- Father(u,Ares)
   F1
u = Zeus
                 □

   Notice that the first step of the refutation matches the condition

              Grandparent(u,Harmonia)

with the conclusion

              Grandparent(x,y).

Top-down inference uses a most general substitution which makes the two atoms identical, in this case

              {x = u, y = Harmonia}.

Any less general substitutions, such as

         {x = Ares, u = Ares, y = Harmonia}
or   {x = Zeus, u = Zeus, y = Harmonia}

which also makes the two atoms identical, need not be considered.

Given any two atoms, all (most general) matching substitutions differ
only in the names they give to variables and are otherwise equivalent.
Consequently, it is necessary to use only one of them in any inference
step. The matching substitution

         {u = x, y = Harmonia}

for example, is equivalent to the one used in the first step of the
refutation above. It gives rise to the equivalent denial

         <- Parent(x,z), Parent(z,Harmonia)

which is a variant of the other.

The possibility of restricting instantiation to the generation of most
general matching substitutions was observed by Prawitz [1960] and
elaborated by Robinson [1965a] who incorporated it into the resolution
rule (Chapter 8), which generalises the top-down and bottom-up inference
rules investigated in this chapter.   Unification algorithms for matching
atomic formulae have been the subject of much investigation [Robinson
1971], [Paterson and Wegman 1976], [Martelli and Montanari 1977].

Inference rules and search strategies

Inference rules are the building blocks of proof procedures. A proof
procedure is a systematic method for showing that a set of assumptions
imply a conclusion.   Proof procedures for the clausal form of logic are
refutation procedures, which show that assumptions imply a conclusion by
demonstrating that the assumptions are inconsistent with the denial of
the conclusion.

Inference rules specify the form of the individual steps which make up
a proof. All possible ways of applying the inference rules, both to an
initially given set of clauses and to the clauses derived from them,
determine the search space for the set of clauses. Specifying a
systematic search strategy for investigating clauses in the search space
determines a proof procedure.

Top-down inference determines search spaces which have the form of a
tree. Individual nodes of the search space are labelled by denials which
contain a selected condition. For each input clause whose conclusion
matches the selected condition there is an arc, labelled by the input
clause, which leads to the denial obtained by applying top-down
inference. A refutation is a path in the search space leading from the
initial denial to the empty clause □.

A top-down search space for the problem of finding a grandparent of
Harmonia is illustrated in the figure below. To save space, abbreviations
such as

```
Ha   for   Harmonia
He   for   Hera
P    for   Parent etc.
```

have been used for constant symbols and predicate symbols, and the input
clauses labelling arcs have been omitted.   Darkened nodes at the tips of
the search tree contain selected conditions which match the conclusion of
no input clause.

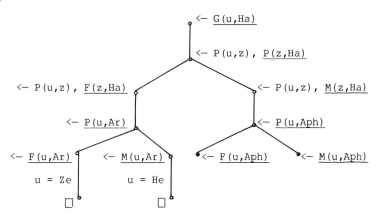

The search space is finite and can be searched completely in a finite
amount of time.   The two main kinds of search strategy are breadth-first
and depth-first search.   Breadth-first search explores all branches of
the search tree to the same depth, n steps away from the root of the
tree, before exploring them to the next depth, n+1 steps away from the
root.   Pictorially, breadth-first search explores the search space above
in the following sequence:

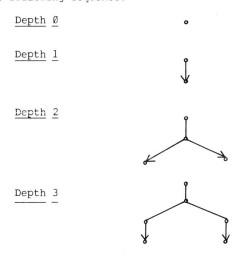

Depth 0

Depth 1

Depth 2

Depth 3

Depth 4

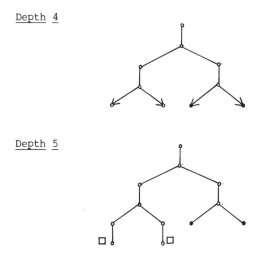

Depth 5

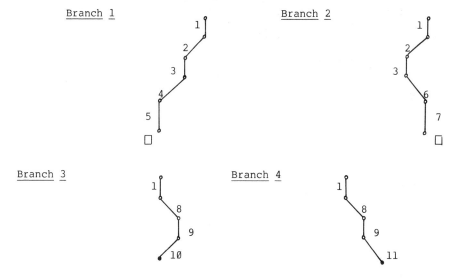

Depth-first search explores one branch of the search space at a time. When it reaches a tip of the tree it backtracks and tries an alternative branch as close to the tip as possible.

The numbers next to arcs indicate the sequence in which the arcs are generated. Here the first branch already contains a solution of the problem. If only one solution is required, then the rest of the search space need not be generated. The whole search space has to be generated, however, if all solutions are desired. In this case there are two refutations, each of which determines a different answer to the question

Who is a grandparent u of Harmonia?
u = Zeus,   u = Hera.

The search space for top-down inference is affected by the selection
of conditions in denials. In the search space above, conditions were
deliberately chosen with the intention of minimising the size of the
search space.   In the search space below, the selection of conditions
maximises its size.

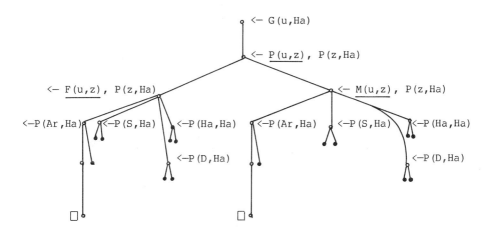

Both top-down search spaces are complete in the sense that they
contain a refutation if the set of clauses is inconsistent. It suffices,
therefore, to search either one search space or the other.   In general,
other things being equal, the larger the search space the more difficult
it is for the search strategy to find a refutation.

In the problem-solving interpretation of top-down inference, the
selection of a condition in a denial is the selection for solution of a
subgoal from a set of subgoals. It is one of the most important
considerations of problem-solving strategy and a major topic of the next
two chapters.

The structure of bottom-up search spaces is more complex than that of
top-down search spaces. Consequently, they are more difficult to search.
The figure below illustrates the bottom-up search space for the family
relationships example. Nodes are labelled by assertions. A bundle of arcs
connects the assertions which match the conditions of an input clause
with the new assertion derived by bottom-up inference. The input clause
which ought to label the bundle is omitted to save space. Darkened nodes
indicate assertions to which no bottom-up inference step applies. The
same abbreviations are used as before. In addition, we use

Ml for Male and
Fl for Female.

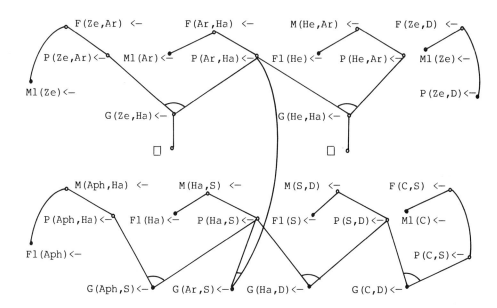

Not included in the figure are the input assertions, such as

God(Zeus) <— and Fairy-Princess(Harmonia) <—

which match no conditions. Notice that the assertion

Male(Zeus) <—

is derived in two different ways, giving rise to two nodes labelled by
the same assertion. In the next chapter, we consider representations of
search spaces in which different nodes are labelled by different clauses.

In practice, few strategies other than breadth-first search have been
applied to bottom-up search spaces. As in top-down search spaces,
breadth-first search explores all assertions of depth n before generating
any of depth n+1.   The depth of an assertion is one greater than the
maximum of the depths of its parent assertions.

Search strategies are an important part of all problem-solving systems
and are investigated in greater detail in the next chapter.

Infinite search spaces: natural numbers

The search spaces for the parsing problem and the family relationships
problems are both finite. Infinite search spaces are normally associated
with clauses containing function symbols. The definition of natural
number using the successor function symbol is a simple example.

```
Numb(0) <-

Numb(s(x)) <- Numb(x)
```

Suppose the problem is to show that three is a number.

```
<- Numb(s(s(s(0))))
```

The top-down search space is finite

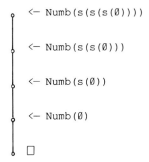

and contains only the solution of the problem. The bottom-up search space, however, is infinite.

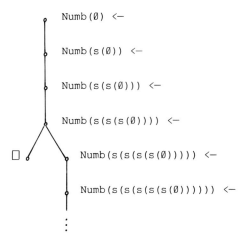

For the problem of finding a number, however, both search spaces are infinite. Moreover, both spaces contain an infinite number of solutions.

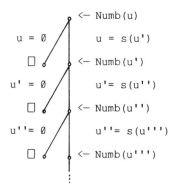

Here each arc of the top-down search space is labelled by that part of
the matching substitution which is needed to find the number u whose
existence is denied in the initial statement of the problem.

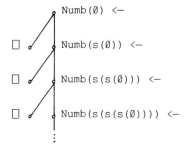

   When search spaces are infinite, depth-first search strategies are
subject to the possibility of following the wrong branch of the search
space and thus failing to find a refutation. In the present example, this
happens in the top-down search space if the clause

            Numb(s(x)) <- Numb(x)

is always used before the assertion

            Numb(0) <-

and in the bottom-up search space if

            Numb(s(x)) <- Numb(x)

is always used before the denial

            <- Numb(u) .

   To guarantee the completeness of a proof procedure, not only must the
search space be complete, but the search strategy must be _exhaustive_:
eventually investigating every node of the search space.

Definitions

Some of the concepts introduced in this chapter are defined more precisely below:

Let S be a set of Horn clauses and let there be given a selection strategy which picks a condition from any denial. A sequence of denials

$$C_1, C_2, \ldots, C_n$$

is a top-down derivation of C_n from S if

1) the first clause C_1 belongs to S and
2) every denial in the sequence, other than the first, is obtained from the preceding denial by an application of top-down inference, using a clause in S.

A derivation of the empty clause from S is a refutation of S.

Given a denial

$$\leftarrow A_1, \ldots, A_{i-1}, A_i, A_{i+1}, \ldots, A_m \qquad m \geq 1$$

with selected atom A_i and an implication

$$B \leftarrow B_1, \ldots, B_n \qquad n \geq 0$$

which shares no variables with the denial, a new denial can be obtained by top-down inference if the selected atom A_i matches the conclusion B of the implication. The new denial consists of all the conditions of the original denial (except for the selected condition) together with all the conditions of the implication, with the matching substitution θ applied:

$$\leftarrow (A_1, \ldots, A_{i-1}, B_1, \ldots, B_n, A_{i+1}, \ldots, A_m)\theta$$

If the denial and the implication contain variables in common, then they have to be renamed, giving equivalent clauses which share no variables, before top-down inference is attempted. Thus to apply top-down inference to the denial

$$\leftarrow Np(y,u), Vp(u,z)$$

using the clause

$$Np(x,y) \leftarrow Det(x,u), Noun(u,y)$$

it is necessary to rename variables first, using, for example, the variant implication

$$Np(x',y') \leftarrow Det(x',u'), Noun(u',y')$$

to obtain the new denial

$$\leftarrow Det(y,u'), Noun(u',u), Vp(u,z)$$

where the matching substitution is

$$\{x' = y, \quad y' = u\}.$$

In general, any condition can be selected in a denial. The selection strategy is of the last-in-first-out kind if the selected condition is always one of the conditions most recently introduced into the denial, in particular one of the conditions

$$B_1\theta, \ldots, B_n\theta$$

in the new denial

$$\leftarrow A_1\theta, \ldots, A_{i-1}\theta, B_1\theta, \ldots, B_n\theta, A_{i+1}\theta, \ldots, A_m\theta .$$

A top-down derivation can be represented as a graph by associating a node with every denial C_j in the derivation and by inserting an arc, from it to the next denial C_{j+1}, labelled by the implication used in the inference step.

The definition of matching substitution is needed to define both top-down and bottom-up inference and will be presented after the top-level of the definition of bottom-up inference.

It is convenient to define a graph-representation of bottom-up inference from the outset. Let S be a set of Horn clauses. A graph D with nodes labelled by assertions is a bottom-up derivation of a clause C from S if

1) D consists of a single node labelled by C, belonging to S and C is either an assertion or the empty clause, or

2) D consists of subderivations,

$$\begin{array}{ll} D_1 \text{ of } & A_1 \leftarrow \text{ from S,} \\ D_2 \text{ of } & A_2 \leftarrow \text{ from S,} \\ \quad \cdot \\ \quad \cdot \\ \quad \cdot \\ D_m \text{ of } & A_m \leftarrow \text{ from S,} \end{array}$$

whose root nodes are connected by arcs to a new node labelled by C and C is obtained from $A_1 \leftarrow$, $A_2 \leftarrow$, ..., $A_m \leftarrow$ by bottom-up inference using a clause C' in S.

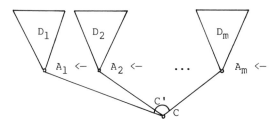

The clause C' labels the bundle of arcs associated with
the inference step.

It is convenient to define the bottom-up inference of clause C from m
assertions

$$A_1 \leftarrow , \quad A_2 \leftarrow , \quad ..., \quad A_m \leftarrow$$

using clause C' by decomposing the inference into a sequence of m simpler
inference steps. Suppose that C' has the form

$$B \leftarrow B_1, B_2, ..., B_m \quad \text{or}$$
$$\leftarrow B_1, B_2, ..., B_m.$$

The clause C is obtained by bottom-up inference using C' from

$$A_1 \leftarrow , \quad A_2 \leftarrow , \quad ..., \quad A_m \leftarrow$$

1) by selecting a condition, say B_1, of C', matching it
with   an assertion,   say $A_1 \leftarrow$,   and deriving   the
intermediate clause C"

$$(B \leftarrow B_2, ..., B_m)\theta \quad \text{or}$$
$$(\leftarrow B_2, ..., B_m)\theta$$

where θ is the matching substitution and

2) deriving C by bottom-up inference from
$A_2 \leftarrow, ..., A_m \leftarrow$ using C".

3) If m=1 then C = C".

4) In step (1) the variables in $A_1 \leftarrow$ need to be distinct
from those in C'. If necessary, variables need to be
renamed to make them distinct.

It can be shown that the conditions in C' can be selected in any order
without affecting the clause C which is finally derived.

The assertions $A_1 \leftarrow$, $A_2 \leftarrow$,   ..., $A_m \leftarrow$ to which bottom-up
inference is applied need not all be distinct. For example, the assertion

Friends(Narcissus, Narcissus) $\leftarrow$

can be derived in one step of bottom-up inference from two copies of the
assertion

Likes(Narcissus, Narcissus) $\leftarrow$

using the clause

Friends(x,y) $\leftarrow$ Likes(x,y), Likes(y,x).

Substitution and matching

It remains to define the notions of substitution and matching.

A substitution

$$\{x_1 = t_1, \ldots, x_m = t_m\}$$

is a set of substitution components of the form

$$x_i = t_i$$

where x_i is a variable and t_i is a term. Distinct substitution components of a substitution

$$x_i = t_i \quad \text{and} \quad x_j = t_j$$

have distinct variables x_i and x_j. Thus a substitution can be regarded as a function which maps variables onto terms. If E is an expression (term, atom, or clause) then the result of applying the substitution

$$\theta = \{x_1 = t_1, \ldots, x_m = t_m\}$$

to E is a new expression

$$E\theta$$

which is identical to E except that for every component $x_i = t_i$ which belongs to θ, wherever E contains an occurrence of x_i, $E\theta$ contains an occurrence of t_i. The new expression $E\theta$ is said to be an instance of E.

A substitution σ unifies the two expressions E_1 and E_2 if it makes them identical, i.e.

$$E_1\sigma = E_2\sigma.$$

$E_1\sigma$ is the common instance of E_1 and E_2 determined by σ. A substitution θ matches E_1 and E_2 (is a most general unifier of E_1 and E_2) if

1) θ unifies E_1 and E_2 and

2) the common instance
$$E_1\sigma$$
determined by any other unifier σ of E_1 and E_2 is an instance of the common instance
$$E_1\theta$$
determined by θ. Thus
$$E_1\sigma = (E_1\theta)\lambda$$
for some substitution λ.

Every pair of expressions which can be unified can also be matched. Moreover, all matching substitutions are equivalent, in the sense that the common instances they determine are variants.

Correctness and completeness of inference systems

A system of inference rules is <u>correct</u> (or <u>sound</u>) if every set of clauses which has a refutation constructed in accordance with the inference rules is inconsistent. The system is <u>complete</u> if every inconsistent set has a refutation. The notions of correctness and completeness connect semantics with the part of syntax concerned with proof theory. An inference system which is both correct and complete is one for which the semantic notion of inconsistency coincides with the proof theoretic notion of refutability. The correctness of top-down and bottom-up inference is easy to verify.

Bottom-up inference is a special case of the hyper-resolution rule defined and proved complete by Robinson [1965b]. Top-down inference is a form of the model elimination rule introduced and proved by Loveland [1968, 1969]. Like hyper-resolution, model elimination applies to arbitrary sets of clauses. In both cases for non-Horn clauses, however, an additional rule of inference, the factoring rule, discussed in Chapter 7, is needed for completeness.

Many forms of top-down inference have been developed, notably linear resolution [Loveland 1970], [Luckham 1970], ordered linear resolution [Reiter 1971], SL-resolution [Kowalski and Kuehner 1971], G-deduction [Michie et al 1972], inter-connectivity graph resolution [Sickel 1976] and analytic resolution [Brand 1976]. Linear resolution employs no restriction on the selection of atoms for top-down inference. Given a denial containing n atoms it potentially investigates the n! redundant sequences in which the atoms can be selected. The other systems, including model elimination, employ last-in-first-out selection procedures. The importance of selecting atoms in a more flexible manner will be studied in the next two chapters. Completeness for top-down inference systems employing arbitrary selection procedures has been proved by several authors including Brown [1973] and Hill [1974].

Top-down and bottom-up inference are special cases of the resolution rule [Robinson 1965a]. A system which mixes top-down and bottom-up inference for Horn clauses has been described by Kuehner [1972]. The connection graph proof procedure [Kowalski 1974a] investigated in Chapter 8 combines both directions of inference for non-Horn clauses as well. A non-resolution system which uses the standard form of logic rather than clausal form has been developed for applications in mathematical theorem-proving by Bledsoe and his colleagues [1971, 1977]. His system also combines bottom-up reasoning forwards from assumptions together with top-down reasoning backwards from conclusions.

Exercises

1) A string of items can be regarded as a directed graph whose nodes are spaces and whose arcs are labelled by items connecting one space to the next. An arc labelled by an item connecting space x to space y

can be represented by means of a three place relationship

$$Conn(x,w,y).$$

Thus the assertions

$$Conn(4,D,2) \leftarrow$$
$$Conn(2,A,3) \leftarrow$$
$$Conn(3,D,f) \leftarrow$$

represent the string

$$D \; A \; D$$

whose spaces are arbitrarily named

$$4, \; 2, \; 3, \; f \; .$$

A string is a <u>palindrome</u> if it reads the same backwards as it does forwards. Express the following more precise definition by means of Horn clauses.

a) A string from space x to space y is a palindrome if the item from x to x' is the same as the item from y' to y and the string from x' to y' is a palindrome.

b) A string from x to y is a palindrome if there is an item from x to y.

c) A string from x to x is a palindrome.

Construct both top-down and bottom-up solutions for the problem of showing that the string D A D is a palindrome.

2) Let strings be represented by means of the three place Conn relation as in exercise (1).

a) Define by means of Horn clauses the relationships

Identical(w,x,u,v) which holds when the string from u to v consists of w copies of the same item x, i.e.

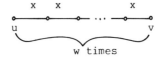

Admissible(u,v) which holds when, for some i, the string from u to v consists of i copies of item a followed by i copies of item b followed by i copies of c, i.e. has the form

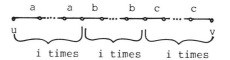

b)   Exhibit the entire top–down and bottom–up search spaces
        for the problem of showing that the string a b c is
        admissible.   In the case of the top–down search space
        select conditions in a manner which minimises the size of
        the search space.

3) Using the clause

          Distance(x,y,w) <— Distance(x,z,u), Distance(z,y,v), Plus(u,v,w)

and any assertions such as

          Plus(3,2,5) <—
          Plus(5,4,9) <—

which are necessary for the Plus relation, construct top–down and bottom–
up solutions to the problem

          <— Distance(A,M,w)

for the graph shown in exercise (7) of Chapter 1. How many distinct
solutions does the top–down search space contain? Is the problem

          <— Distance(x,x,w)

solvable?

4) The relation x ≤ y can be defined by the Horn clauses

          0 ≤ x <—
          s(x) ≤ s(y) <— x ≤ y.

Generate the top–down and bottom–up search spaces (where they are finite)
for the following problems.

          a)   <— s(s(0)) ≤ s(s(s(0)))

          b)   <— s(s(0))) ≤ w

          c)   <— w ≤ s(s(0))

          d)   <— s(s(w)) ≤ s(w)

          e)   <— s(s(w)) ≤ s(0)

5) Define the relation Plus(x,y,z) which holds when x+y = z. You can
use two clauses, one for the case x is 0, the other for the case x is
s(x').

6) Assume that the relations

Plus(x,y,z) and Times(u,v,w)

are defined by variable-free assertions and hold whenever x+y = z and u*v = w respectively.

a)   Let Exp(x,y,z) stand for the relation x to the exponent y is z, written x↑y = z. Express the following sentences in clausal form, without using function symbols.

x↑1 = x   for all x.
x↑(u+v) = y*z   if x↑u = y and x↑v = z.
x↑u = z   if x↑(u+v) = w and x↑v = y and y*z = w.

b)   Using the clauses from part (a) solve the following problems by means of both top-down and bottom-up refutations.

If 2↑a = 10 and a+a = b, then find w such that 2↑b = w.
If 3↑c = 12 and b+1 = c then find w such that 3↑b = w.
Show that for every x there is a z such that x↑0 = z.

You may need to assume such obvious facts about multiplication as Times(1,x,x) ← .

CHAPTER 4

Horn Clause Problem-Solving

When logic is used to express problems and problem-solving methods, proof procedures behave as problem-solvers. We shall argue that Horn clause inference subsumes many of the alternative models of problem-solving developed in artificial intelligence.

In this chapter we compare Horn clause inference both with the path-finding model of the Graph Traverser [Doran and Michie 1966] and the General Problem Solver [Newell and Simon 1963] and with the and-or tree model of problem-reduction [Gelernter 1963], [Nilsson 1971]. In the next chapter we compare Horn clause inference with problem-solving regarded as execution of programs. In subsequent chapters we investigate both the use of non-Horn clauses in problem-solving (Chapters 7 and 8) as well as more global problem-solving strategies (Chapter 9).

The close relationship between problem-reduction and top-down inference has been observed by several authors, including [Kowalski and Kuehner 1971], [Loveland and Stickel 1973], [Pople 1973], [Van der Brug and Minker 1975]. Moreover it is already implicit in the Logic Theorist [1963], The General Problem-Solver and the Geometry Theorem Proving Machine [Gelernter 1963].

Path-finding

It is possible to express any problem as a path-finding problem.

> Given an initial state A, a goal state Z, and operators which transform one state into another, the problem is to find a path from A to Z.

The water containers problem

The water-containers problem can be formulated naturally as a path-finding problem.

Given   7 litres   5 litres   both empty

Goal   4 litres   don't care

Given both a seven and a five litre container, initially empty, the goal is to find a sequence of actions which leaves four litres of liquid in the seven litre container. There are three kinds of actions which can alter the state of the containers:

(1) A container can be filled.

(2) A container can be emptied.

(3) Liquid can be poured from one container into the other, until the first is empty or the second is full.

The water-containers problem has a simple Horn clause formulation. Interpret

State(u,v) as expressing that there is a state in which the 7 litre container contains u litres of liquid and the 5 litre container contains v litres.

Assume that the relations

$$x + y = z \qquad \text{and} \qquad x \leq y$$

are already defined (by infinitely many variable-free assertions, for example).

WC1	State(0,0) $\leftarrow$
WC2	$\leftarrow$ State(4,y)
WC3	State(7,y) $\leftarrow$ State(x,y)
WC4	State(x,5) $\leftarrow$ State(x,y)
WC5	State(0,y) $\leftarrow$ State(x,y)
WC6	State(x,0) $\leftarrow$ State(x,y)
WC7	State(0,y) $\leftarrow$ State(u,v), u+v = y, y $\leq$ 5
WC8	State(x,0) $\leftarrow$ State(u,v), u+v = x, x $\leq$ 7
WC9	State(7,y) $\leftarrow$ State(u,v), u+v = w, 7+$\underline{y}$ = w
WC10	State(x,5) $\leftarrow$ State(u,v), u+v = w, 5+x = w

Clauses WC1 and WC2 express the given and the goal states respectively. WC3 and WC4 define the action of filling a container. WC5 and WC6 define emptying a container. WC7 and WC8 define pouring from one container into another until the first is empty. WC9 and WC10 define pouring from one into another until the second is full.

Before investigating the top-down and bottom-up search spaces, it is useful to define the graph-representation of search spaces. First we shall consider a simplified version of the path-finding problem and its Horn clause formulation.

A simplified path-finding problem

Suppose the problem is to find a path from node A to node Z in the following graph.

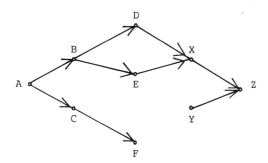

The problem can be formulated with a one-place predicate

Go (x)

which expresses that it is possible to go to node x. Later in the chapter we shall compare this formulation with the one (suggested by semantic networks) which employs a two-place predicate

Go* (x,y)

expressing that it is possible to go from node x to node y.

Go (A) <—	<— Go (Z)
Go (B) <— Go (A)	Go (C) <— Go (A)
Go (D) <— Go (B)	Go (F) <— Go (C)
Go (E) <— Go (B)	Go (X) <— Go (D)
Go (Z) <— Go (X)	Go (X) <— Go (E)
Go (Z) <— Go (Y)	

In this formulation the clauses which describe the graph behave as path-finding procedures which connect adjacent nodes. The top-down and bottom-up search spaces are both trees.

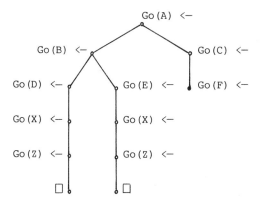

Bottom-up search space

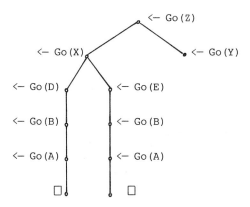

Top-down search space

In both search spaces there is a one-to-one correspondence between refutations and solution paths. Both search spaces, however, contain undesirable redundancies. The bottom-up search space derives the assertion Go(X) <- in two different ways and then redundantly uses it twice in the same way to obtain two refutations. The top-down search space derives the goal statement <- Go(B) in two different ways and then redundantly solves it twice in the same way. These redundancies can be eliminated by representing the search spaces as graphs rather than as trees.

Graph-representation of search spaces

The graph-representation of a search space is obtained from the tree-representation by identifying nodes which have the same label.   Thus no clause occurs in the graph-representation more than once.

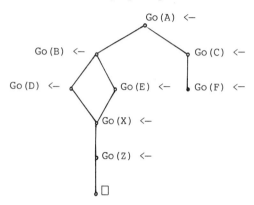

Graph-representation of the bottom-up search space

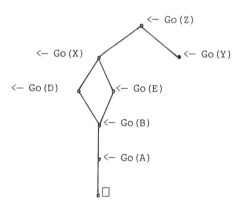

Graph-representation of the top-down search space

Use of the graph-representation suggests that whenever a search strategy generates a clause in the search space, it checks whether the clause has been generated before. If it has, then only one occurrence of the clause is retained. Generally, the new occurrence is deleted.

The graph-representation can turn an infinite search space into a finite one.   The top-down search space for the problem of finding a path from A to Z in the following graph is a simple example.

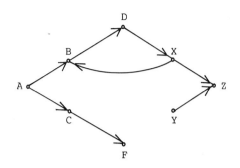

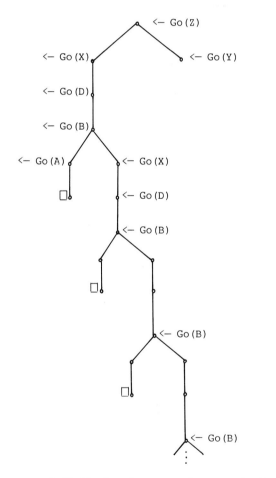

Infinite top-down search space in the tree representation

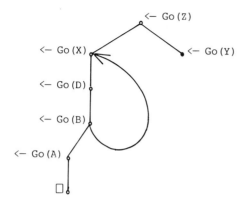

Finite <u>top-down</u> <u>search</u> <u>space</u> <u>in</u> <u>the</u> <u>graph-representation</u>

The Search Spaces for the Water Containers Problem

We can now exhibit the graph representations of the search spaces for the water containers problem. In order to avoid complicating the appearance of the search spaces, arcs which lead to nodes labelled by clauses which already occur elsewhere in the search space are not always shown.

The top-down search space is more complicated than the bottom-up search space. Notice, however, that the matching substitutions which are generated in the first step of both branches of the top-down search space determine that if the goal

<- State(4,x)

has a solution, then x must be either 0 or 5.

Generally speaking, the conclusions of clauses WC3-10 will not match any goal state which cannot have at least one container either full or empty. For this reason, in the clause

<- State(u,v), u+v = 9

it is easier to select the second goal which generates pairs of integers adding up to 9, and to reject those yielding impossible goal states than it is to solve the subgoals in the other sequence.

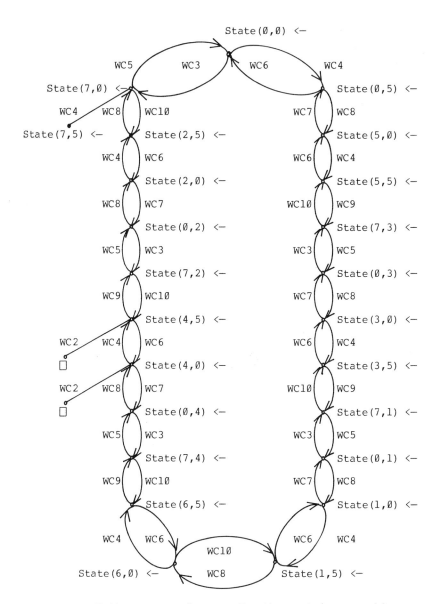

Bottom-up search space for the containers problem

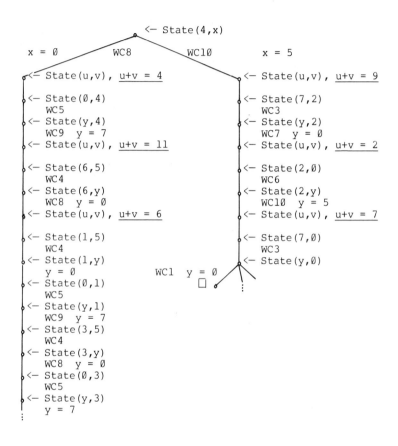

Top-down search space for the containers problem

Search strategies for path-finding

The path-finding model of problem-solving is concerned more with the development of search strategies than it is with the structure of search spaces and the representation of information. Given the task of finding a path in a graph, the search problem becomes one of devising intelligent strategies for searching the graph.

Most search strategies for path-finding employ some form of guidance by evaluation functions. Given a search space, an <u>evaluation function</u> f applied to nodes in the space produces real numbers as values. The value f(N) of a node N is intended to measure the usefulness of continuing the search from that node. The greater the value of the node the more promising it is to apply operators to it. <u>heuristic search</u> strategy, guided by the evaluation function, always searches from the node of currently greatest value.

Breadth-first and depth-first search can be regarded as special cases of heuristic search. In depth-first search, the value of a node is its distance from the start node. In breadth-first search, it is the inverse of its distance from the start node. In both cases, the distance between two nodes is measured simply by the number of arcs contained in the currently shortest path connecting the nodes.

In a typical path-finding problem, a node in the search space represents a state of some collection of objects. If there are n objects, a state can be represented by the n-tuple consisting of the individual states of the objects. In the water containers problem, for example, there are two objects which can be in one of the eight states 0-7. Such <u>state-space</u> path-finding problems can easily be represented with Horn clauses by using a predicate

$$State(x_1, x_2, \ldots, x_m)$$

which expresses that the state in which

> the 1st individual is in state x_1
> the 2nd individual is in state x_2
> .
> .
> .
> the mth individual is in state x_m

is possible.

Special evaluation functions are useful for such state-space problems. In the simplest case, given a node

$$N = State(s_1, s_2, \ldots, s_m)$$

(which is either an assertion or a goal, depending on the direction of the search space) and searching for a node

$$T = State(t_1, t_2, \ldots, t_m)$$

the distance between N and T might be estimated by the sum of the distances between the individual states.

$$dist(t_1, s_1) + dist(t_2, s_2) + \ldots + dist(t_m, s_m)$$

The value of a node is greater the smaller its estimated distance to T. More sophisticated evaluation functions might estimate overall distance by a weighted sum of individual distances or by a more complex function of individual distances (such as the square root of the weighted sum of the squares of the distances).

In many path-finding problems, costs are associated with nodes or arcs of the graph and the problem is to find the least costly path connecting the given and goal nodes. In the water-containers problem, for example, it might be required to find the shortest solution. In such cases, the greater the cost of reaching a node the smaller is its value. Both evaluation function guided search strategies [Nilsson 1971] and branch-and-bound [Lawler and Wood 1966] are useful for such problems.

It is not always possible or desirable to use a numerical-valued evaluation function to guide the search strategy. It may be possible, none the less, to define a merit ordering among nodes in the search space.   The search strategy, guided by the merit ordering, always searches from a node having the greatest merit.

Since a top-down refutation can be regarded as a path from an initial set of goals to the empty clause, the problem of finding a refutation in a top-down Horn clause search space can be regarded as a path-finding problem and the theory of heuristic search can be applied. However, it must be modified when applied to bottom-up search spaces where solutions are more naturally regarded as trees or graphs [Kowalski 1972]. Even in the case of top-down search spaces the heuristic search path-finding model of problem-solving does not address the important problem of selecting subgoals. These deficiencies are remedied by the problem-reduction model of problem-solving and its associated and-or tree representation.

The and-or tree representation of problem-reduction

In the problem-reduction model of problem-solving the task is to find a solution to an initially given problem, using a given collection of assertions and procedures to reduce problems to subproblems. The task is accomplished by repeatedly applying procedures to unsolved problems, replacing them by subproblems, until the initial problem has eventually been replaced by the empty set of subproblems.

In the and-or tree representation of problem-reduction, nodes of the tree are labelled by problems:

(1)   The root node is labelled by the initial problem.

(2)   If a problem A labels a node and a procedure reduces A to the subproblems $A_1, A_2, \ldots, A_m$ then the node is connected by a bundle of directed arcs to nodes labelled by the individual subproblems. The bundle itself may be labelled by the procedure.

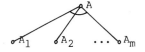

(3) If the problem A labelling a node matches an assertion, then
     it is connected by a single arc to a node labelled by the
     empty collection of subproblems.

The figure below illustrates both the and-or tree representation and
the Horn clause representation for a simple problem-reduction task.

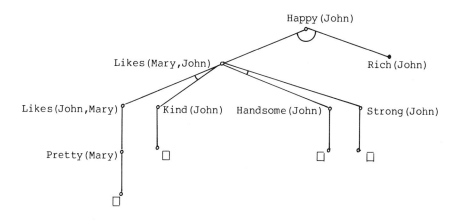

Initial Problem   <- Happy(John)

Procedures   Happy(John) <- Rich(John)
                       Happy(John) <- Likes(Mary,John)
                       Likes(Mary,John) <- Likes(John,Mary), Kind(John)
                       Likes(Mary,John) <- Handsome(John), Strong(John)
                       Likes(John,Mary) <- Pretty(Mary)

Assertions   Pretty(Mary)   <-
                       Kind(John)   <-
                       Handsome(John) <-
                       Strong(John)   <-

    The problem has two solutions which can be represented as subtrees of
the and-or tree:

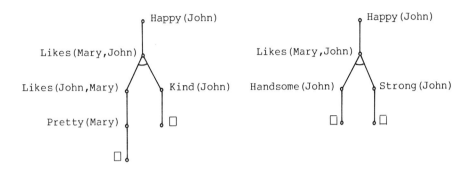

one solution   the other solution

The <u>and-or graph representation</u> is obtained from the and-or tree representation by identifying all nodes which are labelled by the same subproblem. In the example below, the and-or graph representation turns an infinite and-or tree search space into a finite one. The problem has no solution.

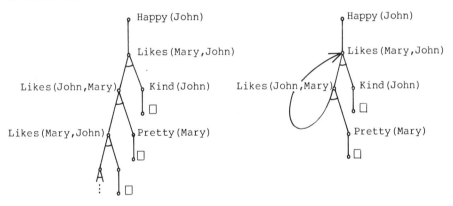

and-or tree representation   and-or graph representation

Initial Problem   <- Happy(John)

Procedures   Happy(John) <- Likes(Mary,John)
                       Likes(Mary,John) <- Likes(John,Mary) , Kind(John)
                       Likes(John,Mary) <- Likes(Mary,John) , Pretty(Mary)

Assertions   Pretty(Mary) <-
                       Kind(John)   <-

Both the and-or tree and and-or graph representations of problem-reduction focus attention on the structure of the search space and on search strategies. However, they ignore both the structure of the problems which label the nodes of the search space and the connection between problems in the form of shared variables. The Horn clause model of problem-reduction represents problems by atomic formulae and makes explicit (in the form of matching substitutions) the information which is generated when a procedure or assertion is applied to a problem.

The problem-solving interpretation of Horn clauses

The problem-solving interpretation of Horn clauses is basically the top-down interpretation.

The atoms in a denial $\leftarrow A_1,\ldots,A_m$ are interpreted as problems, or goals, to be solved. If the denial contains the variables $x_1,\ldots,x_k$ then it is interpreted as stating the goal:

Find $x_1,\ldots,x_k$
which solve the problems $A_1,\ldots,A_m$.

and is called a goal statement.

An implication $A \leftarrow A_1,\ldots,A_m$ is interpreted as a problem-solving method, or procedure:

To solve a problem of the form A,
solve the subproblems $A_1,\ldots,A_m$.

Given a problem B which matches A, the procedure reduces the solution of B to the solution of the subproblems

$$A_1\Theta,\ldots,A_m\Theta$$

where Θ is the matching substitution. We say both that the procedure matches A and that it applies to A.

An assertion $A \leftarrow$ is interpreted as a procedure which solves problems directly without reducing them to further subproblems.

The empty clause □ is interpreted as the empty goal statement.

The and-or tree and and-or graph representations can be extended to Horn clause problem-reduction in general. It is necessary to represent the contribution of a procedure to the values of the variables in the problem to which the procedure is applied. In the extended and-or tree representation, each bundle of arcs is labelled by that part of the matching substitution (called the output component) which affects variables in the problem under consideration. The figure below illustrates the extended and-or tree representation for the fallible Greek problem of Chapter 1.

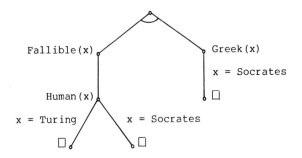

In general, the substitution θ which matches a problem B with a procedure A $\leftarrow$ $A_1,\ldots,A_m$ can be decomposed into two parts $\theta = \theta_i \cup \theta_{\emptyset}$.

(1)   One part θ_i affects variables in the procedure. It passes input from the problem to be solved to the procedure which tries to solve it. θ_i is called the input component of the matching substitution.

(2)   The other part $\theta_{\emptyset}$ affects variables in the problem to be solved. It passes output from the procedure to the problem whose solution is being attempted. $\theta_{\emptyset}$ is called the output component of the matching substitution.

Thus the procedure reduces the problem B to the collection of subproblems

$$A_1\theta_i,\ldots,A_m\theta_i$$

whereas the output component $\theta_{\emptyset}$ is the procedure's contribution to finding the values of the variables in B.

When the matching substitution makes a variable, say x, in the problem identical to a variable, say y, in the procedure, then it is useful to treat the substitution as transmitting input and to include y = x in the input component of the matching substitution.

Splitting and independent subgoals

An important characteristic of the and-or tree representation is that it explicitly exhibits the splitting of a goal statement into separate subgoals. Splitting is especially useful when the subgoals share no variables. Subgoals which share no variables are independent and can be solved by different problem-solvers working independently.

In the family relationships example the two subgoals in the initial goal statement

$\leftarrow$ Parent(x,Ares), Parent(Ares,z)

share no variables and are independent.

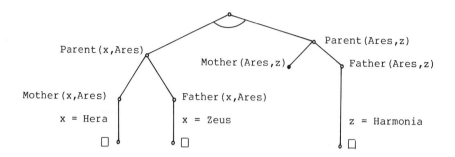

Any solution to the problem of finding an x which is a parent of Ares is compatible with any solution to the problem of finding a z which is a child of Ares. Problem-solvers could work on the separate problems simultaneously without danger of interfering with one another.

Top-down search spaces whose nodes are labelled by goal statements contain redundancies when subgoals are independent. This is illustrated by the goal statement search space for the previous problem. The same abbreviations are used as in the previous chapter.

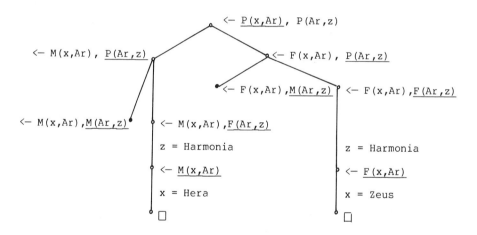

Here the subgoal of finding a child of Ares is redundantly considered twice, once in the context of the goal statement <- M(x,Ar), P(Ar,z) and again in the context of the goal statement <- F(x,Ar), P(Ar,z). In the and-or tree search space the subgoal is represented only once.

More generally, given an initial goal statement <- A, B, n ways of solving A and m ways of solving B, the goal statement top-down search space contains n*m branches, whereas the and-or tree contains only n+m.

Dependent subgoals

The extended and-or tree representation does not specify the relationship between the solution of a goal statement and the solution of its separate subgoals. In particular, the problem-solving interpretation leaves open the possibility that a goal statement

$$\leftarrow A_1, \ldots, A_m$$

might be solved by

(1) independently solving the separate subgoals, obtaining associated substitutions $\theta_1, \ldots, \theta_m$ which solve the subgoals and then

(2) combining the separate substitutions to obtain a solution of the goal statement itself.

If the subgoals are independent then it suffices to combine the separate substitutions by taking their union. If they are dependent then it is necessary to combine them by finding a most general common instance of the substitutions. For example, the combined substitution for the independent subgoals in the goal statement

$$\leftarrow \text{Parent}(x, \text{Ares}), \ \text{Parent}(\text{Ares}, z)$$

is simply the union

$$\{x = \text{Hera}, \quad z = \text{Harmonia}\}$$

of the individual substitutions. But the combined substitution for the dependent subgoals

$$\leftarrow 0 < y, \ \text{Even}(y)$$

given the separate substitutions

$$\{y = s(y')\} \quad \text{and} \quad \{y = s(s(0))\},$$

is obtained by matching the two values for y giving

$$\{y = s(s(0))\}.$$

Top-down goal-statement search spaces make explicit both the dependencies among sub-goals and the effect on the size of the search space of solving different subgoals in different sequences. The and-or tree search space for the problem of the fallible Greek, for example, is independent of the order in which the top level goals are solved. The goal statement search spaces, however, are quite different. Solving goals in one sequence we obtain a search space containing alternative branches, whereas solving them in a different sequence generates a search space consisting only of the solution itself. Notice that, as in the extended and-or tree representation, it is useful to label arcs by the output component of the matching substitution.

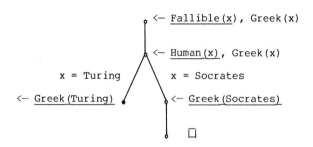

One top-down search space

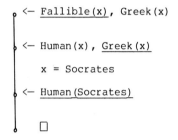

Another search space

For the remainder of the book we shall use goal statement search spaces (in preference to extended and-or tree spaces), because they make it easier to show the effect of the subgoal selection strategy on the size of the search space. In practice, computer implementations of Horn clause problem-solving systems use a representation which combines features of both and-or tree and goal-statement spaces.

The goal statement search spaces for the fallible Greek problem illustrate a general principle. When subgoals are dependent, select one to which the fewest procedures apply. The aim is to minimise the overall size of the search space by locally minimising the number of alternative branches which emanate from any node.

Finding versus showing

Logic does not distinguish between procedures which show that a given relationship holds and procedures which find individuals for which it holds. Thus the grandparent procedure, for example, is able not only to show that one individual is grandparent of another but also to find both grandparents and grandchildren.

The difference between showing and finding is indicated by the presence or absence of variables. In general, the more variables a problem contains, the more finding there is to be done.

Any procedure which applies to a showing problem P(t) also applies to the corresponding finding problem P(x). Thus the search space for a finding problem is generally larger than it is for a showing problem. This suggests the principle of <u>selecting a subgoal which involves least finding and most showing</u>. This principle is subsumed by the one which selects the subgoal to which fewest procedures apply, but it is easier to apply. It requires only an analysis of the subgoals under consideration rather than an analysis of all the matching procedures as well.

Applying these principles to the grandparent procedure

$$\text{Grandparent}(x,y) \longleftarrow \text{Parent}(x,z), \text{Parent}(z,y)$$

results in the selection of different subgoals depending on the form of the problem to be solved:

(1) Given x, to find grandchildren y of x, first find children z of x, then find children y of z.

(2) Given y, to find grandparents x of y, first find parents z of y, then find parents x of z.

(3) Given both x and y, to show x is grandparent of y, compare the number n of children of x with the number m (two) of parents of y.
If n < m, first find children z of x then show they are parents of y.
If n > m, first find parents z of y and then show they are children of x.
If n = m, it doesn't matter which of the two subgoals is selected first.

(4) Given neither x nor y, to find individuals in the grandparent relationship, it doesn't matter which subgoal is selected first.

The principle of preference for subgoals to which fewest procedures apply has two aspects. On one hand, it is a <u>principle of procrastination</u>, which delays as long as possible the selection of explosive subgoals that can be solved in many ways. On the other hand, it is a <u>principle of eager consideration</u> of subgoals which can be solved in few ways.

The principle of procrastination can lead to smaller searches in two ways. When subgoals share variables, delaying the selection of a finding problem (which can be solved in many ways) can turn it into a more manageable showing problem which can be solved in fewer ways. Finding the values of variables may be done more efficiently by selecting other, less explosive, dependent subgoals. Whether subgoals are dependent or not, it may be possible to postpone the consideration of explosive subproblems until after the initial problem has been solved by alternative methods. By then, whether or not the explosive subproblem has been instantiated it can be ignored.

The principle of eager consideration is of particular utility when a subgoal can be solved in at most one way. To solve a goal statement, all its subgoals have to be solved. Therefore, if a goal statement contains an unsolvable subgoal, which matches no procedure, then the selection and recognition of the unsolvable subgoal demonstrates the unsolvability of the goal statement as a whole; hence we avoid the unnecessary consideration of other subgoals in the same goal statement. When only a single procedure matches a given subgoal, then it must be applied sooner or later, if the goal statement has a solution. Early consideration has the advantage that any information in the form of values for variables can be obtained as soon as possible and communicated to other dependent subgoals. Moreover, if the procedure eventually fails to solve the subgoal, then consideration of other more explosive subgoals in the same goal statement may be avoided.

The number of procedures (including assertions) which apply to a given subgoal is only a local approximation to the total number of ways the subgoal can be solved. It can be misleading in some cases. Better approximations can be obtained by employing look-ahead techniques similar to the mini-max methods discussed later in this chapter.

The effect of different strategies for selecting subgoals on the size of the search space is more pronounced when composite terms, constructed by means of function symbols, are involved. The effect of composite terms on the selection of subgoals will be investigated in the next chapter.

Lemmas, duplicate subgoals and loops

Many features of the extended and-or graph representation can be incorporated into the top-down goal statement representation by generating lemmas which record the solution of solved subgoals. When a subgoal is solved, an assertion can be generated which solves the subgoal directly in one step. Such assertions are lemmas, which are found by top-down deduction but could have been generated bottom-up. Thus a lemma which has been generated when a subgoal is solved in the context of one goal statement can be used to solve the same subgoal directly when it arises again in the context of another goal statement.

To achieve the problem-solving power of and-or graphs, negative lemmas also need to be generated when a subgoal is recognised as unsolvable. Negative lemmas can be used to recognise that the same subgoal is unsolvable when it arises again in another context.

The generation of positive lemmas was first described by Loveland [1969] for the top-down model-elimination proof procedure. Both positive and negative lemma generation are incorporated into the top-down parsing procedure for context-free grammars devised by Earley [1970]. An equivalent of lemma generation in Horn clause problem-solving has been proposed by Warren [unpublished] as an extension of the Earley parsing procedure.

The simple case, where duplicate subgoals occur in the same goal statement, can be dealt with directly - simply by deleting all but one of the duplicate occurrences. Such merging of duplicate atoms in the same clause is a special case of the factoring rule described in Chapter 7.

It is also a special case of the rule for deleting redundant subgoals, described in Chapter 9.

Perhaps the most important case of duplicate subgoals arises when a goal occurs as its own subgoal. This is one of the situations that leads to loops and to infinite search spaces. Given a goal B and a matching procedure

$$A \leftarrow A_1, A_2, \ldots, A_m$$

each of the goals $A_1\theta, A_2\theta, \ldots, A_m\theta$ where θ is the matching substitution is a subgoal of B. Moreover, any subgoal of a subgoal of B is also a subgoal of B. Thus one goal is subgoal of another if they both occur on the same branch of the and-or tree search space.

Loop detection procedures, which test whether a goal occurs as its own subgoal, are a feature of Loveland's model elimination procedure and of S1-resolution. More general loop detection strategies, which test whether a goal subsumes a subgoal, have been investigated by Derek Brough [1979] and have been incorporated into a Horn clause problem-solving system implemented at Imperial College.

Search strategies for problem-reduction spaces

Search strategies for and-or trees and graphs are extensions of those for path-finding. They differ primarily because they combine the evaluation of procedures with the selection of subgoals.

The mini-max and alpha-beta strategies [see Nilsson 71] are commonly employed when and-or trees represent game playing problems. Individual subgoals represent states of the game. Alternative procedures which apply to a given subgoal represent the problem-solver's alternative moves for the state represented by the subgoal. The bundle of subgoals which results from the application of a procedure represents the states associated with all the opponent's alternative responses to the problem solver's move.

The value of a move (represented by a procedure) for the problem-solver is only as great as the opponent's strongest response. Thus the value of applying a procedure is the minimum of the values of the subgoals in the bundle associated with the procedure. The value of an individual state of the game (represented by a subgoal) on the other hand, is as great as the problem-solver's best move. Hence the value of a subgoal is the maximum of the values of the procedures which apply to the subgoal.

Given an initial evaluation of subgoals, mini-max evaluation looks ahead into the search space and provides a revised, more accurate evaluation of subgoals. It can be used not only for game playing but for problem-reduction in general. An appropriately modified version of mini-max evaluation can be used specifically to improve the criterion for selecting subgoals. A general method for using 'look-ahead' to improve evaluation functions for clausal theorem-proving has been developed for the connection graph proof procedure [Kowalski 1974a] presented in Chapter 8.

For many problem-reduction applications it is more appropriate to use
some form of depth-first search. This is efficient to implement because
only one branch of the top-down search space is considered at any time.
When no untried procedure applies to the selected subgoal in the goal
statement at the end of the branch, the search strategy backtracks to the
next-to-last node of the branch and tries to solve the selected subgoal
there in an alternative way. For this reason depth-first search is also
called <u>backtracking</u>.

Although backtracking   is effective in   many cases it   can be
distressingly unintelligent in others. Both successful and unsuccessful
applications of backtracking are illustrated by the arch recognition
problem.

Consider, for example, the problem of recognising an arch in the
following scene:

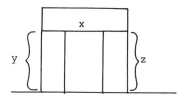

It is convenient to name an arch by means of a function symbol which
collects together the immediate constituents of the arch. We let the term

$$a(y,x,z)$$

name the arch

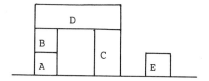

which consists of block x on top of left tower y and right tower z. A
tower can be named by using a function symbol which combines the block on
top of the tower with the subtower beneath it. We let the term

$$t(u,v)$$

name the tower

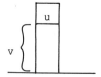

which consists of block u on top of tower v. Thus t(B,A) names the tower comprising block B on top of block A; a(t(B,A),D,C) names the arch in the scene above. The scene and the definitions of arch and tower are represented by clauses A1-12.

A1   Arch(a(y,x,z)) <— Block(x), Tower(y),
                                  Tower(z), On(x,y), On(x,z)

A2   Tower(x)   <— Block(x)
A3   Tower(t(x,y)) <— Block(x), Tower(y), On(x,y)

A4   On(x, t(y,z)) <— On(x,y)

A5   Block(A) <—
A6   Block(B) <—
A7   Block(C) <—
A8   Block(D) <—
A9   Block(E) <—

A10   On(B,A) <—
A11   On(D,B) <—
A12   On(D,C) <—

Clause A4 reduces the problem of determining whether a block is on a tower to that of determining whether the block is on the block which is on top of the tower.

The definition of arch A1 is unsatisfactory for several reasons (see exercise 5). The problems which arise with backtracking, however, are independent of them.

Consider the problem

          <— Arch(a(t(B,A), D, C))

of recognising the arch in which block D is both on the tower B on A and on the tower C. Using A1 and solving subproblems in any sequence, the top-down search space consists of just the single path which solves the problem. No search strategy, including backtracking, behaves unintelligently.

Suppose, however, that the problem is to find an arch in the scene

          <— Arch(w).

Assume that subproblems are selected and procedures are applied in the order in which they are written. Because such strategies are especially easy to implement, they are incorporated in many computer-based problem-solving systems. The initial problem quickly reduces to an unsolvable goal statement.

```
                        o <- Arch(w)
             A1         |
 w = a(y,x,z)           |
                        o <- Block(x), Tower(y), Tower(z), On(x,y), On(x,z)
       x = A            |
             A5         |
                        o <- Tower(y), Tower(z), On(A,y), On(A,z)
             A2         |
                        o <- Block(y), Tower(z), On(A,y), On(A,z)
             A5         |
       y = A            |
                        o <- Tower(z), On(A,A), On(A,z)
             A2         |
                        o <- Block(z), On(A,A), On(A,z)
             A5         |
       z = A            |
                        o <- On(A,A), On(A,A)
```

                   unsolvable

The simple depth-first strategy backtracks to the previous node and searches for another block z. But changing z does not affect the unsolvability of On(x,y) so long as x and y are both A. The backtracker goes into an infinite loop, trying a potentially infinite sequence of towers z which do not affect the unsolvability of the subproblem On(x,y), where x and y are A.

Backtracking can be made more intelligent if, when generating an unsolvable subgoal, it analyses the substitutions which cause the failure (in this case x=A and y=A), and backtracks to a node where it can undo them (in this case to the goal statement containing the selected subgoal Block(y)). Efficiency can be improved by preserving intermediate solved subgoals. The backtracker can be made more intelligent by analysing the failure, not only to identify the subgoal whose solution should be undone, but also to determine how it should be done [Schmidt et al 1978]. In this example, when the subgoal On(x,y) with x=A and y=A is recognised as unsolvable, the assertion On(B,A) <- can be identified as the nearest match. The search strategy can then backtrack to the goal statement containing the selected subgoal Block(x) with substitution x=A and test whether Block(x) with x=B can be solved. Such goal-directed intelligent backtracking has the spirit of Sussman's [1975] model of problem-solving. Instead of carefully evaluating subgoals and alternative procedures, the problem-solver picks them arbitrarily. If they fail, he analyses the mistake in order to find a better method of solution.

Notice, however, that the effect of solving subgoals in an arbitrary sequence and backtracking intelligently when things go wrong can be achieved more directly by selecting the correct subgoals in the first place. In this example, it suffices to select the subgoals

                On(x,y)   and   On(x,z)

before the others in the definition A1 of the arch. Similarly, the subgoal

On(x,y)

should be selected first in the definition A3 of tower. It is necessary, moreover, to try the assertions A10-12, which define the location of blocks resting on blocks, before the procedure A4, which defines the location of blocks on towers.

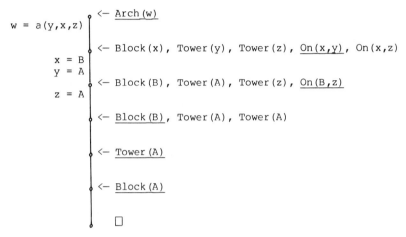

```
                        o  <- Arch(w)
w = a(y,x,z)  |
              |
              |o  <- Block(x), Tower(y), Tower(z), On(x,y), On(x,z)
      x = B   |
      y = A   |
              |o  <- Block(B), Tower(A), Tower(z), On(B,z)
      z = A   |
              |
              |o  <- Block(B), Tower(A), Tower(A)
              |
              |
              |o  <- Tower(A)
              |
              |
              |o  <- Block(A)
              |
              |
              o      □
```

Here the duplicate subgoal Tower(A) has been deleted to avoid redundancy. Notice that the first solution finds the pathological arch:

```
                    ┌───┐
                    │ B │
      a(A, B, A)    ├───┤
                  ──┤ A ├──
                    └───┘
```

Backtracking is employed in both the PLANNER [Hewitt 1969] programming language and the PROLOG [Colmerauer et al 1972] [Roussel 1975] top-down, Horn clause programming system. The inefficiencies of backtracking in PLANNER led to the development of CONNIVER [Sussman and McDermott 1972a, 1972b], a PLANNER-like programming language in which the programmer writes both problem-solving procedures and search strategies. In PROLOG, the problem-solver provides the backtracking search strategy but the programmer can control the extent of backtracking.

Various problem-solvers incorporating intelligent backtracking have been designed and implemented by Sussman and his colleagues [Sussman 1975], [Stallman and Sussman 1977], [Doyle 1978]. Intelligent Horn clause backtracking problem-solvers have also been investigated by Cox and Pietrzykowski [1976], [Cox 1978] and by Bruynooghe [1978]. Limited intelligent backtracking strategies have also been implemented in various Horn clause systems at Imperial College.

Bi-directional problem-solving

The Horn clauses which describe a typical problem-solving task can be classified into three kinds:

(1) general-purpose procedures (including assertions), which
     describe the problem-domain,

(2) problem-specific assertions, which express the hypotheses of
     the problem to be solved, and

(3) a goal statement, which expresses the problem itself.

Problem-specific assertions   can be absent   from a   given task
description. But when they are present, it may be useful to combine top-
down reasoning (from the problem to be solved) with bottom-up reasoning
(from the hypotheses of the problem). However, it is important in this
case to avoid bottom-up reasoning from assertions which are part of the
general description of the problem-domain.   This restricted use of
bottom-up reasoning combined with top-down reasoning is a characteristic
feature of Bledsoe's theorem-proving system [1971].

The majority   of bottom-up proof procedures, however, do not
distinguish betwen different types of assertions. As a result, they
generally lead to combinatorially explosive behaviour, generating
assertions which follow from the general description of the problem-
domain, in addition to assertions which follow from the assumptions of
the particular problem at hand.

A useful criterion for combining problem-specific bottom-up reasoning
with top-down reasoning is a variation of the one proposed by Pohl [1972]
for path-finding problems:

          At every step choose the direction of inference which
          gives rise to the least number of alternatives.

In the top-down direction, the number of alternatives is the smallest
number of procedures which match the selected subgoal in a goal
statement. In the bottom-up direction, it is the smallest number of
assertions which can be derived from any assertion.   The Pohl criterion
is illustrated for a path-finding problem below.

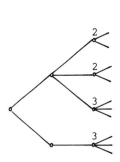

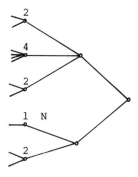

The search space generated   The search space generated
in one direction   in the other direction

The number next to each node indicates the number of successor nodes.
The Pohl criterion selects the direction associated with generating the

successor of N. Given the previous formulation of the path-finding
problem, bi-directional path-finding is accomplished by combining top-
down and bottom-up reasoning.

A notation for describing bi-directional problem-solving

The distinction between top-down and bottom-up inference can be
pictured using arrows to indicate the direction of reasoning. For every
pair of matching atoms in the initial set of clauses (of which one is a
condition and the other a conclusion) an arrow is directed from one atom
to the other.

For top-down inference, arrows are directed from conditions to
conclusions. For the grandparent problem, we obtain the following graph.

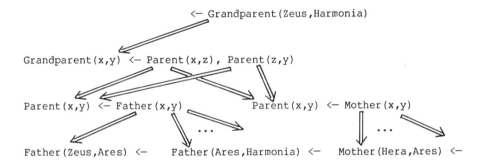

Reasoning is guided by the direction of the arrows. It starts with the
initial goal statement, is transferred within procedures from conclusions
to conditions and ends with the assertions.

For bottom-up inference, arrows are directed from conclusions to
conditions.

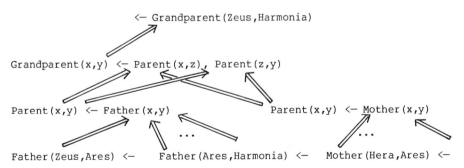

Reasoning begins with the assertions, is transferred within procedures
from conditions to conclusions, and ends with the goal statement.

The grandparent definition can also be used in a combined top-down, bottom-up manner. Different combinations can be represented by using numbers to indicate sequencing. For simplicity, we show only the notation associated with the grandparent definition. The combination of directions

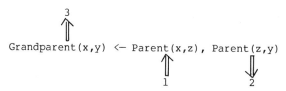

represents the algorithm which

> 1) waits until x is asserted to be parent of z, then
> 2) finds a child y of z, and finally
> 3) asserts that x is grandparent of y.

The combination indicated by

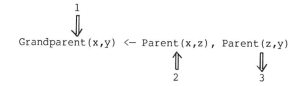

> 1) responds to the problem of showing that
>   x is grandparent of y,
> 2) by waiting until x is asserted to be parent of z, and then
> 3) attempting to show that z is parent of y.

The arrow notation can also be used for non-Horn clauses. In Chapter 8 it is used to control the behaviour of the connection graph proof procedure.

Another formulation of the path-finding problem

The effectiveness of a problem-solving strategy (such as bi-directional reasoning) depends on the problem-formulation rather than on the problem itself. This is shown by comparing the previous formulation of the path-finding problem with the one suggested by the representation of semantic networks.

In this representation we employ a predicate Go*(x,y) which expresses that it is possible to go from node x to node y. Assertions describe the arcs in the initial graph. The following assertions describe the graph at the beginning of the chapter.

```
Go*(A,B) <—          Go*(D,X) <—
Go*(A,C) <—          Go*(E,X) <—
Go*(B,D) <—          Go*(X,Z) <—
Go*(B,E) <—          Go*(Y,Z) <—
Go*(C,F) <—
```

In addition to the assertions, a single procedure is necessary for path-finding

Go*(x,y) <— Go*(x,z), Go*(z,y).

The problem of finding a path from A to Z is described by a single goal statement

<— Go*(A,Z).

Here the assertions are specific to the graph, whereas the path-finding procedure is general-purpose. However, only the goal statement is specific to the particular path in the graph. Bottom-up inference generates assertions about paths which are unmotivated by the particular path to be found. Both forward and backward search, as well as bi-directional search, can be accomplished by top-down inference alone. The direction of search depends on the choice of subgoal in the path-finding procedure. Selecting Go*(x,z) before Go*(z,y) is forward search. Selecting the two subgoals in parallel or timesharing between them gives rise to bi-directional search.

The path-finding problem can be formulated in different ways; the same problem-solving behaviour can be obtained from different formulations by applying different problem-solving strategies. Even the specific behaviour determined by the bi-directional path-finding strategy which at every step chooses the direction which grows least rapidly can be accomplished with both formulations. In the first formulation it is obtained by applying the Pohl criterion for combining top-down and bottom-up inference. In the second formulation it is accomplished by top-down inference alone, applying the strategy of selecting the subgoal to which fewest procedures (including assertions) apply.

Other aspects of problem-solving

Problem-solving can be classified into three main stages.

1) The first stage identifies the problem-domain and formulates problem-solving procedures.
2) The second stage applies the procedures to the solution of problems.
3) The third stage improves the problem problem-solving strategies and procedures.

This chapter has been restricted to a discussion of the second stage. It has not considered the other stages which are concerned with learning. In this respect we have followed the advice of McCarthy [1968] and Minsky [1968] to explore the adequacy of the representation language before dealing with the problems of formulating and improving the representation of the problem domain.

In the next chapter we investigate the interpretation of the Horn clause subset of logic as a programming language. This unifies problem-solving with programming. The first stage of problem-solving is the initial stage of problem formulation and specification. The second stage runs the specification as a program, and the third identifies inefficiencies and remedies them by improving the procedures and tailoring the problem-solving strategies to the problems to be solved.

In subsequent chapters we investigate the role of non-Horn clauses in problem-solving and the use of global problem-solving strategies. In the last chapter we compare the interpretation of logic as a model for problem-solving with the role of logic in philosophy as a model for representing beliefs and formalising arguments.

However, nowhere in this book do we investigate the problems of learning. Nor do we investigate such important strategies as problem-solving by example and by analogy.

Exercises

1)   a) Express the arrow-inversion problem by means of Horn clauses without function symbols:

> Given three arrows in a row D U D, pointed down, up, down respectively, the goal is to reach the state D D D in which all arrows point down. The only action possible is to invert a pair of adjacent arrows, changing both their directions simultaneously.

Hint : Let State(x,y,z) express that there is a possible state in which the first, second and third arrows point in directions x, y and z respectively.

> b) Show that the problem is unsolvable by generating the graph representation of the top-down search space and showing that it contains no solutions.
>
> c) Describe how the clausal formulation of the problem can be modified in order to
>
> i)   invert adjacent arrows only when they have opposite directions,
> ii) add an action which interchanges adjacent arrows,
> iii) deal with a row of four arrows instead of three.

2)   a) Express the farmer, wolf, goat and cabbage problem by means of Horn clauses:

> The farmer, wolf, goat and cabbage are all on the north bank of a river and the problem is to transfer them to the south bank. The farmer has a boat which he can row taking at most one passenger at a time. The goat cannot be left with the wolf unless the farmer is present. The cabbage,

which counts as a passenger, cannot be left with the goat unless the farmer is present.

b)   Compare the graph representations of both the top-down and bottom-up search spaces.

c)   Can you find useful evaluation functions to guide the search for a solution?

3) Given the two different representations of the path-finding problem, compare the problem-solving strategies needed

a)   to recognise that there is no path from A to B if there is no arc leading from A or no arc leading to B and

b)   to show that it is possible to go from A to A.

4) Let sequences be characterised by means of two relations

Item(i,j,k) which holds when i_j = k i.e.
the j-th element in the sequence i is k and
Length(i,u) which holds when the length of sequence i is u.

Thus the sequence

A: $a_1, a_2, \ldots, a_n$

can be characterised by means of the assertions:

Item(A,1,a_1) <—
Item(A,2,a_2) <—
        .
        .
        .
Item(A,n,a_n) <—
Length(A,n) <—

Assume that Plus(x,y,z) holds when x+y = z.

a)   Define by means of Horn clauses the relation Sum(x,v) which holds when v is the sum of the numbers in the sequence x.

b)   Use the clauses of part (a) to find top-down the sum of the numbers in the sequence B: 3,4,10.

c)   Can Sum(x,v) be defined in such a manner that, given x to find v, the search space contains only the solution?

5)   a) List all the solutions to the problem

<— Arch(w)

implied by the definition of arch and the description of the scene given by clauses A1-12.

      b)   Reformulate the definition of arch and tower by means of Horn clauses in order to eliminate as many pathological arches and towers as possible. (This problem can be solved more easily later using negation as failure, investigated in Chapter 11.)

6) Consider the problem

$$\leftarrow \text{Numb}(u), \text{Numb}(v), u > v$$

given the clauses

$$\text{Numb}(0) \leftarrow$$
$$\text{Numb}(s(x)) \leftarrow \text{Numb}(x)$$
$$s(x) > 0 \leftarrow$$
$$s(x) > s(y) \leftarrow x > y.$$

Analyse the behaviour of the backtracking search strategy for solving the problem. Assume that the solution of subgoals is attempted in the order in which they are written and that alternative clauses also are tried in the order given.

CHAPTER 5

The Procedural Interpretation of Horn Clauses

A Horn clause

$$B \leftarrow A_1,\ldots,A_m \qquad m \geq 0$$

is interpreted as a <u>procedure</u> whose <u>body</u> $\{A_1,\ldots,A_m\}$ is a set of procedure calls A_i. Top-down derivations are <u>computations</u>. Generation of a new goal statement from an old one by matching the selected procedure call with the <u>name</u> B of a procedure

$$B \leftarrow A_1,\ldots,A_m$$

is <u>procedure invocation</u>.

A <u>logic program</u> consists of a set of Horn clause procedures and is activated by an initial goal statement.

Conventional programs mix the logic of the information used in solving problems together with the control over the manner in which the information is used. Logic programs are more abstract. They control neither the order in which different procedures are invoked when several match a given procedure call, nor the order in which procedure calls are executed when several belong to the same goal statement.

Logic programs express only the logic of problem-solving methods. They are easier to understand, easier to verify and easier to change. They are especially congenial to inexperienced programmers and database users who do not want to become involved with the details of controlling the program's behaviour.

The first logic programming system, called PROLOG [Colmerauer et al 1973], [Roussel 1975] based on the procedural interpretation of Horn clauses [Kowalski 1974] was designed and implemented in 1972. A PROLOG compiler written in PROLOG for the PDP10 was implemented at the University of Edinburgh by Warren, Pereira and Pereira [1977]. They showed that the PROLOG compiler executes LISP-like logic programs as efficiently as compiled LISP [McCarthy et al 1962].

Terms as data structures

Data in logic programs can be represented by means of terms or relations. The use of terms as data structures gives Horn clause programs many of the characteristics of a list-processing language like LISP. More generally, they function as recursive data structures of the kind advocated by Hoare [1972]. The use of relations in logic programs, on the other hand, is like the representation of data by relations in database formalisms [Codd 1970]. Relations are also like tables and arrays in conventional programming languages. They will be discussed in more detail later in the chapter.

As in LISP, binary trees can be represented by means of a binary function symbol:

cons(x,y)   names the tree

which has the subtree x immediately to the left of the root node and the subtree y immediately to the right. Thus the term

$$cons(A,cons(B,C)) \text{ names the tree}$$

and the program

        Tips(x,1) <— Label(x)
        Tips(cons(x,y), w) <— Tips(x,u), Tips(y,v), u+v = w

defines the relationship Tips(x,y) which holds when y is the number of tips in the binary tree x. Label(x) holds when x is a label:

        Label(A) <—
        Label(B) <—
        Label(C) <—

for example. The goal statement

        <— Tips(cons(A,cons(B,C)), y)

expresses the goal of computing the number of tips in the tree pictured above. The term cons(A,cons(B,C)) names the <u>input</u> and the variable y names the <u>output</u>. The top-down solution

        <— Tips(cons(A,cons(B,C)), y)

          <— Tips(A,u), Tips(cons(B,C), v), u+v = y

          <— Label(A,u), Tips(cons(B,C), v), u+v = y
    u=1
          <— Tips(cons(B,C), v), 1+v = y

          <— Tips(B,u'), Tips(C,v'), u'+v' = v, 1+v = y
    u'=1
    v'=1 <— Label(B), Label(C), 1+1 = v, 1+v = y
    v =2
          <— 1+2 = y
    y =3
          □

is a computation of the output y = 3. The search space contains only the computation.

Lists can be regarded, as in LISP, as a special kind of binary tree.
The term cons(x,y) names the list

x   y

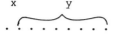

which has <u>first</u> <u>element</u> x followed by the <u>list</u> y. The constant symbol
nil names the <u>empty list</u>. Thus the term cons(A,cons(B,cons(C,nil)))
names the list A,B,C and the program

        Item(cons(x,y), 1, x) <—
        Item(cons(x,y), u, z) <— Item(y,v,z), v+1 = u

defines the relationship Item(x,y,z) which holds when the y-th element of
the list x is z. Notice that the term cons(A,B) does not name the list
A,B because B is not a list. The list consisting of B alone is named by
cons(B,nil) and therefore the list A,B is named by cons(A,cons(B,nil)).

Programs may be easier to read if <u>infix</u> <u>notation</u> is used for function
symbols and conventions are used for suppressing parentheses. It is
especially convenient to use an infix function symbol "." for lists

        x.y stands for cons(x,y)

and to reduce parentheses by letting

        x.y.z stand for cons(x,cons(y,z)).

Thus the list A,B,C can be represented by the term

        A.B.C.nil .

Facilities for defining infix function symbols and for reducing
parentheses are provided in PROLOG. The programmer can further reduce
parentheses by declaring precedence relations among function symbols.
Thus by declaring that the infix function symbol & binds more closely
than the infix function symbol ⊃ , the term

        p & q ⊃ r & s

can be written instead of

        (p & q) ⊃ (r & s).

Computation <u>by</u> <u>successive</u> <u>approximation</u> <u>to</u> <u>output</u>

Horn clause   procedures transmit output   throughout computation.
Partial outputs accumulate and determine successive approximations to the
final output. The approximations are generated whether or not the
computation eventually succeeds.

The figure below illustrates the computation by successive approximation of the list which results from appending 3.nil to 2.1.nil .

```
                <- Append(2.1.nil, 3.nil, x)

    x  = 2.u        (2)

                <- Append(1.nil, 3.nil, u)

    u  = 1.u'       (2)

                <- Append(nil, 3.nil, u')

    u' = 3.nil      (1)

                    □
```

(1)   Append(nil,x,x) <-
(2)   Append(x.y, z, x.u) <- Append(y,z,u)

Clause (1) states that appending any list x to the empty list produces the list x. Clause (2) states that appending a list z to a non-empty list x.y produces a list x.u with the same first element and with a remainder u which is the result of appending z to y.

The successive steps of the computation determine successive approximations to the output

```
        x = 2.u
        x = 2.1.u'
        x = 2.1.3.nil .
```

In general, the output of a computation can be regarded as the collection of all output components of matching substitutions performed in the computation. The output can be compactified, as in the example above, by applying output components lower in the refutation to the terms of output components higher in the refutation.

The variation of input-output parameters

The distinction between the input and output parameters of a procedure depends upon the context in which the procedure is invoked. Any subset of the procedure's parameters can be given as input.   The remaining parameters are then computed as output.

The following computation illustrates the use of Append to compute the list x which produces 2.1.3.nil when 3.nil is appended to it. The search space contains, in addition to the successfully terminating computation, only one other step, which fails because no procedure matches its procedure call.

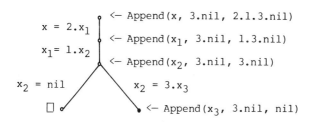

$$x = 2.x_1$$
$$\leftarrow \text{Append}(x, 3.\text{nil}, 2.1.3.\text{nil})$$
$$x_1 = 1.x_2$$
$$\leftarrow \text{Append}(x_1, 3.\text{nil}, 1.3.\text{nil})$$
$$\leftarrow \text{Append}(x_2, 3.\text{nil}, 3.\text{nil})$$
$$x_2 = \text{nil} \qquad x_2 = 3.x_3$$
$$\leftarrow \text{Append}(x_3, 3.\text{nil}, \text{nil})$$

The ability to execute the same procedure with various patterns of input and output is an important feature of logic programs. It implies, for example, that the same procedures which compute derivatives of functions can also be used to compute integrals [Bergman and Kanoui 1973]. Procedures which verify that a given program meets given specifications can also be used to generate programs from specifications [Moss 1977].

Non-determinism$_1$: several procedures match a procedure call

Compared with normal programs, Horn clause programs executed top-down are non-deterministic in two main senses: When several procedures match a given procedure call, the search strategy by means of which the alternative procedures are tried is not determined$_1$. When several procedure calls need to be executed in a single goal statement, the order of execution is not determined$_2$.

In the first case, alternative procedures may compute alternative outputs. If only one output is needed, it is not determined$_1$ which output will be found. If all outputs are required, it is not determined$_1$ in which order they will be generated.

A procedure, which is deterministic$_1$ for one pattern of input and output parameters may be non-deterministic$_1$ for a different pattern. The Append procedure, for example, is non-deterministic$_1$ when it is used to partition a given list into two parts as in the problem

$$\leftarrow \text{Append}(x, y, 2.1.3.\text{nil}).$$

The search space of all computations is illustrated below. Notice the economy which is obtained by structuring the search space as a tree. The two different partitions

$$x = 2.1.\text{nil}, \quad y = 3.\text{nil} \quad \text{and}$$
$$x = 2.1.3.\text{nil}, \quad y = \text{nil}$$

for example, are both obtained from the single initial approximation

$$x = 2.1.x_2 .$$

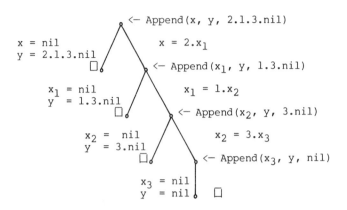

Sequential search regarded as iteration

The ability to specify repeated execution of the same command is an essential feature of all programming languages. Such repetition, also called iteration* , can be accomplished by executing recursive Horn clause procedures. It can also be achieved by using backtracking to search a space of alternativs. The definition of grandparent is a simple example. Suppose that we are given data about individuals in the parenthood relationship

$$
\begin{aligned}
&\text{Parent(Zeus,Ares)} &\leftarrow \\
&\text{Parent(Hera,Ares)} &\leftarrow \\
&\text{Parent(Ares,Harmonia)} &\leftarrow \\
&\text{Parent(Semele,Dionysus)} \leftarrow \\
&\text{Parent(Zeus,Dionysus)} &\leftarrow \\
&\qquad \text{etc.}
\end{aligned}
$$

and the problem is to show that Zeus is a grandparent of Harmonia

$\leftarrow$ Grandparent(Zeus,Harmonia)

using the definition of grandparent

Grandparent(x,y) $\leftarrow$ Parent(x,z), Parent(z,y).

In a conventional programming language, the programmer would have to specify both how the data in the parenthood relationship is stored and how it is retrieved. In a logic program, the same decisions are taken by the program executor instead. In either case, the simplest strategy is to store and retrieve the data sequentially. The parenthood relationship might be stored sequentially, either in a two-dimensional array or in a

----

*Some of the discussion in the next few sections refers to features of conventional programming languages. The reader who is not familiar with such languages can ignore these sections without disadvantage.

linked list. The sequential retrieval strategy is an iteration, consisting of a double loop, one nested inside the other. To show Zeus is a grandparent of Harmonia, the outer loop searches for a child z of Zeus and the inner loop tests whether z is a parent of Harmonia. The iterative algorithm which has to be specified by the programmer in a conventional programming language is identical in this case to the behaviour determined$_1$ by the backtracking strategy for executing non-deterministic$_1$ programs.

In other cases, as when the Append procedure is used to partition lists, backtracking is more general than iteration. In general, whereas iteration searches a tree whose depth is determined by the number of loops which are nested, backtracking searches an arbitrarily deep tree of alternatives,

The suitability of a search strategy depends upon the structure in which the data is stored. Iteration, regarded as sequential search, is suitable for data stored sequentially. Other search strategies are appropriate for such data structures as hash tables, binary trees or semantic networks. Fishman and Minker [1975] for example, store data in a manner which facilitates parallel search, whereas Deliyanni and Kowalski [1979] propose a path-following strategy for retrieving data stored in semantic networks.

"Don't know" versus "don't care" non-determinism$_1$

Non-determinism$_1$ does not always entail the need to search for a solution. The definition of Max(x,y,z) (the maximum of x and y is z) is an example.

$$\text{Max}(x,y,x) \leftarrow x \geq y$$
$$\text{Max}(x,y,y) \leftarrow y \geq x$$

Both procedures apply when x and y are identical, as in the case

$$\leftarrow \text{Max}(3,3,z).$$

Searching for a solution, which is unavoidable in the general case, creates redundancy when it is unnecessary. Backtracking is redundant, for example, when it is applied to the goal statement

$$\leftarrow \text{Max}(3,3,z), \text{Even}(z)$$

and the procedure calls are executed in the order in which they are written. The second procedure call Even(z), which succeeds when z is even, fails no matter how the first procedure call is executed. Backtracking after the first failure, to try a different way of executing the first procedure call, is both unnecessary and redundant.

Searching can be restricted in general whenever the output variables of a procedure call are a function of the input - for example, when the variable y is a function of x in the relation F(x,y) and x is given as input. Backtracking can be suppressed if the first solution of the goal F(A,y) fails to solve the second goal G(y) in the goal statement

$$\gets F(A,y), \; G(y).$$

When searching for a solution is unnecessary, then the program executor "doesn't care" which solution is generated nor how it is obtained. Otherwise, searching is unavoidable when the executor "doesn't know". Don't care non-determinism$_1$ is a dominant feature of Dijkstra's language of guarded commands [1976]. The use of don't care non-determinism$_1$ to restrict search is a form of intelligent backtracking.

Non-determinism$_1$ can have both don't know and don't care characteristics. The path-finding problem is an example. Given the problem of finding a path from A to N

$$\gets Go(A,N)$$

for example, the program executor doesn't care which path is found but normally doesn't know which procedures to apply in order to find it. Searching is necessary to find one path but is unnecessary and redundant thereafter.

The path-finding problem is a special case of the general situation in which a procedure call shares no variables with other calls in the same goal statement. Any non-determinism$_1$ involved in executing the procedure call matters only until the first solution is found. The second procedure call in the body of the procedure

$$Happy(Bob) \gets Teaches(Bob,x), \; Attends(y,x)$$

Bob is happy if he teaches a course
which someone attends.

is an example. If it is executed after the other procedure call, then its only variable y occurs in no other procedure call and it suffices to find only a single solution.

The property that a procedure call contains no variables or that all its variables occur in no other procedure call is a syntactic property which the program executor can easily recognise without the aid of the programmer. The situation, however, in which search can be restricted because a procedure call computes the value of a function is undecidable in principle. It is easier for the programmer to convey such information to the program executor as a comment about the program, than it is for the executor to discover the fact for itself.

Don't care non-determinism$_1$ provides a way of adding extra information to a program without enlarging the search space and even reducing its size. The new information may solve a problem more directly than the original procedures, and if the non-determinism$_1$ doesn't matter then the original procedures can be ignored.

Non-determinism$_2$: The scheduling of procedure calls

In conventional programming languages the program controls the scheduling of procedure calls - usually in some fixed sequence, but sometimes timesharing among them or executing them in parallel. In logic,

however, the body of a procedure specifies only the collection of
procedure calls. The manner in which they are executed is determined$_2$ not
by the program but by the execution mechanism. Different strategies for
scheduling procedure calls affect the efficiency of execution but do not
affect the meaning as determined by the relations which are computed.

The definition of sorted lists is a simple example.   Assume that the
definition of the $\leq$ relation is already given.

Sort(x,y)	holds when y is a sorted version of list x,
Perm(x,y)	y is a permutation of x,
Delete(x,y,z)	z results from deleting any one occurrence of x from y.

S1	Sort(x,y)	$\leftarrow$ Perm(x,y) , Ord(y)
S2	Perm(nil,nil)	$\leftarrow$
S3	Perm(z, x.y)	$\leftarrow$ Delete(x,z,z'), Perm(z',y)
S4	Delete(x, x.y, y)	$\leftarrow$
S5	Delete(x, y.z, y.u)	$\leftarrow$ Delete(x,z,u)
S6	Ord(nil)	$\leftarrow$
S7	Ord(x.nil)	$\leftarrow$
S8	Ord(x.y.z)	$\leftarrow$ x $\leq$ y, Ord(y.z)

In principle, the procedure calls in the body of procedure S1 can be
executed in any sequence. Given a list 1, to generate a sorted version y
of 1, it is possible firstly to execute the procedure call Ord(y),
generating an ordered list y, and then to execute Perm(1,y), testing
whether y is a permutation of 1. If the test fails, other ordered lists
can be generated until the test succeeds. It is more effective, of
course, to execute procedure calls in the opposite sequence - first
generating permutations of x and then testing whether they are ordered.
But no matter in which sequence procedure calls are executed and no
matter what the cost in terms of efficiency, the result in terms of the
input-output relation computed is the same.

Effective scheduling of procedure calls depends upon the pattern of
input and output. Generally it is more efficient to execute a procedure
call which contains the input in preference to one which does not. Thus,
given the problem

$\leftarrow$ Sort(1,y)

$\leftarrow$ Perm(1,y) , Ord(y)

of finding a sorted version y of an input list 1 it is better to select
for execution the procedure call Perm(1,y) which contains the input than
it is to select   Ord(y)   which does not. If both l_1 and l_2 are given
and the problem

$\leftarrow$ Sort(l_1,l_2)

$\leftarrow$ Perm(l_1,l_2) , Ord(l_2)

is to test that l_2 is a sorted version of l_1, then both procedure calls
contain the input and it does not affect efficiency which procedure call
is executed first. Moreover, since the two procedure calls do not share

variables and since they are equally good candidates for execution, they can be executed together - either timesharing between them if only one processor is available or executing them in parallel if several can be used.

In general, it is advantageous to execute procedure calls as soon as sufficient input is available. Given procedures (S1-8) and the goal of sorting the list 2.1.3.nil, generating permutations before testing them for orderedness, the test for orderedness can be initiated just as effectively when the first two elements of the permutation have been determined as it can when the entire permutation has been generated. Executing procedure calls as soon as possible has the advantage that failure can be detected as soon as possible. The figure below illustrates the effectiveness of eagerly executing the orderedness test to reject in one step all permutations which have first element 2 and second element 1.

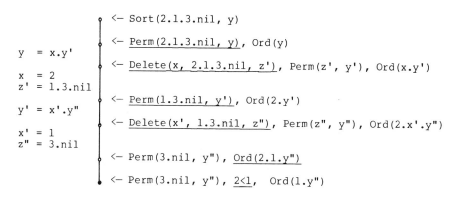

```
                    <- Sort(2.1.3.nil, y)

                      <- Perm(2.1.3.nil, y), Ord(y)
y  = x.y'
                        <- Delete(x, 2.1.3.nil, z'), Perm(z', y'), Ord(x.y')
x  = 2
z' = 1.3.nil
                      <- Perm(1.3.nil, y'), Ord(2.y')
y' = x'.y"
                        <- Delete(x', 1.3.nil, z"), Perm(z", y"), Ord(2.x'.y")
x' = 1
z" = 3.nil
                      <- Perm(3.nil, y"), Ord(2.1.y")

                    <- Perm(3.nil, y"), 2<1, Ord(1.y")
```

The behaviour of the admissible pairs problem is a more dramatic example, which is intolerably non-deterministic[1] if procedure calls are executed last-in-first-out. A pair (a,b) of lists of numbers is admissible if the two lists have the same length and for every i

> if a_i is the i-th element of a and
> b_i is the i-th element of b, then
> $b_i = 2*a_i$ and
> $a_{i+1} = 3*b_i$.

Pictorially:

a:

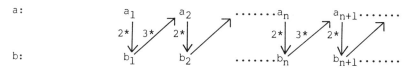

b:

The following clauses, in which lists are represented by means of terms, define the desired relationship:

```
Adm(x,y) <- Double(x,y), Triple(x,y)
Double(nil,nil) <-
Double(x.y, u.v) <- Times(2,x,u), Double(y,v)
Triple(x.nil, u.nil) <-
Triple(x.y.z, u.v)    <- Times(3,u,y), Triple(y.z, v)
```

Consider the problem of generating an admissible pair of lists whose first list begins with with the number 1:

```
<- Adm(1.y, w)
```

The program is intolerably non-deterministic$_1$ if procedure calls are executed last-in-first-out, completing the execution of one call before initiating another. It becomes virtually deterministic$_1$, however, if procedure calls are executed as soon as sufficient input is available. The two procedure calls behave as co-operating sequential processes. As soon as either one of the two processes, Double or Triple, has enough information about its input it runs until it needs more. By that time it has produced enough output for the other process to resume execution.

```
            <- Adm(1.y, u)

            <- Double(1.y, u), Triple(1.y, u)

            u = u'.v

            <- Times(2,1,u'),Double(y,v), Triple(1.y, u'.v)

            u' = 2

            <- Double(y,v), Triple(1.y, 2.v)
y = nil
v = nil     y = y'.z

    □       <- Double(y'.z, v), Times(3,2,y'), Triple(y'.z, v)

            y' = 6

            <- Double(6.z, v), Triple(6.z, v)

            v = u".v'

            <- Times(2,6,u"), Double(z,v'), Triple(6.z, u".v')

            u" = 12

            <- Double(z,v'), Triple(6.z, 12.v')
z = nil
v'= nil
    □           :
```

Coroutines, which cooperatively produce and consume data, can be written in programming languages such as SIMULA. Such coroutines, however, are syntactically and semantically different from normal procedures. However, more recent schemes, in which procedures are called by need [Henderson and Morris 1976] and the activation of processes is controlled by the flow of data [Kahn 1974] [Friedman and Wise 1978], resemble the execution of procedures in logic programs. The strategy for executing procedure calls is not determined by the program but by the program executor.

Bottom-up execution of programs

The procedural interpretation of Horn clauses is primarily the top-down interpretation. It is sometimes possible, however, to give a procedural interpretation to bottom-up inference. Although it is generally more efficient for computers to interpret Horn clauses top-down, it is often more natural for people to understand them bottom-up. Moreover, it is sometimes more efficient to execute programs bottom-up rather than top-down.

A student of mathematics, for example, is more likely to understand the recursive definition of factorial

> The factorial of 0 is 1 <−
> The factorial of x is u <− y+1 = x,
>   the factorial of y is v,
>   x*v = u

bottom-up, as determining the sequence of assertions

> The factorial of 0 is 1 <−
> The factorial of 1 is 1 <−
> The factorial of 2 is 2 <−
> The factorial of 3 is 6 <−
>   etc.

than he is to understand it top-down, as reducing goals to subgoals. In this example, bottom-up derivation of factorials has a computational flavour. It behaves as an iterative computation which accumulates factorials of successively larger numbers until it derives the one which is desired.

The definition of Fibonacci number can be executed more efficiently bottom-up than top-down.

> The 0-th Fibonacci number is 1 <−
> The 1-th Fibonacci number is 1 <−
> The u+2-th Fibonacci number is x <−
>   the u+1-th Fibonacci number is y,
>   the u-th Fibonacci number is z,
>   y+z = x

Here the terms u+2 and u+1 are expressions to be evaluated rather than terms representing data structures. This notation is an abbreviation for the one which has explicit procedure calls in the body to evaluate u+2 and u+1.

Interpreted top-down, finding the u+1-th Fibonacci number reintroduces the subproblem of finding the u-th Fibonacci number. The top-down computation is an and-tree whose nodes are procedure calls, the number of which is an exponential function of u. The problem of computing the Fibonacci of 4, for example, determines a tree, which ignoring additions contains a total of 9 goals and subgoals.

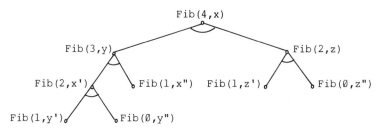

Here Fib(u,x) means the u-th Fibonacci number is x. Executing the same definition bottom-up generates the sequence of assertions

> The 0-th Fibonacci number is 1 <—
> The 1-th Fibonacci number is 1 <—
> The 2-th Fibonacci number is 2 <—
> The 3-th Fibonacci number is 3 <—
>   etc.

The number of computation steps for the Fibonacci of u executed bottom-up is a linear function of u.

In this example, bottom-up execution is also potentially less space-consuming than top-down execution. Top-down execution uses space which is proportional to u, whereas bottom-up execution needs to store only two assertions and therefore can use a small constant amount of storage. That only two assertions need to be stored during bottom-up execution is a consequence of the deletion rules for the connection graph proof procedure (Chapter 8).

Notice that the efficiency of top-down execution approaches that of bottom-up execution if similar procedure calls (i.e. the u-th Fibonacci number is z and the u-th Fibonacci number is z') are executed only once. Such top-down execution is an extension of Earley's parsing algorithm [Earley 1970] as described by Warren [unpublished].

Iteration in conventional programming languages has three different interpretations in logic programs. The classical interpretation regards iteration as a special case of top-down execution of recursive definitions. The iteration

> To do P, repeat Q until R

for example, can be expressed in the form

> P(x) <— R(x)
> P(x) <— Q(x,x'), P(x')

where x is an input parameter which controls the number of iterations through the loop and R(x) and Q(x,x') hold for distinct x. The recursion is a form of iteration if Q(x,x') is executed before P(x'). Consequently each new subgoal P(x') can replace the previous subgoal P(x). Execution, therefore, requires only a constant amount of storage for the current subgoal.

The interpretation of iteration as top-down execution of certain forms of recursive definitions is the only interpretation of iteration possible in the conventional model of computation by recursion. In logic programs, however, it is also possible to regard iteration either as sequential search through a space of alternative responses to a procedure call or as bottom-up execution of recursive definitions.

The pragmatic content of logic programs

It is a common mistake to treat logic simply as a specification language whose statements have semantic content without pragmatic value. Such an attitude is self-fulfilling. To use logic while ignoring its pragmatic aspects is to make information potentially unusable.

Two different statements can express the same information and therefore have the same meaning. But one might be useful for solving problems and the other one useless.

The sorting problem, studied by van Emden [1977], is a good example of the pragmatics of logic. The simple program (S1-8) for sorting lists

$$Sort(x,y) \leftarrow Perm(x,y), Ord(y)$$

is a good specification, but a useless program. Even the scheduling of procedure calls which uses Ord(y) to monitor the partial output of Perm(x,y) is hopelessly inefficient (taking time $2\uparrow n$ in order to sort a list of length n). In contrast, even simple sequential execution of procedure calls produces an efficient algorithm, Quicksort [Hoare 1961], taking time n*log(n), from the program:

$$Sort*(nil,nil) \leftarrow$$
$$Sort*(x.y, z) \leftarrow Partition(x,y,u,v), Sort*(u,u'),$$
$$Sort*(v,v'), Append(u', x.v', z).$$

Here it is intended that Partition(x,y,u,v) holds when u is the list of all members of y which are less than or equal to x and v is the list of all members of y which are greater than x.

Sort and Sort* are equivalent in the sense that Sort(s,t) and Sort*(s,t) hold for the same pairs of terms s, t. Sort is useful as a specification of sortedness but useless for efficiently sorting lists. Sort* is efficient but less obviously correct.

In general, a given problem can be expressed in many different ways. The two representations of the path-finding problem (one using the predicate Go(x), the other using the predicate Go*(x,y)) can be generalised to other problems. Even the definition of factorial can be represented in two ways. The previous definition corresponds to the one-place-predicate formulation of path-finding. The definition below corresponds to the two-place-predicate formulation.

Fact*(x,y,u,v)

expresses that the factorial of x is y if the factorial of u is v.

Fact*(u,v,u,v) <—

Fact*(x,y,u,v) <— u+1 = u', u'*v = v', Fact*(x,y,u',v')

To find the factorial of an integer represented by a term t, a single goal statement incorporates not only the goal but also the information that the factorial of 0 is 1.

<— Fact*(t,y,0,1)

The new formulation of factorial executed top-down behaves in the same iterative manner as the original formulation executed in a mixed top-down, bottom-up fashion. The old formulation is more obviously correct, whereas the new formulation is easier to execute efficiently with more limited problem-solving facilities.

Separation of data structures

For a well-structured program,   it is desirable that the data structures be separated from the procedures which interrogate and manipulate them.   Separation of data structures from procedures means that the representation of the data can be altered without altering the higher-level procedures. It is easier to improve efficiency, therefore, by replacing an inefficient data structure with a more efficient one. In a large complex program the information which needs to be supplied by the data structures is often completely identified only in the final stages of the program design. By separating data structures from procedures, it is possible to write the higher levels of the program before the data structures have been determined.

Data storage and retrieval are automatically separated from procedures when data is represented by relations, as in the family relationships example.   When data is represented instead by terms it is the programmer's responsibility to separate them in the program.

The arch recognition problem is a simple example.   The previous formulation which mixes procedures and data structures can be replaced by one which separates them. Mention of the data structures in the top-level procedures can be replaced by procedure calls which access, compute or construct the data.

Arch(x)   <— Block(v), Tower(u), Tower(w), On(v,u),
             On(v,w), Left(x,u), Right(x,w), Top(x,v)

Tower(x) <— Block(x)

Tower(x) <— Block(u), Tower(v), On(u,v),
             Top(x,u), Bottom(x,v)

On(x,y)   <— Top(y,u), On(x,u)

Here the Top, Left, Right and Bottom relations define the interface
between the procedures and the data structures. It is intended that

```
Top(x,y)        holds when the top of x is y,
Left(x,y)                   the left  subtower of arch x is y,
Right(x,y)                  the right subtower of arch x is y,
Bottom(x,y)                 the bottom of tower x is y.
```

The data structures can be defined separately by defining their
interface with the top-level procedures:

```
Top(a(u,v,w) , v)    <-
Top(t(u,v) , u)      <-
Left(a(u,v,w) , u)   <-
Right(a(u,v,w) , w)  <-
Bottom(t(u,v) , v)   <-
```

In this case the interfacing procedures are defined simply by means of
assertions. But in other cases they might be defined by more general
kinds of procedures.

Comparing the two formulations of the arches program, we notice
another advantage of separating procedures and data structures: with
infix notation for predicate symbols and with well chosen names for the
interfacing procedures, data-structure-independent programs are
virtually self-documenting. For conventional programs which mix data
structures and procedures, the programmer needs to provide documentation
which explains the data structures and is external to the program. For
well-structured programs which separate procedures and data structures,
such documentation is provided by the interfacing procedures and is part
of the program.

Despite the arguments for separating procedures and data structures,
programmers mix them for the sake of run time efficiency. One way of
reconciling efficiency with good program structure is to make use of the
macro-processing facilities provided in some programming languages.
Macro-processing flattens the hierarchy of non-recursive procedure calls
by executing them at compile time before a problem is given. It is also a
feature of the program improving transformations developed by Burstall
and Darlington [1977].

The analogue of macro-processing in logic is bottom-up or middle-out
reasoning combined with deletion of clauses. Such macro-processing is a
special case of more general facilities provided by the connection graph
proof procedure (Chapter 8). In the case of the arches program, the
original formulation can be derived from the new one simply by bottom-up
execution of the interfacing procedure calls.

Terms versus relations as data structures

Data in logic programs can be represented either by means of terms,
as in the Append and Arches examples, or by means of relations, as in
the Parsing and Family Relationships examples.

When data is represented by terms, the input to a program is normally represented by a term in the initial goal statement. Top-down execution is problem-dependent and behaves like recursive evaluation in conventional programming languages. Bottom-up execution, although it sometimes behaves like iteration, as in the Factorial and Fibonacci examples, is more often problem-independent and computationally explosive, unless it can somehow be guided by a global consideration of the problem to be solved. Global strategies for problem-solving are investigated in Chapter 9.

When data is represented by means of relations (defined by assertions and procedures) the input is normally expressed by assertions. Both top-down and bottom-up execution are problem-dependent.   Top-down execution interrogates the input and bottom-up execution manipulates it, deriving new data from that which is initially given.

It is always possible to represent data by means of terms. LISP for example, represents all data by means of constant symbols and a single binary function symbol "cons". Recursion theory represents all data by means of natural numbers using a single constant symbol 0 and a unary function symbol "s". It is instructive to compare the previous formulation of the parsing problem with a formulation which represents data by means of terms.

```
Sent(x)  <- Np(y), Vp(z), Append(y,z,x)
Np(x)    <- Det(y), Adj(z), Noun(v),
            Append(y,z,u), Append(u,v,x)
Vp(x)    <- Aux(y), Verb(z), Append(y,z,x)
Det(the.nil)    <-
Adj(slithy.nil) <-
Noun(toves.nil) <-
Aux(did.nil)    <-
Verb(gyre.nil)  <-
```

Both the input string of words and the problem of showing that it is a sentence are incorporated in the initial goal statement:

```
<- Sent(the.slithy.toves.did.gyre.nil)
```

Notice the procedure calls Append, which have no analogue in the earlier formulation of the parsing problem. When the data is represented by means of assertions, the program has direct access to the data, similar to that given by arrays in conventional programming languages. When the data is represented by means of terms, then special procedures like Append are needed to provide access to the contents of the data structures.

It is possible to represent data entirely by means of relations as in relational databases [Codd 1970]. Instead of representing the list

a, c, b, a

by the term

cons(a, cons(c, cons(b, cons(a, nil))))

or   a.c.b.a.nil

we can give it a name, say A, and represent it by the assertions

$$Item(A,1,a) \leftarrow$$
$$Item(A,2,c) \leftarrow$$
$$Item(A,3,b) \leftarrow$$
$$Item(A,4,a) \leftarrow$$
$$Length(A,4) \leftarrow$$

where Item(x,y,z) means that

                z is the y-th item of x

and Length(x,y) means that

                y is the length of x.

    Instead of writing an explicitly recursive program for reversing lists, either

$$Reverse(nil,nil) \leftarrow$$
$$Reverse(x.y, z) \quad \leftarrow Reverse(y,u), Append(u, x.nil, z)$$

or more efficiently

$$Reverse(x,y) \leftarrow Rev(x,nil,y)$$
$$Rev(nil,y,y) \leftarrow$$
$$Rev(x.y, z, u) \leftarrow Rev(y, x.z, u)$$

we can write a non-recursive program:

$$Item(rev(x), u, y) \leftarrow Item(x,v,y), Length(x,w),$$
$$u+v = w', w+1 =w'$$
$$Length(rev(x), y) \quad \leftarrow Length(x,y)$$

Here the term rev(x) names the list which is the reverse of x.

    When data is represented by means of terms, the program needs to specify how data is stored and retrieved and it needs to take responsibility for the separation of the data from the higher levels of the program. Data located closer to the surface of a term can be accessed more directly than data located deeper inside. When data is represented by relations, the program defines the data at an abstract level which is independent of the storage and retrieval scheme adopted by the programming system. When a relation is defined by means of assertions, the program has direct access to the information.

Database formalisms and programming languages

    Conventional database formalisms are different from the formalisms used for programming languages. Logic, in contrast, is the same whether it is used for databases, database queries and programs or for database integrity constraints and program specifications. Indeed, especially

when relations are used as data structures, the use of logic blurs the
normal distinction between databases and programs. General laws for data
description are indistinguishable from procedures in programs,   and
database integrity constraints are the same as program properties.

The conventional distinction between databases and programs is not
reflected by the nature of computational problems.   A representation in
logic of the symbolic integration problem, for example, like the one
written in PROLOG by Bergman and Kanoui [1973] can be regarded as both a
database and a program. The relationship of a function to its integral is
defined by means of assertions such as

    sin(x) is the integral of cos(x) with respect to x

and by general rules, such as

    u + v is the integral of u' + v' with respect to x
           if u is the integral of u' with respect to x
           and v is the integral of v' with respect to x.

The definition of the relation can be viewed both as the definition of a
recursive procedure and as the description of a database by a combination
of explicit assertions and implicit rules.

The desirability of combining databases and programs more intimately
than is possible with conventional formalisms is beginning to be
appreciated by the database community. The design of a programming
language [Zloof and deLong 1977]   based on query-by-example is a
significant development of this kind.

Algorithm = Logic + Control

Conventional algorithms and programs expressed in conventional
programming languages combine the logic of the information to be used in
solving problems with the control over the manner in which the
information is put to use.   This relationship can be expressed
symbolically by the equation

    Algorithm = Logic + Control   (A = L + C).

Logic programs express only the logic component L of algorithms. The
control component C is exercised by the program executor,   either
following its own autonomously determined control decisions or else
following control instructions provided by the programmer.

The conceptual separation of logic from control has several
advantages:

    (1) Algorithms can be constructed by successive refinement,
         designing the logic component before the control component.

    (2) Algorithms can be improved by improving their control
         component without changing the logic component at all.

(3) Algorithms can be generated from specifications, can be verified and can be transformed into more efficient ones, without considering the control component, by applying deductive inference rules to the logic component alone.

(4) Inexperienced programmers and database users can restrict their interaction with the computing system to the definition of the logic component, leaving the determination of the control component to the computer.

In the systematic development of well-structured algorithms it is appropriate for the logic component to be specified before the control component. The logic component expresses the domain-specific part of an algorithm. It both determines the meaning of the algorithm and influences the way it behaves. The control component, on the other hand, determines the general-purpose problem-solving strategy. It affects only the efficiency of the algorithm without affecting its meaning.

Thus different algorithms A_1 and A_2, obtained by applying different control C_1 and C_2 to the same logic L, are equivalent in the sense that they solve the same problems with the same results. Symbolically

$$A_1 \text{ and } A_2 \text{ are equivalent if } \begin{aligned} A_1 &= L + C_1 \text{ and} \\ A_2 &= L + C_2. \end{aligned}$$

The equivalence of different algorithms having the same logic can be used to improve the efficiency of an algorithm by improving its control without changing its logic. In particular, replacing bottom-up by top-down control often, though not always, improves efficiency, whereas replacing top-down sequential execution of procedure calls by top-down consumer-producer and parallel execution almost always improves efficiency, and never harms it.

The arguments for separating logic from control are like the arguments for separating procedures from data structures. When procedures are separated from data structures, it is possible to distinguish what functions the data structures perform from the manner in which they perform them. An algorithm can be improved by replacing an inefficient data structure by a more efficient one, provided that the new data structure performs the same functions as the old one. Similarly, when logic is separated from control, it is possible to distinguish what the algorithm does, as determined by the logic component, from the manner in which it is done, as determined by the control component. An algorithm can be improved by replacing an inefficient control strategy by a more efficient one, provided that the logic component is unaltered. In both cases, it is easier to determine the meaning of the algorithm and to improve efficiency without affecting meaning.

The separation of logic from control simplifies the problem of relating programs to specifications. By ignoring the control component entirely, it is possible to use rules of deduction to show, for example, that the logic component of an algorithm is correct, because it is implied by its specification. The same techniques of deduction can also be used to generate a logic program from its specification or to transform an inefficient program into a more efficient one. These techniques have been developed by Bibel [1976a, 1976b, 1978], Clark and Tarnlund [1977] Clark and Sickel [1978], Clark and Darlington [1978] and

Hogger [1979] for logic programs and are similar to ones developed for recursion equations by Burstall and Darlington [1977] and for LISP by Manna and Waldinger [1978]. A brief introduction to these methods is presented in Chapter 10, which deals with the standard form of logic and its relationship to clausal form.

The analysis of algorithms into logic and control components provides two distinct methods for improving the efficiency of an algorithm. Given a fixed control component, incorporated in a program executor with limited problem-solving capabilities, efficiency can be improved by changing the representation of the problem in the logic component; or, given a fixed logic component, it can be improved by improving the problem-solving capabilities of the program executor. Changing the logic component is a useful short-term strategy, since the representation of the problem is generally easier to change than the problem-solver. Changing the control component, on the other hand, is a better long-term solution, since improving the problem-solver improves its performance for many different problems.

Specification of the control component

The control component can be expressed by the programmer in a separate control language; or it can be determined by the program executor itself. The provision of a separate control language allows the programmer to advise the problem-solver about program execution and is suitable for the more experienced programmer. The determination of control by the program executor, on the other hand, relieves the programmer of the need to specify control altogether and is more useful for the inexperienced programmer, the casual database user, and even the expert programmer during the early stages of program development.

A completely satisfactory, autonomous control strategy, however, has not yet been designed. The problem of designing an efficient algorithm for scheduling procedure calls, in particular, has still to be solved. The principle of procrastination, which delays execution when a procedure call can be executed in many ways, and the complementary principle, which initiates execution as soon as a procedure call can be executed in no more than one way, work efficiently in a large number of cases. But they are inadequate when all procedure calls are non-deterministic[1]. Annotations for controlling the execution of procedure calls as coroutines have been provided in the PROLOG system [Clark and McCabe 1979] at Imperial College. They are similar to the annotations for recursion equations proposed by Schwarz [1977].

Autonomous search strategies have been designed for both top-down and bottom-up search spaces in theorem-proving. These strategies use merit orderings or evaluation functions to guide the generation of clauses in the search space. Arguments against such search strategies have been advanced by Hayes [1973]. He argues that the kind of information they provide is not adequate for effective problem-solving and proposes that more suitable information can be supplied by the programmer in an auxiliary control language. That a given relation is a function of certain arguments is an example of such information.

Control primitives for guiding search strategies have been provided in programming languages like PLANNER [Hewitt 1969], MICROPLANNER [Sussman, Winograd and Charniak 1971], CONNIVER [Sussman and McDermott 1972], POPLER [Davies 1973], SAIL [Feldman et al 1972], QA4 [Rulifson et al 1973] and QLISP [Reboh and Sacerdoti 1973]. The recommendation lists of PLANNER and MICROPLANNER in particular enable the programmer to specify the order in which procedures should be tried in order to execute a given procedure call. Such information might be useful in fault diagnosis programs, for example, when the programmer knows that a symptom P is more likely to be caused by Q than by R. This might be indicated to the problem-solver by the recommendation that the procedure

$$P \leftarrow Q$$

be tried before $P \leftarrow R$.

Both autonomous and user-specified control over the direction of execution have been provided in theorem-proving and in artificial intelligence programming languages. In programming languages of the PLANNER family, the direction in which procedures are executed is specified in advance by the types associated with procedure declarations (consequent theorem type if the direction is top-down, antecedent theorem type if it is bottom-up). Moreover each procedure call is assigned the type of the procedures which it is allowed to invoke. Autonomous, system-determined strategies for controlling direction of execution are more common in operational research and theorem-proving. Few strategies have been investigated, however, other than the one which chooses the direction having the current least branching rate. Both system-determined and user-specified control over direction are investigated in Chapter 8, which describes the connection graph proof procedure.

Despite the difficulties involved, the desirability of separating logic from control and of allocating responsibility for exercising control to the problem-solver is generally accepted in the field of databases. Given, for example, a data base which defines the relations

Supplier(x,y,z)   supplier number x has name y and status z,
Part(x,y,z)   part number x has name y and unit cost z,
Supply(x,y,z)   supplier number x supplies part number y
                  in quantity z.

the query   Who supplies books?

      <- Answer(y)
      Answer(y) <- Supplies(x,y,z), Supply(x,u,v), Part(u,book,w)

specifies only the logic component of the problem. The data retrieval system needs to determine that, for the sake of efficiency, the procedure call Part(u,book,w) (containing the input) should be executed first. Given the structurally similar query

      What parts are supplied by John?

      <- Answer(y)
      Answer(y) <- Supplier(x,John,z), Supply(x,u,v), Part(u,y,w)

however, it needs to recognise that Supplier(x,John,z) should be executed first.

For inexperienced database users it is desirable that queries be expressed in a formalism as close to natural language as possible. Since logic originates from the analysis of natural language, it is not surprising that database query languages express only the logic component of algorithms. Restricting query languages to the logic component has other advantages. It has the consequence that storage and retrieval schemes can be changed and improved in the control component without affecting the user's view of the data as defined by the logic component. In general, the higher the level of the programming language and the less advanced the level of the programmer, the more the system needs to assume responsibility for efficiency and to exercise control over the use of the information it is given.

The notion that

> computation = controlled deduction

was first proposed by Hayes [1973] and more recently by Bibel [1978], Kowalski [1976], Pratt [1977] and Schwarz [1977]. The similar thesis that database systems be decomposed into a relational component which defines the logic of the data, and a control component which manages data storage and retrieval, has been advocated by Codd [1970]. Hewitt's argument [1969] for the programming language PLANNER, though generally regarded as an argument against logic, can be regarded more positively as an argument for the thesis that algorithms consist of both logic and control components.

Natural Language = Logic + Control

The procedural interpretation of Horn clauses reconciles the classical role of logic in the analysis of language with the interpretation of natural language statements as programs [Winograd 1972]. Like algorithms, natural language combines logic with control. The sentence

> If you want Mary to like you then give her presents and
> be kind to animals.

combines the declarative information

> Mary likes you if you give her presents and
> are kind to animals.

with the advice that it be used top-down to solve problems of being liked by Mary to subproblems of giving her presents and being kind to animals.

Exercises

1) Let the Delete relation be defined by the procedures

Dl   Delete(x, x.y, y) <—
Dl   Delete(x, z.y, w) <— Delete(x,y,w)

a)   Use Dl-2 top-down to delete 1 from the list 2.1.nil .
      Exhibit the entire top-down search space.

b)   Use Dl-2 top-down to add 1 to the list 2.nil . Exhibit
      the entire search space.

c)   Assume that Diff(x,y) holds when   x and y are not
      identical.   Define the relation Delallocc(x,y,w) which
      holds when w is the list which results from deleting all
      occurrences of x from the list y.

2) Describe a representation of the path-finding problem which makes
it possible to find the list of all nodes in a path from one node to
another.

3) Reformulate the   water containers problem of   Chapter 4 to
incorporate loop checking into the program, so that it can be executed
efficiently even if the problem-solver does not recognise and delete
loops.

4) Let Partition(x,y,u,v) be defined by

            Partition(x,y,u,v) <— Shuffle(u,v,y), Small(x,u), Big(x,v)
            Shuffle(nil, v, v) <—
            Shuffle(v, nil, v) <—
            Shuffle(x.y, z, x.u) <— Shuffle(y,z,u)
            Shuffle(y, x.z, x.u) <— Shuffle(y,z,u)

            where Small(x,u) holds when x $\leq$ all members of u,
                  Big (x,u)   x $\geq$ all members of u,
                  Shuffle(u,v,y)   the lists u and v can
                                          be shuffled together
                                          to obtain the list y.

Consider the problem <— Partition(s,t,u,v) where s and t are given as
input and u and v are desired as output.

a)   Define Small(x,u) and Big(x,u) recursively in terms of the
      relations $\leq$ and $\geq$.

b)   Describe the behaviour of the procedures given above and
      in part a) when backtracking is used to solve the problem
      top-down, executing procedure calls sequentially, left-to-
      right.

c)   Describe a more deterministic way of executing procedure
      calls for the same problem.

d)   Redefine Partition(x,y,u,v) so that behaviour similar to
     that of part c) is achieved by simple left-to-right
     execution of procedure calls.

   5) Let the relation   Is(x,y) which holds when x is   an initial sublist
of y

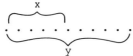

be defined by

          Is(x,y) ← Append(x,z,y)

a)   Define Is(x,y) recursively without using Append.

b)   The relation Sl(x,y) which holds when x is a sublist of y

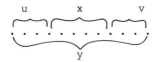

     can be specified by

          Sl(x,y) ← Append(u,x,w), Append(w,v,y)

     Define Sl(x,y) recursively in terms of Is without using
     Append.

c)   Describe an execution strategy for the two procedure calls
     in the specification of Sl above which behaves in the same
     way as top-down sequential execution of the recursive
     definition of Sl.

   7)   a) Express the 8-queens problem by means of Horn clauses:

          Given an 8 by 8 checker board, find a list of eight
          queen positions such that no queen can take another. One
          queen can take another if both are located on the same
          row, same column or same diagonal of the checker board.
          Assume that the Plus relation

               Plus(x,y,z)   (x+y = z)

          is already defined by variable free assertions.

b)   Modify the 8-queens problem and show that the 2-queens
     problem (placing 2 queens on a 2 by 2 checker board) is
     unsolvable by generating the entire top-down search space.
     Execute procedure calls in a manner which minimises the
     size of the search space.

8) Any binary tree can be regarded as representing a list.   For example, the tree

A   B   C   D

named by the term
cons(cons(tip(A), tip(B)), cons(tip(C), tip(D)))
represents the list A.B.C.D.nil .

In general the relationship Represents(x,y) which holds when the tree x represents list y can be defined by the clauses:

R1   Represents(nil,nil) <—
R2   Represents(tip(x), x.nil) <—
R3   Represents(cons(tip(x), y), x.z) <— Represents(y,z)
R4   Represents(cons(cons(x,y), z), w) <—
                                  Represents(cons(x, cons(y,z)), w)

a)   Define the relationship Samelists(x,y) which holds when the trees x and y represent the same lists.

b)   Use procedures R1-4 and (a) to reduce the problem of showing the two trees

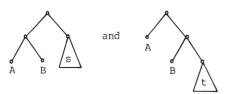

and

represent the same lists to the problem of showing that the subtrees named by s and t represent the same lists.

c)   Use procedures R1-4 and (a) to show that the problem of showing the two trees

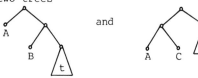

and

represent the same lists, where t and s name any subtrees, is not solvable.

d)   Generalise the execution strategies employed in (b) and (c) and describe an efficient general strategy for executing   the   procedure   calls   in   R1-4   and   (a) cooperatively rather than sequentially.

CHAPTER 6

Plan-Formation and the Frame Problem

In the plan-formation problem we are given an initial state, a goal
state, and a set of actions which transform one state into another. The
problem is to construct a plan, consisting of an appropriate sequence of
actions, which transforms the initial state into the goal state.

The plan-formation problem is identical, therefore, to the state-space
problem. The n-tuple representation of state-space problems is not
feasible, however, when the number n of individuals is large or unknown.
In this chapter, we investigate a version of the binary representation of
state space problems.

The use of logic, in both the n-ary and binary representations, runs
into the frame problem: how to deal with the fact that almost all
statements which hold true of a given state continue to hold after an
action has been performed. It has often been assumed that such facts
cannot be expressed naturally in logic and cannot be used efficiently.

The supposed inadequacies of logic have led to the development of
special systems, such as STRIPS [Fikes and Nilsson 1971] and PLANNER
[Hewitt 1969], specifically intended to deal with the frame problem. We
shall argue that an equally satisfactory treatment of the frame problem
can be obtained in logic: by using terms to name statements and by using
the frame axiom, which describes the statements which continue to hold
after an action has been performed, top-down rather than bottom-up.

Plan-formation and the blocks world

We shall consider the simple blocks world plan-formation problem
[Sacerdoti 1977] in detail. There are three manipulatable blocks A, B
and C and three unmanipulatable places p, q and r. The location of
objects in the initial and goal states is illustrated below:

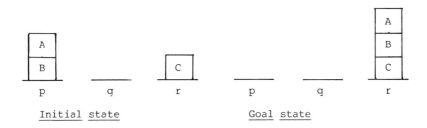

Initial state   Goal state

There is a single action

> trans(x,y,z)

which transfers x from y to z. The action can be performed in a given state if

> x is manipulatable,
> x and z are clear,
> x is on y, and
> x is different from z.

The new statement that

> x is on z and
> y is clear

holds true of the new state which results when the action has been performed. All statements which held in the previous state, except that

> x is on y and
> z is clear,

continue to hold in the new state.

   In general, an action is defined by specifying its preconditions and postconditions. Preconditions are statements which must hold in a state before an action can be performed; whereas postconditions are statements which hold in the new state after the action has been performed. Postconditions are of two kinds: new statements which are added to the description of the new state and old statements which continue to hold from the previous state. The old statements are described by means of a frame axiom which expresses that all statements which held in the old state, except for those explicitly stated as exceptions to be deleted, continue to hold in the new state. The explicit specification for every action of preconditions, added statements and deleted statements is due to STRIPS.

A clausal representation of the blocks world problem

   In this formulation, both states and statements are regarded as individuals and are represented by means of terms. That a statement x holds true in a state y is represented by a binary relationship

> Holds(x,y).

States are named by constant symbols or by composite terms. It is convenient to let the constant symbol O name the initial state and to let the term

> result(u,v)

name the state which results from applying the action u to the state v.

The representation of statements by means of terms is discussed in Chapter 12 concerned with formalising part of the meta-language. Here it is sufficient to let the term

> on(x,y)

name the statement that x is on y and

> clear(x)

that x is clear. An alternative representation, in which the term

> atom(x,y)

names the atomic formula with predicate symbol x and list of arguments y, is more flexible but not necessary here.

In the following clauses

> Poss(x)   expresses that state x is possible,
> Manip(x)   object x is manipulatable,
> Diff(x,y)   x is different from y.

Initial state 0   (1)   Poss(0) <—
                   (2)   Holds(on(A,B), 0) <—
                   (3)   Holds(on(B,p), 0) <—
                   (4)   Holds(on(C,r), 0) <—
                   (5)   Holds(clear(A), 0) <—
                   (6)   Holds(clear(q), 0) <—
                   (7)   Holds(clear(C), 0) <—
State-independent
assertions   (8)   Manip(A) <—
                   (9)   Manip(B) <—
                  (10)   Manip(C) <—

Goal state   (11)   <— Holds(on(A,B),w), Holds(on(B,C),w),
                          Holds(on(C,r),w), Poss(w)

State space and
preconditions   (12)   Poss(result(trans(x,y,z),w)) <— Poss(w),
                          Manip(x), Diff(x,z), Holds(clear(x),w),
                          Holds(clear(z),w), Holds(on(x,y),w)

Added statements (13)   Holds(on(x,z), result(trans(x,y,z), w)) <—
                  (14)   Holds(clear(y), result(trans(x,y,z), w)) <—

Frame axiom and deleted
statements   (15)   Holds(u, result(trans(x,y,z), w)) <—
                                     Holds(u,w), Diff(u, on(x,y)),
                                     Diff(u, clear(z))

Clauses (1)-(6) describe the initial state, whereas clauses (7)-(10) describe the state independent facts about the manipulatability of blocks and clause (11) describes the goal state. The remaining clauses describe the action of transferring an object from one location to another. Clause (12) defines the structure of the state-space search space. It expresses

the preconditions which need to hold before an action can be applied to a
possible state in order to produce a new one. Clauses (13) and (14)
express the postconditions which are added by the action, whereas (15)
expresses those which hold in the new state because they held in the
previous state and were not destroyed by the action.

The relationship $Diff(s,t)$ holds, for variable-free terms s and t,
when s and t are syntactically distinct. It is useful to imagine that
clauses (1)-(15) are supplemented by infinitely many clauses of the form

$$Diff(s,t) \leftarrow$$

for every pair of terms s and t which do not match. Equivalently, the
same relation can be defined by the axioms

$$Diff(f(x_1,\ldots,x_m), g(y_1,\ldots,y_n)) \leftarrow$$

for every pair of distinct function symbols f and g, including the cases
$m = 0$ and $n = 0$ when f and g are constant symbols, and

$$Diff(f(x_1,\ldots,x_m), f(y_1,\ldots,y_m)) \leftarrow Diff(x_i,y_i)$$

for every function symbol f and for every argument i of f, excluding the
case $m = 0$ when f is a constant symbol. In practice, it is more efficient
to define Diff as the negation of identity

$$Diff(x,y) \leftarrow not\text{-}(x = y)$$
$$x = x \quad \leftarrow$$

and to determine that $not\text{-}(x = y)$ holds by showing that $x = y$ fails to
hold. Such an interpretation of negation as failure and its relationship
to the normal interpretation of negation has been studied by Clark [1978]
and is discussed in Chapter 11 which is concerned with definitions
expressed in terms of "if-and-only-if".

This formulation of the plan-formation problem is similar to the one
employed by Green [1969b], based upon proposals of McCarthy and Hayes
[McCarthy and Hayes 1969]. It differs from their formulations, however,
in its use of the Holds relation. They add an extra state parameter to
relations instead, writing, for example, $On(x,y,w)$ to express that x is
on y in state w and $Clear(x,w)$ that x is clear in w. The treatment of
statements as individuals, which is implied by the use of the Holds
relation, can be regarded as a formalisation of part of the meta-
language. The advantages of using logic as its own meta-language are
discussed later in Chapter 12. Here it suffices to note that treating
sentences as individuals avoids that part of the frame problem which is
concerned with expressing the frame axiom. Instead of employing a
separate frame axiom for every relation, writing, for example,

$$On(u, v, result(trans(x,y,z), w)) \leftarrow On(u,v,w), Diff(u,x)$$
$$Clear(u, result(trans(x,y,z), w)) \leftarrow Clear(u,w), Diff(u,z)$$

it suffices to employ a single frame axiom

$$Holds(u, result(v,w)) \leftarrow Holds(u,w), Preserves(v,u)$$

where $Preserves(v,u)$ expresses that the action v preserves the truth of

statement u. The use of the Preserves relation separates the frame axiom
from the specification of the statements which are deleted by individual
actions. In the case of the trans-action:

$$\text{Preserves(trans}(x,y,z), u) \leftarrow \text{Diff}(u, \text{on}(x,y)),$$
$$\text{Diff}(u, \text{clear}(z))$$

As we shall see in the next chapter, clause (15), which combines the
frame axiom and the specification of the deleted statements, can be
obtained by macro-processing the procedure call to the relation
Preserves. Macro-processing executes procedure calls at compile time
before problems are given, rather than at run time during the course of
trying to solve them. It can be regarded as a form of middle-out
reasoning, which in turn is a special case of the resolution rule
[Robinson 1965a]. Resolution also generalises top-down and bottom-up
inference and applies to non-Horn clauses as well.

    It is useful to classify relations into two kinds: primitive
relations, which are independent of other relations, and defined
relations, which can be defined in terms of the primitives. In the blocks
world, the relationship which holds when one object is above another can
be defined in terms of the primitive relationship which holds when one
object is located directly on another.

$$\text{Holds(above}(x,y), w) \leftarrow \text{Holds(on}(x,y), w)$$
$$\text{Holds(above}(x,y), w) \leftarrow \text{Holds(above}(x,z), w),$$
$$\text{Holds(above}(z,y), w)$$

It suffices to specify added and deleted statements only for primitive
relations. The effect of actions on defined relationships is determined
by their effect on primitive relationships and by the definition of the
defined relations in terms of the primitives. The classification of
relations and its use in plan-formation was introduced with STRIPS.

    We have treated the On and Clear relations as primitive. It would be
more natural, however, to define the Clear relation in terms of the On
relation:

$$\text{Holds(clear}(y), w) \leftarrow \text{for all } x \text{ not-Holds(on}(x,y), w)$$

We shall discuss this possibility in Chapter 11, which investigates if-
and-only-if definitions and the interpretation of negation as failure.

    The logic of the blocks world problem is separate from its use.
Clauses can be used either top-down or bottom-up. They can also be used
in a mixture of directions. If the state space axiom (12) is used bottom-
up, then the problem-solver reasons forward from the initial state,
deriving new states from old ones, until the goal state is generated. If
the axiom is used top-down, then the problem-solver reasons backward from
the goal-state, until the initial state is generated.

    The second part of the frame problem arises when the frame axiom (15)
is used bottom-up to derive, from an assertion that a given statement
holds in a given state, a new assertion that the same statement holds in
a following state. For more realistic plan-formation tasks than the
blocks world problem, a typical state needs to be described by a large
number of assertions, many of which are unrelated to the problem at hand.

In such situations it is not computationally feasible to use the frame
axiom bottom-up to copy preserved facts from state to state.

Both PLANNER and STRIPS deal with the frame problem by abandoning the
frame axiom and using special-purpose procedures instead. Similar results
can be obtained by retaining the frame axiom but interpreting it top-
down:

> To determine whether a statement u holds in a state result(v,w)
>
> (i)   show u is added by v,
> (ii)   alternatively, if u is not deleted by v,
>   determine whether u holds in the previous state w.

Changing the direction of execution of the frame axiom exemplifies the
general strategy of improving an algorithm by improving its control
without changing its logic.

We shall illustrate the different solutions determined for the blocks
world problem by using the state space and frame axioms in different
directions.

Bottom-up execution of the state space axiom (12)

The following illustration displays part of the search space of states
determined by executing (12) bottom-up.

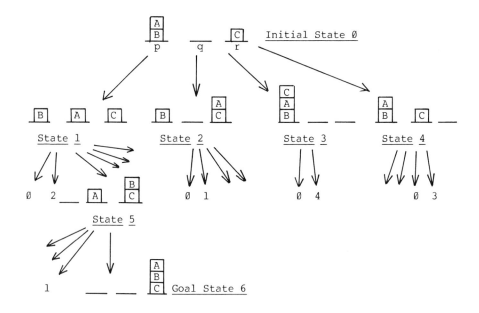

Distinct nodes represent distinct states. However, distinct states labelled by the same number are characterised by the same statements. In this case, the redundancy arises because it is never useful to pick up the same object twice in a row.

The assertions which are generated by bottom-up execution of the state space axiom describe the search space of states illustrated above and are independent of the direction of execution of the frame axiom.

Bottom-up execution of the frame axiom (15)

The following assertions, concerning states which belong to the solution path, are generated by bottom-up execution of the frame axiom.

Holds(on(B,p), 1) <—	Holds(on(C,r), 1) <—
Holds(on(A,q), 5) <—	Holds(on(C,r), 5) <—
Holds(on(B,C), 6) <—	Holds(on(C,r), 6) <—
Holds(clear(A), 1) <—	Holds(clear(C), 1) <—
Holds(clear(B), 5) <—	Holds(clear(A), 5) <—
Holds(clear(A), 6) <—	Holds(clear(p), 6) <—

The additional assertions

Holds(on(A,q), 1) <—	Holds(clear(B), 1) <—
Holds(on(B,C), 5) <—	Holds(clear(p), 5) <—
Holds(on(A,B), 6) <—	Holds(clear(q), 6) <—

which are needed for a complete description of the same states are instances of the clauses (13) and (14) which specify the statements added by the trans-action. As in the previous illustration,

1	abbreviates	result(trans(A,B,q), 0),
5		result(trans(B,p,C), 1),
6		result(trans(A,q,B), 5).

In the general case, a search strategy might need to generate many assertions concerning states which are not relevant to the solution as well as assertions such as

Holds(on(B,p), result(trans(A,C,B), 0)) <—
Holds(on(B,p), result(trans(B,q,C), 0)) <—
Holds(on(B,p), result(trans(B,B,B), 0)) <—

which describe impossible states. The generation of such undesirable assertions is avoided if the frame axiom is used top-down. It can also be avoided when the frame axiom is used bottom-up by adding the extra condition

Poss(result(trans(x,y,z), w))

to the frame axiom.

Mixed top-down and bottom-up execution of the frame axiom

Top-down execution of the frame axiom may be combined with bottom-up
execution of the state space exiom. This can be pictured in arrow
notation:

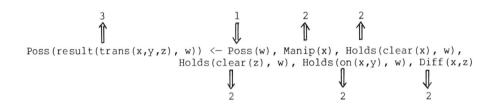

It can be simulated by top-down execution alone. It suffices to rewrite
clauses (1), (11) and (12) using a predicate symbol Nposs which is the
negation of Poss. Clauses (1), (11) and (12) become (1'), (11') and
(12') respectively.

```
(1')              <- Nposs(Ø)
(11')         Nposs(w) <- Holds(on(A,B), w), Holds(on(B,C), w),
                           Holds(on(C,r), w)
(12')         Nposs(w) <- Nposs(result(trans(x,y,z), w)), Manip(x),
                           Holds(clear(x), w), Holds(clear(z), w),
                           Holds(on(x,y), w), Diff(x,z)
```

The renaming of predicate symbols, of the kind involved in rewriting
clauses (1), (11) and (12), has been investigated by Meltzer [1966] and
will be considered again in the next chapter.

A small part of the search space is illustrated below. The mixed top-
down, bottom-up execution strategy is equivalent to pure top-down
execution using clauses (1'), (11') and (12') instead of (1), (11) and
(12). All arcs which diverge from the solution path are illustrated.
Nodes which are labelled by clauses containing unsolvable subgoals are
darkened   to indicate that they are terminal failure nodes. The circled
numbers preceding underlined atoms indicate the order in which they or
their descendants are selected. Unlabelled arcs indicate execution of
procedure calls containing the predicate symbol Diff. Some nodes are left
unlabelled in order to suppress distracting details. t(x,y,z) abbreviates
trans(x,y,z).

Notice that many alternatives to the solution path fail after only a
few steps. The alternatives which do not fail correspond to genuine
alternative actions in the search space of states.

Poss(0) <—
(12)

(11)   Poss(result(t(x,y,z),0)) <—②Manip(x),①Holds(clear(x),0),
(7)   (5)   Holds(clear(z),0),
  (6)   ③Holds(on(x,y),0), Diff(x,z)
        (8)

        (2)
        Poss(result(t(A,B,z),0)) <—①Holds(clear(z),0),②Diff(A,z)
(7)   (6)
  (5)   Poss(result(t(A,B,q),0)) <—
        (12)
(11)   Poss(result(t(x,y,z),1)) <—②Manip(x),①Holds(clear(x),1),
        (14)   Holds(clear(z),1),
  (15)   ③Holds(on(x,y),1), Diff(x,z)
(5)   (9)
 (6) (7)
        (15)

        (3)

        Poss(result(t(B,p,z),1)) <—①Holds(clear(z),1),②Diff(B,z)
(14)   (15)
(5)   (7)
  (6)

        Poss(result(t(B,p,C),1)) <—
        (12)
(11)   Poss(result(t(x,y,z),5)) <—②Manip(x),①Holds(clear(x),5),
        (15)   Holds(clear(z),5),
(14)   Holds(on(x,y),5), Diff(x,z)
        (15)
(14)
(7)   (5)
  (6)

        (8)
        Poss(result(t(A,y,z),5)) <— Holds(clear(z),5),
        (15)   Holds(on(A,y),5),Diff(A,z)
(15)   (13)

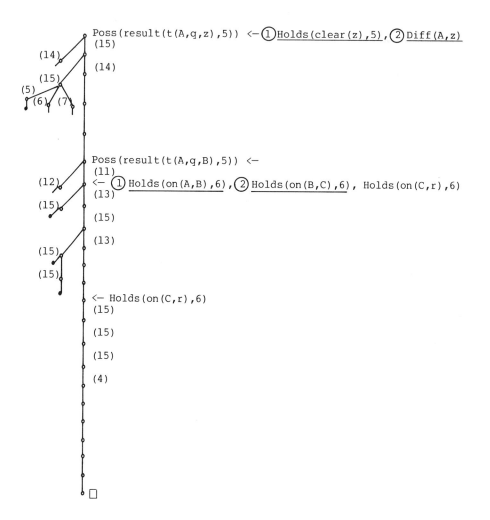

The eventual failure of the alternative attempts to solve the subgoals

            Holds(on(A,y),5)
            Holds(on(A,B),6)   and
            Holds(on(B,C),6)

can be hastened by strengthening the restrictions on the frame axiom. The
more restrictive version of the frame axiom

        Holds(u, result(trans(x,y,z), w)) <- Holds(u,w),
                                             Diff(u, on(x,v)),
                                             Diff(u, clear(z)),
                                             Diff(u, clear(y))

in particular, fails immediately whenever one of the clauses (13) or (14) succeeds.

Top-down execution of the state space and frame axioms

Part of the search space of states determined by executing the state space axiom top-down is illustrated below. As in the case where the state space axiom is executed bottom-up, redundancy arises when the same object is picked up twice in succession. The variables y and y' name locations which have not yet been determined.

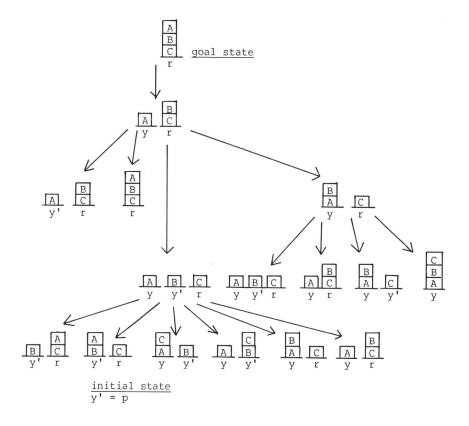

In the following solution all clauses are executed top-down. Subgoals are considered breadth-first and left to right in the order in which they are written. Duplicate subgoals are deleted. To save space, steps involving the solution of subgoals containing the predicate symbol Diff are not illustrated.

```
      ⟵ Holds(on(A,B),w), Holds(on(B,C),w),
13         Holds(on(C,r),w), Poss(w)
15
15         w = result(trans(A,y,B),w₁)
12
      ⟵ Holds(on(B,C),w₁), Holds(on(C,r),w₁), Poss(w₁),
13         Manip(A), Holds(clear(A),w₁), Holds(clear(B),w₁),
15         Holds(on(A,y),w₁), Diff(A,B)
12
 8
15         w₁ = result(trans(B,y',C),w₂)
15
15
      ⟵ Holds(on(C,r),w₂), Poss(w₂), Manip(B),
15         Holds(clear(B),w₂), Holds(clear(C),w₂),
12         Holds(on(B,y'),w₂), Diff(B,C), Holds(clear(A),w₂),
 9         Holds(clear(B),w₂), Holds(on(A,y),w₂)
14
15
15         w₂ = result(trans(A,B,y),w₃)
15
13
      ⟵ Holds(on(C,r),w₃), Poss(w₃), Manip(A),
 4         Holds(clear(A),w₃), Holds(clear(y),w₃),
 1         Holds(on(A,B),w₃), Diff(A,y), Holds(clear(C),w₃),
 8         Holds(on(B,y'),w₃), Holds(clear(A,w₃)
 5
 6
 2         w₃ = ∅   y = q   y' = p
 7
 3
           ☐
```

Applications of plan-formation

The principal application of plan-formation has been the construction
of plans for robot-like machinery. Plan-formation has also been applied
to the automatic construction of programs from specifications. The
description of the input and the output states constitutes a
specification of a program. The definition of the preconditions and of
the statements added and deleted by actions expresses the semantics of
the machine operations. A plan consists of a sequence of machine
operations and represents a program. More elaborate systems of plan-
formation include procedures for constructing plans with conditional
statements, loops and other operations. Horn clause plan-formation
programs written by Warren [1974, 1976] and Moss [1977] have been applied
to program construction.

An application of plan-formation to the synthesis of organic compounds
was developed by Fogel, while a high school student, at Imperial College
during the summer of 1977. Chemical compounds, like states in plan-
formation, can be described by assertions concerning the objects (atoms
and bonds) which belong to them. The statement that

bond b of strength s holds between the
atoms a_1 and a_2 in the compound c

can be expressed by a single n-ary relationship

Bond(b,s,a_1,a_2,c) $\leftarrow$

or by several binary relationships:

b has strength s $\leftarrow$
b bonds a_1 $\leftarrow$
b bonds a_2 $\leftarrow$
b belongs to c $\leftarrow$

An initial compound functions as an initial state and a goal compound as
a goal state. Chemical reactions are actions which transform one compound
into another. They are defined by specifying (1) the preconditions which
must hold before a reaction can take place, (2) the new bonds which the
reaction introduces and (3) the old bonds which the reaction destroys. A
frame axiom states that bonds which are not destroyed by a reaction are
preserved by it. Both the program written by Moss and the one written by
Fogel were implemented as Horn clause programs and run on a PROLOG-like
system developed at Imperial College.

   Programs for drug analysis have been written in PROLOG at the Ministry
of Heavy Industry in Budapest [Futo, Darvas and Szeredi 1978]. These use
relational data structures similar to those in the organic synthesis
program. Because many of the properties of a given drug may be unknown,
the drug analysis programs employ binary rather than n-ary relations. The
programs have led to useful discoveries concerning previously unknown
drug interactions and concerning inconsistencies in descriptions of drugs
in the pharmaceutical literature.

Limitations

   The approach taken in this chapter stores information about the
initial state explicitly and uses the frame axiom to compute information
about later states. It can be argued that this is unnatural and
potentially inefficient. The alternative, when using depth-first search
and reasoning forward from the initial state, is to store the current
state explicitly and to compute information about earlier states. The two
approaches are intuitively equivalent. The problem of formally explaining
and justifying the equivalence, however, has still to be solved.

   The treatment of plans as sequences of actions is another limitation,
which creates redundancies when actions do not interact and can be
performed in parallel. Performing the actions in sequence produces the
same results redundantly in any sequence. Systems for generating plans
which are partially ordered collections of actions have been described by
Sacerdoti [1975] and Tate [1974]. A Horn clause program which generates
partially ordered plans has also been written in PROLOG by Warren. A
survey of plan-formation systems and a comparison with the one presented
in this chapter has been made by Waldinger [1977].

Exercises

1) Formulate an n-tuple representation of the blocks world problem.
Let State(x,y,z) hold when it is possible for block A to be on x, B on y
and C on z simultaneously. Compare problem-solving strategies for the n-
tuple representation with those for the binary representation of the
problem.

2) Reformulate the water container problem investigated in Chapter 4
as a plan-formation problem using the binary representation investigated
in this chapter. Compare the problem-solving strategies needed for
efficient solution of the problem in both the n-ary and binary
representations.

3) The assigment statement of conventional programming languages can
be regarded as an action which transforms one state of a computer into
another. The new state

          assign(u,v,w)

differs from the preceding state w in that the location u contains v.

Assume that A, B and C are locations and that in the initial state 0
they contain a, b and c respectively. The problem is to find a state in
which the initial values of A and B are interchanged.

Formulate and solve the problem as a plan-formation task.

CHAPTER 7

Resolution

We shall extend the Horn clause model of problem-solving to non-Horn clauses. With non-Horn clauses

(1) goals and assertions can be negative as well as positive,

(2) the application of procedures to goals can generate assertions as well as subgoals,

(3) the solution of subgoals can require the analysis of several alternative cases and

(4) solutions can be disjunctions: $x = t_1$ or t_2 or ... or t_m.

Top-down and bottom-up inference can be extended to non-Horn clauses. The new rules, as well as the old ones, are all special cases of the general resolution rule introduced by Robinson [1965a].

Negative goals and assertions

In many cases a set of non-Horn clauses can be reexpressed as Horn clauses by renaming predicate symbols [Meltzer 1966]. The non-Horn clause

Pleasant(x), Nightmare(x) $\leftarrow$ Dream(x)

for example, can be rewritten as the Horn clause

Nightmare(x) $\leftarrow$ Dream(x), Unpleasant(x)

by reexpressing the negative atom not-Pleasant(x) as the positive atom Unpleasant(x).

Similarly the non-Horn clause problem of showing that every boletus is poisonous can be transformed into a Horn clause problem by eliminating the predicate symbol "Mushroom" and using the new predicate symbol "Nonmushroom" instead. The unnegated atom, Nonmushroom(x), means the same as the negated atom, not-Mushroom(x). The new Horn clause problem Fung'1-6 can be solved top-down or bottom-up.

Fung'1   Toadstool(x) <- Fungus(x), Nonmushroom(x)
Fung'2   Poisonous(x) <- Toadstool(x)
Fung'3   Fungus(x) <- Boletus(x)
Fung'4   Nonmushroom(x) <- Boletus(x)
Fung'5   Boletus(🍄) <-
Fung'6   <- Poisonous(🍄)

A <u>bottom-up</u> solution:

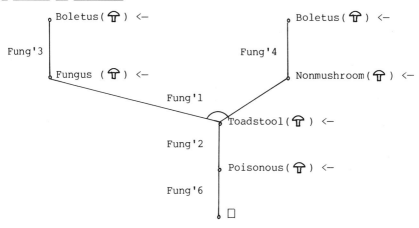

A <u>top-down</u> solution:

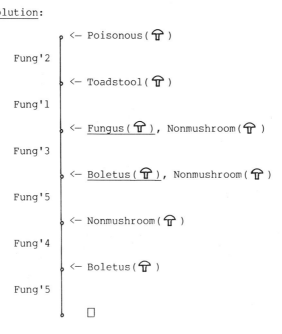

The bottom-up derivation of the assertion

    Nonmushroom(🍄) ←

from the Horn clauses Fung'4 and Fung'5 is equivalent to the derivation of the negative "assertion"

        ← Mushroom(🍄)

directly from the original clauses Fung 4-5,

        ← Boletus(x), Mushroom(x)

        Boletus(🍄) ← .

Similarly the top-down derivation of the positive subgoals

        ← Fungus(🍄), Nonmushroom(🍄)

from the goal statement

        ← Toadstool(🍄)

by means of the Horn clause Fung'1 is equivalent to the direct derivation of the clause

    Mushroom(x) ← Fungus(x)

from the same goal statement

        ← Toadstool(🍄)

by means of the non-Horn clause

Fung1   Toadstool(x), Mushroom ← Fungus(x).

Resolution

In general, top-down and bottom-up inference for both Horn clauses and non-Horn clauses are special cases of the resolution rule: To create a resolvent of two clauses it is necessary first to rename variables so that different clauses contain different variables.

> Given a condition in one clause and a conclusion in the other, the resolvent exists if the condition and the conclusion match. The two clauses are said to be the parents of the resolvent clause. An atom is a condition of the resolvent if it is obtained by applying the matching substitution to a condition, different from the matched condition, of one of the parents. Similarly, an atom is a conclusion of the resolvent if it is obtained by applying the matching substitution to a conclusion, different from the matched conclusion, of one of the parent clauses.

The definition can be expressed by means of Horn clauses. Let

```
res(x,u,y,v)      name the  resolvent which  exists  when,  after
                  appropriate renaming of variables,  the condition u
                  in x matches the conclusion v in y,
cond(x)           the collection of conditions of clause x,
concl(x)          the collection of conclusions of clause x,
union(x,y)        the union of x and y,

Apply(x,w,x')     express that  the  result of  applying  to  x  the
                  substitution w is x',
Rename(x,y,w)     the  substitution w  applied  to clauses x  and  y
                  results  in  clauses which  contain  no  variables in
                  common,
Match(u,v,w)      substitution w matches the atoms u and v,
Member(u,x)       u is a member of x,
```

Combine(w_1,w_2,w)   the substitution w has the combined effect of
                  first applying substitution w_1 and then applying
                  substitution w_2,
Resolves(x,u,y,v,w) the resolvent of x and y on atoms u and v
                  exists and w is the combined substitution which
                  both renames variables and matches atoms.

Resolves(x,u,y,v,w) $\leftarrow$ Rename(x,y,w_1),Member(u,cond(x)),Apply(u,w_1,u'),
                  Member(v,concl(y)),Apply(v,w_1,v'),Match(u',v',w_2),
                  Combine(w_1,w_2,w)

Member(z, cond(res(x,u,y,v))) $\leftarrow$ Resolves(x,u,y,v,w),
                  Member(z', union(cond(x),cond(y))),
                  Diff(z',u), Apply(z',w,z)

Member(z, concl(res(x,u,y,v))) $\leftarrow$ Resolves(x,u,y,v,w),
                  Member(z', union(concl(x),concl(y))),
                  Diff(z',v), Apply(z',w,z)

Member(z, union(x,y)) $\leftarrow$ Member(z,x)

Member(z, union(x,y)) $\leftarrow$ Member(z,y)

Notice that the definition can be used either top-down or bottom-up. The
Boyer-Moore structure-sharing implementation of resolution [1972] can be
regarded as using the definition top-down but saving solved subgoals of
the form Resolves(x,u,y,v,w) as lemmas.

The definition given here is less general than Robinson's which also
incorporates the factoring rule described later in the chapter.

Middle out reasoning with Horn clauses

In addition to top-down and bottom-out inference, resolution includes
middle-out reasoning with Horn clauses. The resolvent of the two clauses

$$\text{Fallible}(x) \; \leftarrow \; \text{Human}(x)$$
$$\text{Mortal}(x) \; \leftarrow \; \text{Fallible}(x)$$

for example, is the clause Mortal(x) $\leftarrow$ Human(x).

Middle-out reasoning can also be applied to different copies of the same clause. From two copies of the definition of ancestor, for example

Ancestor(x,y) <— Ancestor(x,z), Ancestor(z,y)
Ancestor(u,v) <— Ancestor(u,w), Ancestor(w,v)

we can derive the resolvent

Ancestor(x,y) <— Ancestor(x,w),Ancestor(w,z),Ancestor(z,y).

Propositional logic example

The clauses which define the semantics of propositional logic provide instructive examples of the resolution rule. Here if x and y name propositions x* and y* respectively then

x & y	names the proposition	x* and y*
x V y		x* or y*
x ⊃ y		if x* then y*
x<=>y		x* if and only if y*
¬ x		it is not the case that x*.

where &, V , ⊃, <=> and ¬ are infix function symbols. Read True(x) as stating that x is true. The following set of clauses cannot be reexpressed as Horn clauses by renaming predicate symbols.

T1	True(x&y) <— True(x), True(y)
T2	True(x) <— True(x&y)
T3	True(y) <— True(x&y)
T4	True(xVy) <— True(x)
T5	True(xVy) <— True(y)
T6	True(x), True(y) <— True(xVy)
T7	True(x⊃y),True(x) <—
T8	True(x⊃y) <— True(y)
T9	True(y) <— True(x), True(x⊃y)
T10	True(x<=>y) <— True(x⊃y), True(y⊃x)
T11	True(x⊃y) <— True(x<=>y)
T12	True(y⊃x) <— True(x<=>y)
T13	True(¬x), True(x) <—
T14	<— True(¬x), True(x)

Clauses T1-3 state that

x & y is true if and only if
x is true and y is true.

Clause T1 is the if-half of the statement and clauses T2-3 are the only-if-half. Similarly the remaining clauses state that

T4-6   x V y is true if and only if
x is true or y is true;

T7-9   x ⊃ y is true if and only if
                if x is true then y is true;
T10-12   x <⇒ y is true if and only if
                x ⊃ y is true and y ⊃ x is true;

T13-14   ¬ x is true if and only if
                x is not true.

    This set of clauses is based upon a more general definition of "truth"
for sentences in the   standard form   of logic   formulated by Colmerauer
[unpublished].

    The if-halves of the statements are useful top-down to reduce problems
concerning the truth of a complex proposition to subproblems concerning
the truth of simpler propositions. The only-if halves, on the other hand,
are useful bottom-up to derive conclusions concerning the truth of simple
propositions from assumptions concerning the truth of more complicated
ones.

    For example, to show that

                p & ¬q is true if p is true and q is not true

it is natural to reason top-down from the goal

                <— True (p & ¬q)

using the assumptions

A1   True (p) <—
A2   <— True (q)

and regarding the second assumption A2 as a negative assertion.

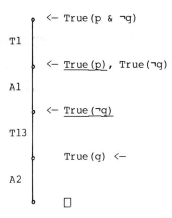

        T1

                     <— True (p & ¬q)

                     <— True (p), True (¬q)

        A1

                     <— True (¬q)

        T13

                     True (q) <—

        A2

                     □

Here the clause T13 can be regarded as reducing the problem of showing
that ⁻q is true to the problem of showing that q is not   true, which is
solved directly by assumption A2.*

    On the other hand, to show that

                p is true and q is not true if p & ⁻q is true

it is more natural to reason bottom-up from the assumption

                True(p & ⁻q) <− .

The clause

G   True(q) <− True(p)

can be interpreted as expressing the goal of showing that p is true and q
not true.

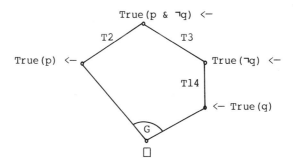

Clause T14 can be regarded as deriving the negative assertion that q is
not true, which solves the negative goal in G. Notice that the bundle of
arcs labelled G represents two successive resolution steps. The order in
which the steps are performed is not significant.

    The problem of showing that

                p V ⁻p is true

illustrates another characteristic feature of top-down problem-solving
with non-Horn clauses: No one method adequately solves the problem, but
several alternative methods exhaust all the cases.

                    ----

*Throughout this chapter only resolution refutations are exhibited.
Search spaces will be investigated in the next chapter.

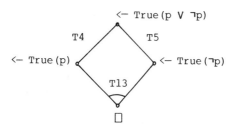

Methods T4 and T5 reduce the original problem to subproblems which
exhaust the two cases asserted by the non-Horn clause T13.

   A bottom-up solution of the same problem would involve reasoning by
cases. Case analysis by bottom-up reasoning can be seen more clearly,
however, for the problem of showing that

              r is true if p ∨ q is true,

assuming that

              r is true if p is true, and r is true if q is true.

(1)   <— True(r)
(2)   True(p ∨ q) <—
(3)   True(r) <— True(p)
(4)   True(r) <— True(q)

              True(p ∨ q) <—
      T6

              True(p), True(q) <—

         (3)

              True(r), True(q) <—

         (1)

              True(q) <—

         (4)

              True(r) <—

         (1)

              □

Clause T6 derives a non-Horn clause which expresses that there are two
cases. The solution reasons bottom-up, first solving the goal in the
case that p is true and then solving it in the case that q is true. It
"remembers" the second case while it is working on the first one.

Given a goal and a Horn clause which reduces the goal to subgoals, non-Horn clauses can be used to derive assumptions to assist the solution of the subgoals. Such non-Horn clauses typically arise from non-clausal sentences of the form

$$A \leftarrow [B \leftarrow C], D$$

in which a condition is an implication. In the problem-solving interpretation, the clausal form of such a sentence

$$A, C \leftarrow D$$
$$A \leftarrow B, D$$

can be regarded as stating that

in order to solve A, solve D, and solve B assuming C.

The clauses T7-8 arise from such a non-clausal sentence:

$$True(x \supset y) \leftarrow [True(y) \leftarrow True(x)]$$

To show that $x \supset y$ is true,
show that y is true assuming that x is true.

In some cases only one of the clauses T7-8 is needed to solve the problem. If x is not true as in the case

$$\leftarrow True((p \ \& \ \neg p) \supset q)$$

then only the non-Horn clause T7 which derives the assertion

$$True(p \ \& \ \neg p) \leftarrow$$

is needed. But if y is true as in the case

$$< \ True(q \supset (p \lor \neg p))$$

then only the Horn clause T8 which derives the subgoal

$$\leftarrow True(p \lor \neg p)$$

is needed.

In most cases, however, both clauses need to be used. The simplest problem which requires the cooperation of clauses T7-8 is that of showing that p p is true.

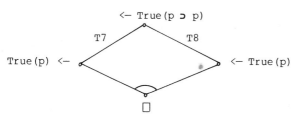

The derived subgoal of showing that p is true is solved by the derived assertion that p is true. The bundle of arcs associated with the resolution step is unlabelled, because only derived clauses are involved in the inference.

The problem of showing that

$p \supset q$ is true if $p \supset r$ is true and $r \supset q$ is true

is more interesting. Here it is natural to reason bi-directionally, both forward from the two assumptions and backward from the conclusion. Moreover, when reasoning backward from the conclusion

$\leftarrow$ True $(p \supset q)$

it is natural to reason forward from the derived assertion

True (p) $\leftarrow$

and backward from the derived subgoal

$\leftarrow$ True (q)

The following resolution proof formalises the argument.

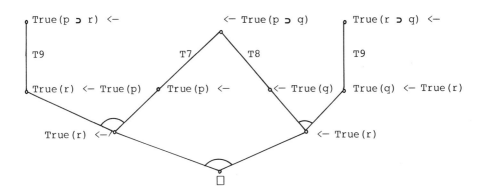

Arrow notation for non-Horn clauses

The arrow notation used earlier for Horn clauses, to indicate the combination of top-down and bottom-up inference, can also be used for non-Horn clauses. The problem-solving interpretation, in particular, of sentences of the form

A $\leftarrow$ [B $\leftarrow$ C]

can be indicated by arrows associated with the corresponding clauses

The notation associated with the first clause indicates that it should wait for a subgoal of the form A and then derive the assertion C <— . The notation associated with the second clause indicates that it should wait for a subgoal of the form A and then derive the subgoal B.

The use of arrow notation to control the behaviour of a problem-solver will be investigated in the next chapter.

Disjunctive solutions to non-Horn clause problems

Plan-formation tasks, described by means of non-Horn clauses, may require the construction of conditional plans from disjunctive solutions.

Consider, for example, the problem of putting the maximum of two numbers A and B in a location L:

M1	<— Holds(val(L,x), w), Max(A,B,x)
M2	Numb(A) <—
M3	Numb(B) <—
M4	Location(L) <—
M5	u $\leq$ v, v $\leq$ u <— Numb(u), Numb(v)
M6	Max(u,v,u) <— v $\leq$ u
M7	Max(u,v,v) <— u $\leq$ v

Suppose that the only action available is the <u>assignment</u> operation. Given a state w, it generates the new state

          assign(u,v,w)

which results from w by putting v in location u. The "semantics" of the action are described by specifying its preconditions and the statements which are added and deleted when the action is performed. To simplify matters, the single precondition, that u be a location, can be incorporated into the clauses which specify the added (M8) and deleted (M9) statements:

M8	Holds(val(u,v), assign(u,v,w)) <— Location(u)
M9	Holds(x, assign(u,v,w)) <— Holds(x,w), Diff(x, val(u,y)), Location(u)

Before solving the problem top-down it is convenient to reason one step bottom-up:

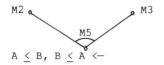

M10   A ≤ B, B ≤ A ←—

The top-down solution using the derived lemma M10 requires that the two
procedures M6 and M7 cooperate to solve the single subgoal Max(A,B,x).

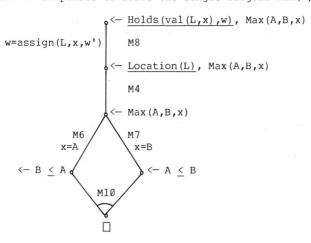

The solution is a disjunction of two possibilities

w = assign(L,A,w') or assign(L,B,w'), for any w'.

A solution exists, but it is not determined$_3$ which of the two
possibilities it is.

Non-determinism$_3$ contrasts with non-determinism$_1$. A problem is non-
deterministic$_3$ if its solution

x = t$_1$ or t$_2$ or ... or t$_m$

is underspecified. It is non-deterministic$_1$ if its solution is
overspecified

x = t$_1$ and t$_2$ and ... and t$_m$.

The treatment of program construction as an application of plan-
formation was first proposed by Green [1969b] and Lee and Waldinger
[1969].   Lee and Waldinger, in particular, present an algorithm for
extracting conditional programs, such as

If A ≤ B then w = assign(C,B,w')
        else w = assign(C,A,w')

from disjunctive solutions. The relationship between plan-formation and
axiomatic semantics of programming languages has been investigated by
Moss [1977].

Factoring

The resolution rule alone is complete for demonstrating the inconsistency of Horn clauses. Moreover, it is also adequate for many, but not all, non-Horn clause problems. The combination of factoring and resolution, first described in Robinson's original, unpublished paper is equivalent to the published version of the resolution rule [Robinson 1965a]. Consequently, the completeness proof in the published paper establishes completeness of resolution and factoring combined.

The barber paradox is a simple example which requires the use of factoring.

> Suppose that all barbers shave all people who do not shave themselves and no barber shaves anyone who shaves himself. Then there are no barbers.

To establish the conclusion we assert that there is a barber and attempt to derive a contradiction.

B1   Shave(x,y), Shave(y,y) <— Barber(x)
B2   <— Shave(x,y), Shave(y,y), Barber(x)
B3   Barber(☺) <—

That the three clauses are inconsistent can be demonstrated by instantiating the first two clauses

> Shave(☺,☺), Shave(☺,☺) <— Barber(☺)
> <— Shave(☺,☺), Shave(☺,☺), Barber(☺)

deleting duplicate atoms

> Shave(☺,☺) <— Barber(☺)
> <— Shave(☺,☺), Barber(☺)

and applying resolution.

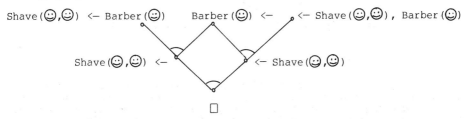

Shave(☺,☺) <— Barber(☺)   Barber(☺) <—   <— Shave(☺,☺), Barber(☺)

Shave(☺,☺) <—   <— Shave(☺,☺)

□

That resolution alone is inadequate for demonstrating inconsistency can be seen more clearly by considering a simpler example:

S1   S(x), S(y) <—
S2   <— S(u), S(v)

The two clauses are inconsistent because they have instances

> S(x), S(x) <—
> <— S(u), S(u)

which, after removal of duplicate atoms, are directly contradictory:

        S(x) <—
        <— S(u)

However, no matter how many times resolution is applied to clauses S1-2 and their descendants, every resolvent contains exactly two atoms, and consequently no resolvent is the empty clause (which contains no atoms).

The __factoring__ rule, which needs to supplement resolution in these examples, generates instances of clauses in order to delete duplicate atoms. The instantiating substitution can be restricted so that it matches the two atoms which become duplicates. Applied to the two clauses B1 and B2, factoring generates instances which are more general than the two instances considered before.

B1   Shave(x,y), Shave(y,y) <— Barber(x)
              (match underlined atoms)

              Shave(x,x), ~~Shave(x,x)~~ <— Barber(x)
              (delete duplicates)

B'1   Shave(x,x) <— Barber(x)

B'1 is the only factor of B1. Similarly B'2 is the only factor of B2:

B'2   <— Shave(x,x), Barber(x)

Application of factoring and the combined resolution and factoring refutation can be exhibited in a graph.

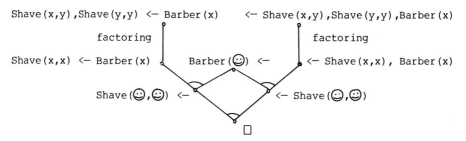

Factoring is only necessary infrequently and it creates redundancy if it is applied too often. Perhaps the most restrictive constraint on the use of factoring, without affecting completeness, is the one incorporated in the model elimination proof procedure [Loveland 1968, 1969, 1978].

Exercises
─────────

  1) Use resolution and factoring to show that the assumptions

        John likes anyone who doesn't like himself.
        John likes no one who likes himself.

are inconsistent.

2) Suppose I believe:

> (a) There exists a dragon.
> (b) The dragon either sleeps i. its cave or hunts in the forest.
> (c) If the dragon is hungry then it cannot sleep.
> (d) If the dragon is tired then it cannot hunt.

Use resolution to answer the following questions:

> What does the dragon do when it is hungry?
> What does the dragon do when it is tired?
> What does the dragon do when it is hungry and tired?

To answer the questions it is necessary to make explicit the assumption:

> If x cannot do y then x does not do y.

3) Express the following assumptions in clausal form:

> Everyone admires a hero.
> A failure admires everyone.
> Anyone who is not a hero is a failure.

Use resolution and factoring to find a pair of individuals (not necessarily distinct) who admire one another.

4) This problem is discussed by Moore [1975]. Suppose there are three blocks A, B and C.

> A is on B which is on C.
> A is green, C is blue and
> the colour of B is unknown.

A	green
B	
C	blue

Use resolution (and factoring if necessary) to find a green block on a block which is not green. You must assume that blue is not green. What block does the proof find?

5) Using resolution and factoring, show that the following conclusions follow from assumptions T1-14.

> (a) If p ⊃ (r & q) is true
>   then (p ⊃ r) & (p ⊃ q) is true.
>
> (b) If p ⊃ q is true
>   then there is an r such that (p ⊃ r) & (r ⊃ q).
>   What r does the proof find?

6) The relation Plus(x,y,z) which holds when x+y = z can be defined
using non-Horn clauses

        Plus(x,y,z), Add(0,y) <—
        Plus(x,y,z) <— Add(x,z)
        Add(s(x),s(z)) <— Add(x,z)

where s(x) names the successor of x.   Use resolution and factoring to
solve the problem

        <— Plus(x,y,s(y)), Plus(x,x,y).

CHAPTER 8

The Connection Graph Proof Procedure

The search space determined by unrestricted application of the resolution rule is highly redundant. Redundancy can be avoided, at the expense of flexibility, by restricting resolution to top-down or bottom-up inference. It can also be avoided, however, without the loss of flexibility by employing the connection graph proof procedure.

Clauses are stored in a graph and occurrences of matching atoms on opposite sides of the arrow are connected by arcs. Associated with each arc in the graph is the resolvent obtained by resolving the clauses connected by the arc. The main operation of the connection graph proof procedure is the selection of an arbitrary arc and the incorporation of the associated resolvent into the connection graph. Top-down inference is performed by selecting an arc connected to a goal statement; bottom-up inference, by selecting an arc connected to a clause which contains no conditions. Redundancy is avoided by deleting the selected arc and by restricting the number of new arcs which are added when the resolvent is incorporated into the graph.

The initial connection graph

The first step of the connection graph proof procedure is the construction of the initial connection graph. In addition to the initial set of clauses, the initial connection graph contains an arc for every pair of matching atoms on opposite sides of the arrow in different clauses. The arc connects the atoms and is labelled by the matching substitution. Later in the chapter we consider the case in which an arc links atoms in the same clause.

The initial connection graph for a simple non-Horn clause problem is illustrated below.

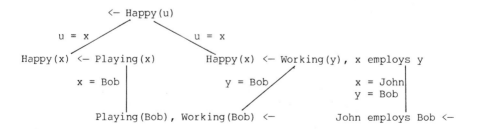

Associated with each arc in the graph is the resolvent obtained by matching the atoms linked by the arc. Conversely, for every resolvent which can be generated from different parent clauses there is an associated arc in the graph.

According to Robinson's purity principle [Robinson 1965a], a clause which contains an unlinked atom can be deleted from a set of clauses without affecting its consistency (or inconsistency). Such a clause can not contribute to a resolution refutation because the unlinked atom can not be resolved upon.

Deletion of clauses containing unlinked atoms is an important feature of the connection graph proof procedure. In addition to the clause itself, all links connected to its atoms must also be deleted from the graph. Deletion of such links, however, may cause atoms in other clauses to become unlinked. Thus deletion of clauses can create a chain reaction in which a succession of clauses is deleted from the graph. Deletion of clauses simplifies the connection graph, reduces the search space, and makes it easier to find a solution.

The effect of deleting clauses can be illustrated by assuming that Bob is unemployed and modifying the preceding example.

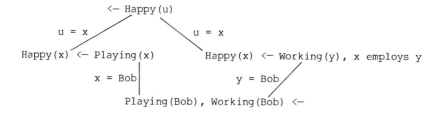

We delete the clause which contains the unlinked atom.

```
                        <- Happy(u)
                      /
          u = x    /
                /
Happy(x) <- Playing(x)
                     |
         x = Bob     |
                     |
           Playing(Bob), Working(Bob) <-
```

The new graph contains a new unlinked atom. Deletion of clauses continues until we are left with the empty set of clauses. The empty set of clauses is trivially consistent, because it contains no clauses which can be false in an interpretation. Therefore the original set of clauses is consistent as well.

The Resolution of links in connection graphs

The basic operation of the proof procedure is the selection of a link
and the generation of the associated resolvent. The link is deleted and
the resolvent is added to the graph. New links are added connecting atoms
in the resolvent to atoms in the rest of the graph. The new links can be
constructed, without searching the graph, from the links which are
already connected to the atoms in the parent clauses.

For example, in the initial connection graph at the beginning of the
chapter, we can reason bottom-up by selecting the link which matches the
two atoms containing the predicate symbol Playing. In the resolvent,
the atom Happy(Bob) descends from the atom Happy(x) in the parent
clause. All new links connected to the new atom descend from the links
connected to the parent atom. In this case the new link connecting
Happy(Bob) to Happy(u) is derived from the old link connecting
Happy(x) to Happy(u) . The new connection graph, which results from
selecting the link, generating the resolvent, adding new links and
deleting both parent clauses (which now contain unlinked atoms) is
illustrated below.

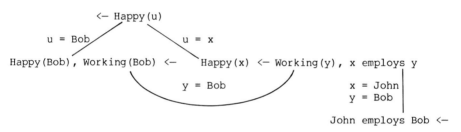

The substitution u = Bob which labels the new link can be computed from
the substitution x = Bob which labelled the selected link and the
substitution u = x which labelled the "parent" link from which the new
link descends.

Before continuing with the example we outline the definition of the
proof procedure in general.

The connection graph proof procedure begins with an initial connection
graph and processes it repeatedly until the empty clause is generated. It
processes a connection graph by

      (1) repeatedly deleting clauses containing unlinked atoms
          and deleting their associated links until all such
          clauses have been deleted and then

      (2) selecting a link, deleting it and adding the resolvent
          and its associated new links to the graph.

This definition of the top-most level of the connection graph proof
procedure is given in the "repeat-until" iterative style of algorithm
description associated with Algol-like programming languages. At the end
of the chapter, we shall reexpress the definition in the Horn clause
logic programming style.

We return to the example. Any link may be selected from the graph. We
shall continue, however, with the bottom-up analysis of the case
Playing(Bob) by selecting the link labelled   u =Bob. Deletion of the
selected link leaves one of the parents with an unlinked atom. The parent
is deleted.

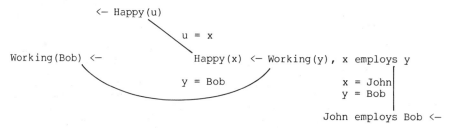

The goal has now been solved in the first case Playing(Bob). Next we
investigate the remaining case Working(Bob), also reasoning bottom-up.
When the selected link is deleted, both parent clauses contain unlinked
atoms and are deleted as well.

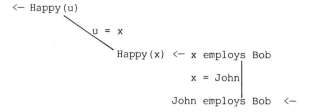

We continue to reason bottom-up and delete both parents because they
contain unlinked atoms.

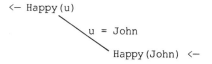

The resolvent associated with the remaining link is the empty clause and
both parents are deleted.

☐

Notice that the proof gives a disjunctive answer to the question:

    Is anyone happy?

    Yes, Bob or John.

The sequence of successive connection graphs generated by the proof
procedure constitutes both a proof of inconsistency as well as a search
for the proof. In this example, every step in the search contributes to
the proof itself. In the general case, however, according to a theorem of
Ehrenfeucht and Rabin [Bundy 1971] [Meltzer 1972], it is not always

possible to avoid steps which are not relevant to the proof.

At every stage during the course of searching for a proof, any link
can be selected to generate a resolvent. The selection of different links
leads to the generation of different search spaces, some of which may be
easier to search than others. In the following sequence of connection
graphs we illustrate a top-down search for a solution to the previous
problem. Selected links are indicated by bold lines. Several links may be
marked for selection in the same graph when the order of selection does
not matter, in order to reduce the number of separate graphs displayed.
Deletion of clauses containing unlinked atoms is not exhibited
explicitly.

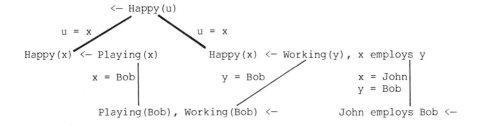

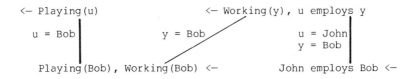

□

As in the bottom-up search for a solution, every step contributes to the
proof.

Notice that unrestricted application of the resolution rule is
redundant in the sense that it determines a search space which contains
many unnecessary clauses including, in particular, all those which belong
to both the top-down and the bottom-up search spaces exhibited above.

Mixed top-down and bottom-up search - the parsing problem

Top-down and bottom-up inference can be mixed, simply by mixing the selection of links connected to atoms in goal statements with the selection of links connected to atoms in clauses which contain no conditions. In general it is useful always to select a link which results in the least complicated new graph. This strategy applied to a version of the parsing problem of Chapter 3 results in a mixed top-down, bottom-up search. As in the preceding example, selected links are indicated by bold lines. Substitutions, which label links, are omitted from the graph.

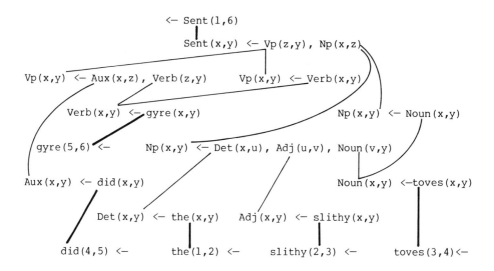

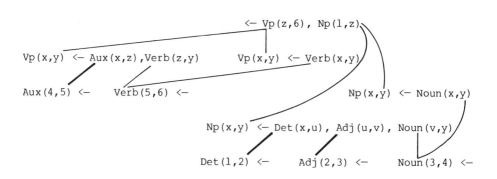

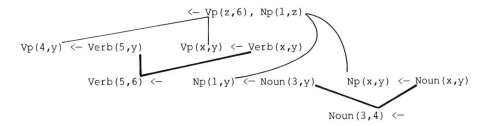

```
                        <- Vp(z,6), Np(1,z)

Vp(4,y) <- Verb(5,y)       Vp(x,y) <- Verb(x,y)

     Verb(5,6) <-        Np(1,y) <- Noun(3,y)     Np(x,y) <- Noun(x,y)

                                            Noun(3,4) <-


                    <- Vp(z,6), Np(1,z)

        Vp(4,6) <-  Vp(5,6) <-   Np(1,4) <-   Np(3,4) <-


                <- Vp(4,6)

        Vp(4,6) <-            Vp(5,6) <-


                    □
```

Macro-processing and middle-out reasoning

In conventional programming languages, macro-processing transforms a
program by eliminating all calls to a given procedure, executing them in
advance of the particular problems to be solved. The original procedures
are replaced by the new ones. The analogue of macro-processing in logic
is middle-out reasoning combined with deletion of the parent clauses
because they contain unlinked atoms.

Macro-processing has the advantage that procedure calls are executed
once and for all before the problems are given, rather than repeatedly
during the course of trying to solve them.

Macro-processing can be illustrated by eliminating all calls to the Np
and Vp procedures in the parsing problem.

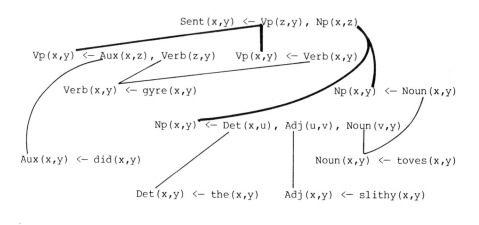

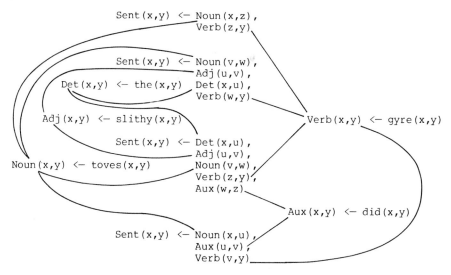

Arrow notation for controlling selection of links

The arrow notation, introduced informally earlier in the book, can be used to control the selection of links in the connection graph proof procedure. The links of a connection graph can be turned into arrows by giving them a direction. A clause is regarded as _active_ if all links connected to its atoms are outgoing. A link may be _selected_ if it is connected to an atom in an active clause. The new links connected to atoms in a resolvent inherit their direction from the parent links from which they descend.

The connection graph proof procedure can be restricted to top-down inference, by directing all arrows from conditions to conclusions. Then a

clause is active if and   only if it is   a goal statement. The following
sequence of graphs illustrates the use of arrow notation to impose a top-
down problem-solving interpretation on the problem of the fallible Greek.
Despite notational   similarities, there   is no   connection between   arrow
notation in connection graphs and arcs in semantic networks.

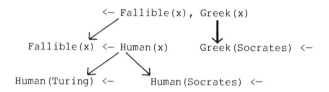

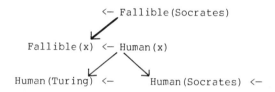

The proof procedure can be restricted to bottom-up inference, by
directing all arrows from conclusions to conditions. Then a clause is
active if and only if it has no conditions. The use of arrow notation for
bottom-up inference is illustrated below.

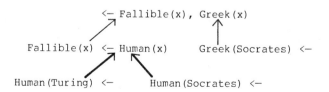

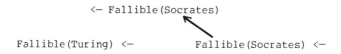

                    <- Fallible(Socrates)

    Fallible(Turing) <-   Fallible(Socrates) <-

                    □

    The arrow notation can be used with non-Horn clauses to control the
generation of assertions for use in the solution of subgoals. The non-
Horn clause in the connection graph below, for example, generates the
assertion

        Studentof(☺,Bob) <-

to assist the solution of the subgoal

        <- Likes(☺,logic).

The two clauses from which the assertion and subgoal are derived,
together with the associated arrow notation, attempt to show that Bob is
happy by asserting that   is a student of Bob and showing that
even   likes logic. Since nothing else is said about the individual   ,
if it can be shown that   likes logic, then anyone who is a student of
Bob likes logic. The two clauses, therefore, state in effect that

        Bob is happy if all his students like logic.

    The arrows in the following connection graph direct the   search for a
solution top-down from the top-level goal and the derived subgoal, but
bottom-up from the assertion to be used in solving the subgoal.

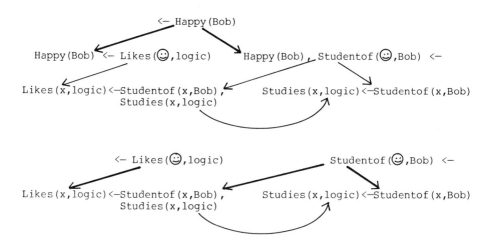

<- Studies(☺,logic)   Studies(☺,logic) <-

□

Notice that Bob would also be happy if he had no students

<- Studentof(x,Bob)

or if everyone liked logic unconditionally

Likes(x,logic) <- .

There is no guarantee that every assignment of direction preserves the solvability of a connection graph. It seems sensible, moreover, to restrict the direction of arrows so that all links connected to the same atom have the same direction.

Self-resolving clauses

A self-resolving clause is one which resolves with a copy of itself. For example, the clause

Append(x.y, z, x.y') <- Append(y,z,y')

resolves with the copy

Append(u.v, w, u.v') <- Append(v,w,v').

For the sake of completeness, it is necessary to connect resolving atoms in a self-resolving clause by means of a link.

Append(x.y, z, x.y') <- Append(y,z,y')

Such a link is a pseudo-link in the sense that is stands for a link between atoms in different copies of the same clause.

Pseudo-links can be selected for processing, but it is simpler for the purposes of exposition to restrict their use to the derivation of new links. This is illustrated in the following example.

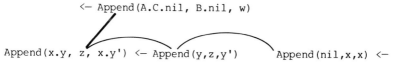

<- Append(A.C.nil, B.nil, w)

Append(x.y, z, x.y') <- Append(y,z,y')   Append(nil,x,x) <-

The single atom in the resolvent descends from an atom having two links, one of which is a pseudo-link. The pseudo-link gives rise to a descendant which is a normal link. The other link connected to the assertion has no descendant. The original goal statement contains an unlinked atom and therefore is discarded when the resolvent is added to the graph.

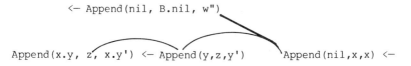

$\leftarrow$ Append(C.nil, B.nil, w')

Append(x.y, z, x.y') $\leftarrow$ Append(y,z,y')   Append(nil,x,x) $\leftarrow$

The new graph is similar to the initial connection graph. However, this time, when the resolvent is generated, it is the pseudo-link which has no descendant and the link to the assertion which has.

$\leftarrow$ Append(nil, B.nil, w")

Append(x.y, z, x.y') $\leftarrow$ Append(y,z,y')   Append(nil,x,x) $\leftarrow$

The resolvent of the new link is the empty clause. Independently, the recursive clause can be deleted because its conclusion has only a pseudo-link. Once the recursive clause has been deleted, the assertion can be deleted as well. The resulting connection graph consists of the empty clause alone.

□

In general, a self-resolving clause can be deleted if one of its atoms has no normal (non-pseudo-) links. The inheritance of links and pseudo-links in connection graphs has been studied by Bruynooghe [1977]. Note that, although in all of the preceeding examples the final connection graph contains only the empty clause, in the general case it may contain other clauses as well.

Deletion of links whose resolvents are tautologies

A clause is a tautology if it contains the same atom both as a condition and as a conclusion. The use of tautologies in top-down problem-solving leads to loops in which a goal reoccurs as its own subgoal. For that reason, because they do not positively contribute to the solution of problems, tautologies can be deleted from a set of clauses without affecting inconsistency [Robinson 1965a]. In the connection graph proof procedure, the effect of deleting tautologies can be obtained by deleting links whose resolvents are tautologies.

The set of clauses describing the concept of even number is an example.

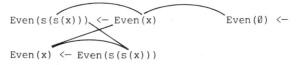

Even(s(s(x))) $\leftarrow$ Even(x)   Even(0) $\leftarrow$

Even(x) $\leftarrow$ Even(s(s(x)))

The two links connecting the two recursive clauses have resolvents which are tautologies. The links are deleted from the graph:

Even(s(s(x))) <- Even(x)   Even(0) <-

Even(x) <- Even(s(s(x)))

The collection of three clauses is consistent because it contains no
goal statement. The two recursive clauses can be deleted because they
contain atoms with only pseudo-links. The basis assertion can then be
deleted as well. Given the goal statement

          <- Even(s(s(s(s(0)))))

moreover, the condition of the second recursive clause still has no non-
pseudo-link. Consequently, the clause can be deleted, leaving the
simpler graph:

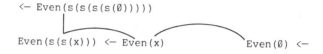

          <- Even(s(s(s(s(0)))))

     Even(s(s(x))) <- Even(x)   Even(0) <-

In more complex examples it is not so easy to recognise that a clause
cannot contribute to a solution. In such cases a more global analysis may
be useful. Global problem-solving strategies are investigated in the next
chapter.

The connection graph proof procedure

We summarise here the definition of the connection graph proof
procedure in a style of English which corresponds to the procedural
interpretation of Horn clauses.

To demonstrate the inconsistency of a set of clauses by the
connection graph proof procedure, generate and solve its initial
connection graph.

The initial connection graph for a set of clauses contains all
clauses in the set, a (non-pseudo-) link connecting each pair of
matching atoms on opposite sides of the arrow in different clauses,
and a pseudo-link connecting atoms on opposite sides of the arrow in
the same clause if the atoms match in different copies of the clause.

A connection graph is solved if it contains the empty clause.

To solve a connection graph which does not contain the empty
clause,

> either delete a link whose resolvent is a tautology, and
> solve the resulting connection graph,
> or delete a clause containing an unlinked atom, together
> with its associated links, and solve the resulting
> connection graph,
> or select a link which is not a pseudo-link, delete it,
> add the resolvent together with its new links to the
> graph, and solve the resulting connection graph.
>
> A (non-pseudo-) link connects an occurrence L of an atom in a
> resolvent to an occurrence K of an atom in another clause if L and K
> match, L descends from an occurrence L' of an atom in a parent
> clause, and there is a link (possibly a pseudo-link) between L' and
> K.
>
>
>
> A pseudo-link connects L and K in a resolvent if L and K match, L
> and K descend from L' and K' in the (same or different) parent
> clauses, and there is a link between L' and K'.
>
>

The four different ways of solving a connection graph correspond to
four clauses having the same conclusion. Ignoring the deletion of links
whose resolvents are tautologies, the resulting three procedures express
the logic and top-down control of the iterative algorithm described at
the beginning of the chapter. The earlier algorithm can be obtained from
the new one by further specifying the control over the use of the
procedures given here. In particular,

> (1) the alternative ways of solving a connection graph
> should be tried one at a time in the order in which they
> are written above and
>
> (2) backtracking should not be employed, as the non-
> determinism$_1$ of the procedures doesn't matter.

The proof procedure which has been described is incomplete as it
stands, because the factoring operation has been omitted. In order to
avoid redundancy, severe restrictions need to be imposed on its use.
Since adequate restrictions have not yet been devised, and since it
simplifies the description of the proof procedure, we have decided to
ignore the factoring operation altogether. A definition of the proof
procedure including factoring can be found in the original publication
[Kowalski 1974a].

The completeness of the connection graph proof procedure cannot be
assured if the selection of links which are needed for a proof is
postponed indefinitely. Such indefinite postponement might arise, for

example, when the selection strategy carries out a depth-first search along a non-terminating path of a top-down search space. The requirement that every link eventually be scheduled for selection is the analogue of the exhaustiveness of search strategies for more conventional proof procedures.

A completeness proof for a variant of the connection graph proof procedure has been constructed by Brown [unpublished]. In the case of Horn clauses, his proof applies also to the proof procedure which has been described here. Other completeness proofs for the general case have been announced by Siekmann and Stephan [1976] and by Bibel [1979].

A number of proof procedures employ connection graphs but process them in a manner different from the one described here. Noteworthy among these are those of Sickel [1976] and Kellogg, Klahr and Travis [1978]. Closer to the connection graph procedure, however, is the unpublished cancellation system of Colmerauer.

Exercises

1) Express the top-level of the definition of the connection graph proof procedure by means of Horn clauses.

2) Using the methods described later in Chapter 10 for transforming sentences from the standard form of logic into clausal form, the definition of subset can be expressed by means of the following two clauses:

$$x \subseteq y, \quad arb(x,y) \in x \leftarrow$$
$$x \subseteq y \leftarrow arb(x,y) \in y$$

Used top-down these clauses behave as procedures which given a subgoal of the form $x \subseteq y$,

> assert that some arbitry individual, say $arb(x,y)$, belongs to x and try to show that it belongs to y.

Use the connection graph proof procedure to prove the following theorems.

a) The empty set ϕ defined by

$$\leftarrow x \in \phi$$

is a subset of any set S.

b) Every set S is a subset of the universal set defined by

$$x \in U \leftarrow$$

c) Every set is a subset of itself.

d) The set A such that

a(x), b(x) <— x ϵ A

is a subset of the set B such that

x ϵ B <— a(x)
x ϵ B <— b(x)
x ϵ B <— c(x).

This is a formulation without equality of the problem of showing that

{a,b} ⊆ {a,b,c,}.

3) Verify the claim made in Chapter 5 that, using the connection graph proof procedure, bottom-up execution of the definition

Fib(0, s(0)) <—
Fib(s(s(x)), w) <— Fib(s(x), u), Fib(x,v), Plus(u,v,w)

of Fibonacci number requires only a constant amount of storage. Assume that the Plus relation is defined by means of variable-free assertions and ignore the space that would be needed to store them.

CHAPTER 9

Global Problem-Solving Strategies

In this chapter we investigate problem-solving strategies which deal with problems as a whole rather than with subproblems individually. Goal transformation deals with the combination of goals in goal statements, whereas analysis of differences deals with the effect of procedures on the difference between goals and assertions.

Goal transformation consists of a number of related strategies which are concerned with the logical relationships among subgoals. It includes deletion of redundant subgoals, which are implied by other subgoals, addition of implicit subgoals which are easier and more useful to solve than those which are explicitly given, rejection of inconsistent subgoals, which are mutually incompatible, and rejection of subgoals which are contradicted by an example.

The techniques of goal transformation are similar to those of program transformation developed for recursion equations by Burstall and Darlington [1977]. Program transformation transforms programs before problems are given, whereas goal transformation transforms goals during the course of attempting to solve them. Goal transformation techniques have also been used in robot plan-formation, mathematical programming and geometry theorem-proving.

Analysis of the differences between goals and assertions involves an even more global approach to problem-solving. It attempts to identify both procedures which reduce differences as well as those which increase them or leave them invariant. Preference can be given to procedures which reduce differences over those which do not. Goals can be rejected as unsolvable if it can be demonstrated that no procedure reduces differences at all.

The techniques of difference analysis are similar to ones used in program-proving. Demonstrating that programs reduce differences is involved in proving program termination, whereas demonstrating that programs leave properties invariant is used for proving program properties. The strategy of selecting procedures for their effectiveness at reducing differences is the basis, moreover, of the General Problem Solver developed by Newell, Shaw and Simon [1963].

Although the methods we describe can also be applied to non-Horn clauses, we shall simplify matters by limiting attention to top-down problem-solving by Horn clauses alone. Moreover, we shall not concern ourselves with the heuristics which would be needed for the effective utilisation of these methods.

Deletion of redundant subgoals

A subgoal can be deleted from a goal statement, if the assumption that
the other subgoals have a solution implies that the redundant subgoal has
a compatible solution as well. According to this criterion, assuming the
transitivity of the $\leq$ relation,

$$x \leq y \leftarrow x \leq z, z \leq y$$

the goal statement

$$\leftarrow r \leq s, s \leq t, r \leq t$$

contains the redundant subgoal $r \leq t$. For, assuming that the other
subgoals have a solution, it follows that the assertions

$$r' \leq s' \leftarrow$$
$$s' \leq t' \leftarrow$$

hold for appropriate instances r', s' and t' of the terms r, s and t
respectively. But those assertions together with the transitivity of $\leq$
imply the assertion

$$r' \leq t' \leftarrow$$

which expresses that the third subgoal is compatibly solvable also. It is
unnecessary to solve the redundant subgoal explicitly. It suffices to
know that any solution of the other subgoals guarantees the existence of
a compatible solution of the third subgoal as well.

The transitivity clause does not need to be part of the program or
even a logical consequence of it. To justify deletion of the redundant
subgoal, it suffices that transitivity be a property of the program. This
is the case, for example, if the $\leq$ relation is defined by the clauses

$$0 \leq y \leftarrow$$
$$s(x) \leq s(y) \leftarrow x \leq y.$$

A statement is a property of a Horn clause program P, if it is consistent
with P and together with P implies no variable-free assertions not
already implied by P. A program property, therefore, adds no solutions to
those which can be obtained by the program itself.

Deleting a duplicate occurrence of a subgoal is a special case of
deleting a redundant subgoal, since any one occurrence of a subgoal
implies any other occurrence. Thus the goal statement

$$\leftarrow P, Q, P$$

for example, can be replaced by

$$\leftarrow P, Q.$$

Addition of surrogate subgoals

Although it is often useful to delete redundant subgoals, it is
sometimes beneficial to add them instead.

The strategy of deriving additional subgoals is common in mathematical
programming, where subgoals are regarded as constraints to be satisfied.
A surrogate constraint, whose solution is implied by the solution of the
original constraints, can be added and then solved before the others.
This is useful if the surrogate constraint is easier to solve and aids
the solution of the original constraints by determining the values of
some of their variables.

Consider, for example, the initial collection of two constraints
involving the variables x and y:

$$\leftarrow x+y = 2, \; x-y = 0$$

A sequential, top-down problem-solver would generate pairs of numbers
satisfying one of the constraints and then test whether they solve the
other. A more intelligent problem-solver, programmed by Warren in PROLOG,
coroutines between the two subgoals solving them simultaneously by
successive approximation. The program, a general-purpose, Horn clause
problem-solver, always selects a subgoal which contains fewest variables
at the top-most level.

The normal, mathematical problem-solving method, however, derives and
solves a surrogate constraint instead. It assumes that the original
constraints have a solution and concludes (by adding the two equations
together) that the additional constraint

$$\leftarrow 2*x = 2$$

must also be satisfied by the same solution. The new constraint is
redundant in the new goal statement

$$\leftarrow x+y = 2, \; x-y = 0, \; 2*x = 2$$

but it can be solved without any search. Moreover, once it has been
solved, the remaining instantiated original constraints

$$\leftarrow 1+y = 2, \; 1-y = 0$$

can then be solved without search as well. In fact, it suffices to solve
just one of the remaining constraints, because the other constraint is
now redundant.

The strategy of surrogate subgoals is useful for plan-formation
problems. Consider, for example, the problem of finding a state w in
which the robot is in the room and next to the box

$$\leftarrow In(Rob,room,w), \; Nextto(Rob,box,w).$$

Assuming that the box is not in the room initially and that the robot is
more mobile than the box, it is useful to derive the surrogate subgoal

$$\leftarrow In(box,room,w)$$

from the original subgoals using the program properties

$$In(x,y,w) \leftarrow In(z,y,w), Nextto(x,z,w)$$
$$Nextto(x,z,w) \leftarrow Nextto(z,x,w).$$

If the surrogate subgoal is added to the original goal statement

$$\leftarrow In(Rob,room,w), Nextto(Rob,box,w), In(box,room,w)$$

and is selected for solution before the others, then the simplest solution (where the robot pushes the box into the room) finds a state w which directly solves the remaining subgoals.

Rejection of inconsistent goal statements

An entire goal statement can be rejected as unsolvable, if the assumption that it can be solved leads to contradiction.

A simple case is the one in which a goal statement is subsumed by a program property or an integrity constraint. The goal statement

G $\leftarrow On(A,B,w), Clear(B,w), On(B,C,w)$

for example, is subsumed by the clause

C $\leftarrow On(x,y,z), Clear(y,z)$

which expresses that nothing is clear and has something on it at the same time. In general, one clause C_1 subsumes another C_2 if all the conditions and conclusions of some instance of C_1 are contained among the conditions and conclusions of C_2. The subsuming clause is more general than the subsumed clause and possibly has fewer conditions or fewer conclusions. In the example above, the instance of the subsuming clause C (in which x = A, y = B and z = w) contains one fewer condition than the subsumed clause G.

A clause can be deleted from a set of clauses if it is subsumed by another clause in the same set. Deletion of the subsumed clause does not affect the consistency (or inconsistency) of the set of clauses as a whole. A thorough discussion of the completeness of deleting subsumed clauses is contained in the book by Loveland [1978].

The strategy of deleting a subsumed goal statement can be regarded as a special case of deleting an inconsistent one. In the preceding example, the assumption

$$On(A,B,s) \leftarrow$$
$$Clear(B,s) \leftarrow$$
$$On(B,C,s) \leftarrow$$

that there exists a solution w = s of the goal statement G is inconsistent with C.

Rejection of an inconsistent goal statement, however, is more general than deletion of a subsumed one. It can involve an arbitrary amount of deduction. The database query

<— Teaches(John,y)

for example, is not subsumed by any of the clauses

Tl	Teacher(x) <— Teaches(x,y)
T2	<— Teacher(x), Student(x)
T3	Student(John) <—

but is unsolvable because the assumption that it is solvable, namely

Teaches(John,A) <—

say, is inconsistent with Tl-3.

Similar strategies for rejecting queries which are inconsistent with type information have been developed by McSkimin and Minker [1977] who augment a resolution theorem-prover with a semantic network which stores and processes type information. Subsumption of unsolvable goal statements is also a feature of plan-formation systems developed by Dawson and Siklossy [1977], Hewitt [1975] and, more generally, of the logic programming system developed by Robinson and Sibert [1978].

Generalising the use of diagrams in geometry

In order to justify the addition or deletion of a redundant subgoal, it is necessary that the assumptions used to derive the subgoal be properties of the procedures which can be used to solve it. In order to justify rejection of an inconsistent goal statement, however, a weaker condition suffices: The assumptions A used to derive inconsistency need only be consistent with the procedures P.

For, suppose that

(i)   P is consistent with A,
(ii)   G* expresses that the goal statement G is solvable,
(iii)   G* is inconsistent with P and A, but
(iv)   P solves G.

Then, since P solves G, P implies G* and therefore P together with A implies G*. But then, since P is consistent with A, G* is consistent with P and A , contradicting (iii). It follows that

if P is consistent with A, but
G* is inconsistent with P and A, then
P does not solve G.

The use of diagrams to reject unsolvable subgoals in Gelernter's Geometry Theorem Proving Machine [1963] can be regarded as a case of using assumptions which are consistent with the problem-solving procedures to reject inconsistent goal statements. The axioms of geometry function as procedures and the description of the diagram functions as the additional assumptions. The use of a diagram is justified, provided its description is consistent with the general axioms

of geometry and with the particular hypotheses of the theorem to be
proved. Gelernter estimated that the use of diagrams reduced the size of
search spaces on the average to 1/200 their original size. The argument
above shows that the use of examples to recognise the unsolvability of
problems need not be restricted to geometry. Examples can be used to
recognise and reject unsolvable subgoals in any problem-domain.

Goals as generalised solutions

It is sometimes useful not to solve subgoals explicitly but to regard
them instead as standing for the general class of all their solutions.

Consider, for example, an initial goal statement

$$\leftarrow G(x)$$

which eventually reduces to the subgoal

$$\leftarrow x > 0.$$

Instead of generating an arbitrary positive number x as an explicit
solution, it is more informative to report that any positive number is a
solution. This can be effected by regarding the subgoal $x > 0$ as a
generalised solution which stands for the class of all its individual
solutions.

Solving subgoals by generalised solutions is a feature of Bledsoe's
approach to theorem-proving [1971, 1977]. To be effective, it needs to
be combined with goal transformation. Given a goal statement

$$\leftarrow x > 0, x > 1, G(x)$$

for example, deletion of the redundant subgoal is necessary to transform
the goal statement to the new one:

$$\leftarrow x > 1, G(x)$$

Given

$$\leftarrow x < 0, x > 1, G(x)$$

on the other hand, rejection of inconsistent subgoals is necessary to
recognise that the goal statement is unsolvable.

Treating certain kinds of goals as generalised solutions is also
useful for database queries, and is a feature both of Darlington's [1969]
resolution information retrieval system and of McSkimin and Minker's
[1977] semantic network theorem-prover. Given the query

Who teaches programming?
$\leftarrow$ Teaches(x,programming)

and the general rule

All professors teach programming.
Teaches(x,programming) $\leftarrow$ Professor(x)

it is better to regard the resulting subgoal as a generalised solution

<-- Professor(x)

than it is to report   one or more of the answers which qualify as
solutions as a result of the assertions

Professor(Mary) <--
Professor(John) <--
Professor(Bob) <-- .

Goal transformation and the information explosion

It is a characteristic of human problem-solving that the assimilation
of additional information generally improves problem-solving efficiency.
This contrasts with the simple model of problem-solving in which all
knowledge is used as problem-solving procedures. Additional information
only increases the size of the search space and makes problems harder to
solve (except in those cases where only one solution is required and the
non-determinism$_1$ doesn't matter). In the goal transformation model,
however, additional information can be used to transform goal statements
and to reduce the size of the search space.

Loop detection by analysis of differences

Like goal transformation, analysis of   differences adds to the
possiblities of recognising that a procedure goes into a loop.

Consider, for example, the procedure

Numb(x) <-- Numb(s(x))

given the goal

<-- Numb(s(s(0)))

and the assertion

Numb(0) <-- .

Repeated top-down execution of the procedure gives rise to the non-
terminating, infinite sequence of subgoals:

<-- Numb(s(s(0)))

<-- Numb(s(s(s(0))))
.
.
.

In this case the connection graph proof procedure avoids the loop,
because the procedure call Numb(s(x)) has only a pseudo-link to the head
of the procedure. It follows that the procedure is unusable and can be

deleted from the graph. If the assertion Numb(∅) <− is replaced by the
assertion

          Numb(s(∅)) <−

however, application of the procedure gives rise to the same infinite
loop, but the procedure can no longer be deleted, because its procedure
call has an additional non-pseudo-link to the new assertion. The loop can
be avoided in all these cases, though, if it can be recognised that
application of the procedure cannot reduce the difference between the
goal and the assertion. The goal differs from the assertion in that it
contains a greater number of occurrences of the function symbol s.
Application of the procedure only increases the difference by generating
subgoals which contain even more occurrences of s.

    The global nature of difference analysis becomes apparent if the
assertion is replaced by the new assertion

          Numb(s(s(s(s(∅))))) <− .

Now, application of the procedure reduces the difference between the goal
and the assertion and eventually solves the problem.

          <− Numb(s(s(∅)))

          <− Numb(s(s(s(∅))))

          <− Numb(s(s(s(s(∅)))))

              □

    A procedure might be needed for a solution even if it increases the
difference between the goal and the assertions. Given, for example, the
goal

          <− Numb(s(s(s(∅))))

and the assertion

          Numb(∅) <−

the procedure

          Numb(s(s(x))) <− Numb(x)

decreases the difference, whereas the procedure

          Numb(x) <− Numb(s(x))

increases it. But both procedures are necessary to solve the problem.

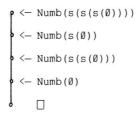

```
  ⟵ Numb(s(s(s(0))))
  ⟵ Numb(s(0))
  ⟵ Numb(s(s(0)))
  ⟵ Numb(0)
     □
```

In the preceding examples the application of a procedure which increases differences either generates a loop or else is essential for a solution. More often, increasing differences neither contributes to a solution nor prevents its being found. Such is the case with the pair of procedures

$$Numb(s(x)) \;\leftarrow\; Numb(x)$$
$$Numb(x) \;\leftarrow\; Numb(s(x)).$$

If one of them unnecessarily increases differences, the other can be used to restore them to their previous state. Indeed using one procedure after the other simply generates the kind of loop which can be avoided in the connection graph proof procedure by deleting links whose resolvents are tautologies.

In all of these examples, the difference between subgoals and assertions can be measured simply by the number of occurrences of the function symbol s. In other cases the characterisation of differences is more complicated.

The factorial example

The definition of factorial is a more realistic example. The non-clausal sentence

$$Times(s(x),u,v) \;\rightarrow\; [Fact(x,u) \;\leftrightarrow\; Fact(s(x),v)]$$

gives rise to two Horn clause procedures:

(1) $Fact(s(x),v) \;\leftarrow\; Fact(x,u), Times(s(x),u,v)$
(2) $Fact(x,u) \;\leftarrow\; Fact(s(x),v), Times(s(x),u,v)$

Given the assertion

$$Fact(0,s(0)) \;\leftarrow$$

there is no goal for which the second procedure is necessary. However, given the assertion

$$Fact(10,3628800) \;\leftarrow$$

instead, the second procedure is necessary for solving the problem

$$\leftarrow Fact(s(0),x)$$

and the first procedure is unnecessary. Here the natural number n is used as an abbreviation for the term

$$s(s(s(...(0)...)))$$

$$\underbrace{\qquad\qquad\qquad\qquad}_{n \text{ times}}$$

containing n occurrences of the function symbol s.

More generally, it may be useful to have several assertions, e.g.

    Fact(0,1) <—
    Fact(10,3628800) <—

and, using analysis of differences, to apply the procedure which most quickly narrows the gap between the problem and the assertions, using (1), for example, for the problem

    <— Fact(3,x)

and using (2) for

    <— Fact(8,x).

Notice that the last example is a case of "don't care" non-determinism$_1$. There are several ways of finding the factorial, all of which lead to the same result. It doesn't matter which method is chosen. But, if backtracking is used, then it does matter (for the sake of efficiency) that only one method is tried.

Invariant properties of procedures

The unsolvability of a problem can be detected not only by analysing the effect of procedures on differences but also by analysing the properties which procedures leave invariant. A problem can be recognised as unsolvable if it can be shown that it differs from the assertions in a property which is not affected by the procedures. A typical property of this kind is parity.

Suppose we are given the clauses

        Even(8) <—
        Even(s(s(x))) <— Even(x)
        Even(x) <— Even(s(s(x)))
        <— Even(17)

By analysis of differences, the second procedure can be rejected as useless. Used alone it only increases differences. Used together with the other procedure it only generates loops. By analysis of invariants the first procedure can also be rejected. It reduces a problem of a given parity to a subproblem of the same parity. No matter how many times the procedure is used it cannot change the parity of the original problem. Since the original problem has an odd number of occurrences of "s" and the assertion has an even number, the procedure cannot be used to solve the problem. Here parity can be determined by counting occurrences of the function symbol "s". In more realistic cases the invariant property is more complex.

Such is the case in the following example, where the invariant property is another form of parity. Given a sequence of six arrows (or coins) each of which can face up or down, the problem is to transform them from one state to another - for example, from

$$U\ U\ U\ D\ D\ D \quad to \quad U\ U\ D\ D\ U\ U$$

There is only one action available: it is possible simultaneously to change the direction of two adjacent arrows.

A simple n-tuple representation in which

$$State(d_1,\ d_2,\ d_3,\ d_4,\ d_5,\ d_6)$$

expresses that

the first arrow can have direction d_1,
the second arrow can have direction d_2,
and in general
the i-th arrow can have direction d_i

simultaneously, is the following.

$$State(U,U,U,D,D,D) \leftarrow$$

$$\leftarrow State(U,U,D,D,U,U)$$

$$State(x,y,z,u,v,w) \leftarrow State(x',y',z,u,v,w),\ Opp(x,x'),\ Opp(y,y')$$

$$State(x,y,z,u,v,w) \leftarrow State(x,y',z',u,v,w),\ Opp(y,y'),\ Opp(z,z')$$

$$State(x,y,z,u,v,w) \leftarrow State(x,y,z',u',v,w),\ Opp(z,z'),\ Opp(u,u')$$

$$State(x,y,z,u,v,w) \leftarrow State(x,y,z,u',v',w),\ Opp(u,u'),\ Opp(v,v')$$

$$State(x,y,z,u,v,w) \leftarrow State(x,y,z,u,v',w'),\ Opp(v,v'),\ Opp(w,w')$$

$$Opp(U,D) \leftarrow$$

$$Opp(D,U) \leftarrow$$

The problem is unsolvable, because, whereas the procedures leave invariant the parity of the number of arrows in either direction, in the assertion there is an odd number of arrows in both directions and in the goal there is an even number. To show that the procedures leave parity invariant it is necessary to consider the two cases: Either the two inverted arrows have the same direction before inversion or they have different directions. If they have the same direction, then inversion increases the number of arrows in one direction by two and decreases the number in the other by two, but leaves the parity the same. If they have different directions, then inversion leaves the number of arrows in both directions unchanged and therefore does not affect the parity. In both cases parity is an invariant property of the procedures.

The mutilated checker board problem   is similar. Given a checker-board with two opposite corners removed,

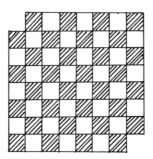

the problem is to cover it with dominoes, each one of which covers two adjacent squares. Since adjacent squares have different colours, the procedures leave invariant the difference between the number of uncovered squares of different colours. The problem is unsolvable, therefore, because in the goal state the difference is zero, but in the initial state it is two.

There is an obvious relationship between proving that logic procedures leave a property invariant and proving a property of a flowchart program using invariants. In both cases the objective is to show that if a property holds at the beginning of a repetitive process then it holds at the end. This is done by showing that if it holds at the beginning of one step of the process then it holds at the end of the step. The desired result then holds by induction.

Exercises

1) Suppose y is a function of x in the relation F(x,y), i.e.

        y = z <— F(x,y), F(x,z)

where the only clause defining equality is

        x = x <— .

Show how goal transformation can be used to eliminate redundancy when a goal statement contains a pair of subgoals of the form

        F(r,s) and F(r,t)

where r, s and t are terms.

2) Show that "goal transformation" can be used to justify transforming the clause

        Tower(t(x,y)) <— Block(x), Tower(y), On(x,y)

into the clause

Tower(t(x,y)) <— Tower(y), On(x,y).

What property of the On relation is needed for the transformation?

3) In Chapter 6, the precondition Diff(x,z) can be eliminated from the definition of the action trans(x,y,z) and its use can be replaced by that of the integrity constraint

<— Holds(on(x,x), w)

instead. Compare the problem-solving behaviour needed for these two alternative formulations of the plan-formation task.

4) Analyse the English sentence

S1   Reject stealing as a way of having something if you also
                want to be virtuous.

as a recommendation concerning the use of the procedure

Have(u,x) <— Steal(u,x)

applied to goal statements containing two subgoals of the form

Have(r,s) and Virtuous(r).

Can the notions of goal transformation be used to establish a logical relationship between the sentences S1, S2 and S3?

S2   Do not steal if you want to be virtuous.
S3   Anyone who steals is not virtuous.

5) Discuss the formalisation of the following problems and the problem-solving strategies needed to solve them intelligently.

a)   Find an assignment of digits 1,2,3,...,9 to the cells of a
      3 by 3 matrix such that:

row 1

row 2

row 3

(i)   Exactly one digit is assigned to each cell.

(ii) No digit is assigned to more than one cell.

(ii) The three digit number in row 3 is the sum of the three digit numbers in rows 1 and 2.

(iv) If the digit i is assigned to a cell then the digit i+1 is assigned to a cell which is horizontally or vertically adjacent.

b)   Find an assignment of digits 1,2,3,...,9 to letters in the names such that:

$$\begin{array}{r} \text{DONALD} \\ +\text{GERALD} \\ \hline \text{ROBERT} \end{array}$$

(i)   Exactly one digit is assigned to each letter.

(ii) No digit is assigned to more than one letter.

(iii) The 6 digit number assigned to the word "ROBERT" is the sum of the 6 digit numbers assigned to "DONALD" and "GERALD".

(iv) 5 is assigned to "D".

CHAPTER 10

Comparison of Clausal Form with Standard Form

Clausal form is simpler than the standard form of logic and bears greater resemblance to other formalisms used for databases and programming. Moreover, the resolution rule resembles conventional rules for information processing and problem-solving more closely than does standard form.

Although any problem can be converted from standard form to clausal form, the standard form is often more economical and more natural than the resulting collection of clauses. The specification of programs, in particular, is an area in which the standard form of logic (or some appropriate extension of Horn clause form) is more suitable than simple clausal form. Moreover, the derivation of programs from specifications can be achieved more naturally by reasoning with the standard form of logic directly. Useful inference systems for the standard form of logic, however, may be obtained by combining inference rules for clausal form with rules for converting from standard form to clausal form.

Introduction to the standard form of logic

We shall present only the informal semantics of the standard form of logic, by associating expressions of English with expressions of the symbolic language. Such notions as "consistency" for expressions in standard form can be understood informally in terms of their English language counterparts.

The standard form of logic provides explicit symbolism for the propositional connectives "and", "or", "not", "if" and "if and only if" and for the quantifiers "for all" and "there exists". The propositional connectives construct more complex propositions from simpler ones. The symbol

$$\begin{array}{ll} \& & \text{stands for "and"} \\ \lor & \text{stands for "or"} \\ \lnot & \text{stands for "not"} \\ \rightarrow & \text{stands for "if... then... " or "implies"} \\ \longleftrightarrow & \text{stands for "if and only if".} \end{array}$$

A clause

$$A_1,\ldots,A_m \leftarrow B_1,\ldots,B_n$$

not containing variables, is written

$$[B_1 \& \ldots \& B_n] \rightarrow [A_1 V \ldots V A_m]$$

in standard form. If n=0, the standard form omits the arrow

$$A_1 V \ldots V A_m$$

If m=0, the arrow becomes a negation symbol.

$$\neg [B_1 \& \ldots \& B_n].$$

In standard form the direction of the implication sign $\rightarrow$ is opposite to the one we have been using in clausal form. But like the inequality sign $<$ or $>$ of arithmetic the direction of the implication sign is not significant. Thus the expressions

$$A \rightarrow B \text{ and } B \leftarrow A$$

are equivalent. But notice that

$$A \rightarrow B \text{ and } A \leftarrow B$$

are not.

Sentences in standard form can also be constructed by means of the two quantifiers.

The <u>universal</u> <u>quantifier</u>

$\forall x$ stands for "for all x".

The <u>existential</u> <u>quantifier</u>

$\exists x$ stands for "there exists an x".

<u>Example</u>   Some oysters can be crossed in love.

<u>Clausal Form</u>   Oyster(Σ) $\leftarrow$
                 Crossed-in-Love(Σ) $\leftarrow$

<u>Standard form</u> $\exists x$ [Oyster(x) & Crossed-in-Love(x)]

In the clausal formulation, in order to refer to an individual, it is necessary to give it a name. The existential quantifier allows individuals to be referred to without being named. In clausal form sentences are implicitly connected by "and". In standard form the conjunction & can be written explicitly.

<u>Example</u>   Every human has a mother.

<u>Standard Form</u> $\forall x \exists y$ [Human(x) $\rightarrow$ Mother(y,x)]

<u>Clausal Form</u>   Mother(mum(x),x) $\leftarrow$ Human(x)

In the clausal form it is necessary to use a function symbol to name the individual y which exists as a function of x.

Changing the order of the quantifiers changes the meaning.   The sentence

$$\exists y \forall x [\text{Human}(x) \rightarrow \text{Mother}(y,x)]$$

states there is a single individual who is the mother of us all. The clausal form uses a constant symbol to name the individual.

$$\text{Mother}(\odot,x) \leftarrow \text{Human}(x)$$

For the precise definition of sentence, it is necessary to define the more general notion of formula. Formulae may contain free (unquantified) variables, whereas sentences do not. Thus the formula

$$\forall x \exists y \text{Loves}(x,y)$$

is a sentence, but the formula

$$\forall x \text{Loves}(x,y)$$

is not. It contains the bound (quantified) variable x and the free variable y.

Terms and atomic formulae are defined just as for clausal form.

An expression Z is a formula if and only if it is an atomic formula or an expression of the form

$$[X \ \& \ Y]$$
$$[X \ V \ Y]$$
$$[X \rightarrow Y] \text{ or } [Y \leftarrow X]$$
$$[X \leftrightarrow Y]$$
$$\neg \ X$$
$$\forall v \ X \ \text{ or}$$
$$\exists v \ X$$

where X and Y are formulae and v is any variable.

Any formula Z is a subformula of itself.   In the first four cases above, any subformula of X or Y is a subformula of Z; and in the last three cases, any subformula of X is a subformula of Z.

An occurrence of a variable v in a formula Z is free (or unbound) if it belongs to no subformula of Z of the form $\forall v \ X$ or $\exists v \ X$.   If an occurrence of v is free in X then it is bound in $\forall v \ X$ and $\exists v \ X$ by the quantifiers $\forall v$ or $\exists v$ respectively.

A formula is a sentence if and only if it contains no free occurrence of a variable.

The definitions above permit sentences such as

$$\exists x \ [Oyster(x) \ \& \ \exists x \ Tasty(x)]$$

in which the same variable x is bound by different occurrences of a quantifier. Such sentences create complications which are better avoided. Consequently we shall restrict formulae Z to those which satisfy the condition that

> for every variable v which occurs in Z, either all occurrences of v in Z are free in Z or all occurrences of v in Z are bound by the same quantifier occurrence.

Any formula Z which violates the restriction can be transformed into an equivalent one which satisfies it by renaming variables. This can be done by applying the equivalences

---

$\forall u \ X \ <-> \ \forall v \ X'$
$\exists u \ X \ <-> \ \exists v \ X'$
where X' is obtained from X by replacing all occurrences of u by v and v does not occur in X.

---

to subformulae of Z. Any subformula can be replaced by an equivalent one without affecting the meaning of the formula in which it occurs.

Notice also that the definitions permit quantification $\forall v \ X$ or $\exists v \ X$ of a variable v which does not occur in the formula X. Such quantification is _vacuous_ in the sense that the resulting formula is equivalent to the unquantified formula X. Deletion of vacuous quantifiers is justified by the equivalences:

$\forall v \ X \ <-> \ X$
$\exists v \ X \ <-> \ X$
where the variable v does not occur in X.

Several conventions can be employed to improve the readability of formulae by reducing the number of brackets. Outermost brackets can always be omitted, writing $A \rightarrow B$, for example, rather than $[A \rightarrow B]$.

The associativity of conjunction justifies omitting brackets when several formulae are conjoined together. Since the formulae

    A & [B & C]   and
    [A & B] & C

are equivalent, it is permissible to ignore brackets altogether, writing

    A & B & C.

Similarly, the associativity of disjunction justifies writing

                A V B V C
    instead of   A V [B V C]   or
                [A V B] V C.

Brackets can be reduced further by establishing precedence rules for the quantifiers and the propositional connectives. We shall follow the conventions that

The negation symbol ¬ and the quantifiers ∃, ∀ bind more closely than the other symbols and conjunction & and disjunction V bind more closely than implication —> and equivalence <->.

Thus we may safely write

A V B V C <— D & E & F

instead of   [[A V [B V C]] <— [[D & E] & F]]

for example.

Readability can be improved further by omitting universal quantifiers at the beginning of sentences, writing, for example,

Grandparent(x,y) <— Parent(x,z) & Parent(z,y)

instead of   ∀x∀y∀z[Grandparent(x,y) <— Parent(x,z) & Parent(z,y)]

as in clausal form.   Such omission of universal quantifiers can be performed safely only when the context makes it clear that the expression is a sentence rather than a formula containing occurrences of free variables.

Conversion to clausal form

Any sentence in standard form can be converted to clausal form.   The resulting set of clauses is consistent if and only if the sentence in standard form is consistent.   Thus conversion to clausal form can be used to demonstrate the inconsistency of a set of sentences in standard form:

> A set of sentences in standard form is inconsistent if and only if the corresponding set of clauses is inconsistent.

The rules for converting to clausal form can be expressed more simply, to begin with, if implications and equivalences are reexpressed in terms of negation, conjunction and disjunction by using the equivalences:

> [X —> Y] <—> ¬X V Y
> [X <—> Y] <—> [X —> Y] & [Y —> X]   i.e.
> [X <—> Y] <—> [¬X V Y] & [¬Y V X]
> where X and Y are any formulae.

Once implications and equivalences have been rewritten, the rest of the conversion consists of

> (1) moving   negations   inside   the   sentence   past conjunctions, disjunctions and quantifiers, until they stand only in front of atomic formulae,

(2) moving disjunctions inside the sentence past conjunctions and quantifiers, until they connect only atoms or negated atoms,

(3) eliminating existential quantifiers and

(4) reexpressing disjunctions

$$A_1 \vee \ldots \vee A_m \vee \neg B_1 \ldots \vee \neg B_n$$

of atoms and their negations as clauses

$$A_1, \ldots, A_m \longleftarrow B_1, \ldots, B_n.$$

Negations can be moved in front of atoms by repeatedly applying the following equivalences:

> $\neg[X \& Y] \longleftrightarrow \neg X \vee \neg Y$
> $\neg[X \vee Y] \longleftrightarrow \neg X \& \neg Y$
> $\neg \exists v\, X \qquad \longleftrightarrow \forall v\, \neg X$
> $\neg \forall v\, X \qquad \longleftrightarrow \exists v\, \neg X$
> $\neg \neg X \qquad \longleftrightarrow X$
> where X and Y are any formulae
> and v is any variable.

Disjunctions can be moved inside a sentence until they connect only atoms and their negations by using the equivalences:

> $X \vee [Y \& Z] \longleftrightarrow [X \vee Y] \& [X \vee Z]$
> $X \vee \exists v\, Y \qquad \longleftrightarrow \exists v\, [X \vee Y]$
> $X \vee \forall v\, Y \qquad \longleftrightarrow \forall v\, [X \vee Y]$
> where the variable v does not occur in X.

The commutativity of disjunction

> $X \vee Y \longleftrightarrow Y \vee X$

is needed to justify the similar equivalences

> $[Y \& Z] \vee X \longleftrightarrow [Y \vee X] \& [Z \vee X]$
> $\exists v\, Y \vee X \qquad \longleftrightarrow \exists v\, [Y \vee X]$
> $\forall v\, Y \vee X \qquad \longleftrightarrow \forall v\, [Y \vee X]$
> where v does not occur in X.

The preceding equivalences are sufficient to transform any sentence without quantifiers in standard form into an equivalent one in clausal form. The elimination of an existential quantifier, however, produces a sentence which is not equivalent. It introduces a constant or function symbol in order to name an individual which is referred to only implicitly in the original sentence. The new sentence implies, but is not implied by, the original sentence. Nevertheless, the elimination of the existential quantifier does not affect the consistency of the set of sentences as a whole.

Given a conjunction (or set) of sentences S, in order to eliminate existential quantifiers from S it is necessary to eliminate them from sentences of the form

$$\forall v_1 \forall v_2 \ldots \forall v_n \exists u \; X$$

belonging to S. Such a sentence can be replaced by the new sentence

$\forall v_1 \forall v_2 \ldots \forall v_n \; X'$
where X' is obtained from X by replacing
all free occurrences of u in X by the term
$f(v_1, \ldots, v_n)$ where f is a function symbol
which does not occur in S.

If n=0 the term $f(v_1, \ldots, v_n)$ reduces to a constant symbol. Note that the replacement is not an equivalence and it only applies to sentences, not to formulae. The new conjunction (or set of sentences) is consistent (or inconsistent) if and only if S is.

In order to transform sentences belonging to S into the correct form, it is useful to move universal quantifiers inside conjunctions.

$$\forall v \; [X \& Y] \longleftrightarrow \forall v \; X \& \forall v \; Y$$

Repeated application of the preceding rules will   convert any conjunction (or set) of sentences in standard form into a conjunction (or set) of sentences, each of which has a form

$$\forall v_1 \ldots \forall v_k \; [A_1 V \ldots V \, A_m V \neg B_1 V \ldots V \neg B_n]$$

which is equivalent to a clause

$$A_1, \ldots, A_m \longleftarrow B_1, \ldots, B_n.$$

The preceding rules express the logic of a family of algorithms for converting from standard form to clausal form.   All non-determinism[1] is of the don't care variety. An efficient algorithm is obtained by always applying the   rules to an   outermost propositional   connective or quantifier, replacing the formula on the left hand side of an equivalence by the formula on the right hand side. Moreover, it is more convenient in practice to leave the implication sign intact and to apply derived equivalences. The following derived equivalences (see exercise 2) are the most useful.

$[X \longrightarrow Y \& Z]$ $\longleftrightarrow$ $[X \longrightarrow Y] \& [X \longrightarrow Z]$
$[X V Y \longrightarrow Z]$ $\longleftrightarrow$ $[X \longrightarrow Z] \& [Y \longrightarrow Z]$
$[X \& \neg Y \longrightarrow Z]$ $\longleftrightarrow$ $[X \longrightarrow Y V Z]$
$[X \longrightarrow \neg Y V Z]$ $\longleftrightarrow$ $[X \& Y \longrightarrow Z]$
$[X \longrightarrow [Y \longrightarrow Z]]$ $\longleftrightarrow$ $[X \& Y \longrightarrow Z]$
$[[X \longrightarrow Y] \longrightarrow Z]$ $\longleftrightarrow$ $[X V Z] \& [Y \longrightarrow Z]$
$X \longrightarrow \forall v \; Y$ $\longleftrightarrow$ $\forall v \; [X \longrightarrow Y]$
$X \longrightarrow \exists v \; Y$ $\longleftrightarrow$ $\exists v \; [X \longrightarrow Y]$
$\forall v \; Y \longrightarrow X$ $\longleftrightarrow$ $\exists v \; [Y \longrightarrow X]$
$\exists v \; Y \longrightarrow X$ $\longleftrightarrow$ $\forall v \; [Y \longrightarrow X]$
where v does not occur in X.

In addition, generalisations of the equivalences:

$[U \& [X V Y] \longrightarrow Z]$ $\longleftrightarrow$ $[U \& X \longrightarrow Z] \& [U \& Y \longrightarrow Z]$
$[U \& [X \longrightarrow Y] \longrightarrow Z]$ $\longleftrightarrow$ $[U \longrightarrow X V Z] \& [U \& Y \longrightarrow Z]$

for example, are often useful as well. In order to apply them may require application of the commutativity of conjunction:

$$X \;\&\; Y \;\langle -\rangle\; Y \;\&\; X$$

Comparison of clausal form with standard form

Clausal form is a restricted subset of standard form. It has the advantage that simple, efficient, and reasonably natural resolution theorem provers have been developed for it. Standard form, however, allows more liberal means of expression. Some kinds of sentences can be expressed more economically and others more naturally than in clausal form. The analysis in the next few sections, of the cases in which standard form provides greater expressive power than clausal form, suggests that what is needed is not full unrestricted standard form but a limited extension of clausal form. In most cases it suffices to allow non-atomic formulae as conditions and conclusions of implications.

$$A_1, \ldots, A_m \;\langle-\; B_1, \ldots, B_n$$

It is useful, in particular, to allow conclusions A_i which are conjunctions of atoms and conditions B_j which are implications. In addition it is useful to employ equivalences $\langle-\rangle$ for definitions instead of writing the two halves separately.

The ideal system of logic would combine the advantages of clausal form with those of standard form. In order to do so, it would need both to reduce to resolution for sentences already in clausal form and to resemble the natural deduction systems of Bledsoe [1971], Brown [1977], Bibel and Schreiber [1975], and Nevins [1974]. Such a system might result from combining the resolution rule with the rules which convert sentences from standard form to clausal form.

The satisfactory solution of the problem of deriving Horn clause programs from program specifications in standard form requires such a proof procedure. The problem has been investigated by Bibel [1976a, 1976b, 1978], Clark and Sickel [1977], and Hogger [1978a, 1978b, 1979]. Their derivation rules resemble both the rules for converting to clausal form as well as the resolution rule which behaves as procedure invocation. Proof procedures for the standard form of logic, which have some of the necessary properties, have been developed by Murray [1978] and by Manna and Waldinger [1978].

In the following sections we investigate a number of examples which illustrate the limitations of clausal form and the inadequacy of dealing with standard form simply by converting to clausal form and applying resolution. At the end of the chapter we shall consider the problem of deriving Horn clause programs from non-clausal specifications.

Conjunctive conclusions and disjunctive conditions

Standard form is more economical than clausal form when the same conditions imply several conclusions or when the same conclusion is implied by alternative conditions.

Example   Everyone makes mistakes.

Standard form   ∀x∃y [Human(x) —> Does(x,y) & Mistake(y)]

Conversion   (a) Human(x) —> Does(x, m(x)) & Mistake(m(x))

                (b) ¬Human(x) V [Does(x, m(x)) & Mistake(m(x))]

                (c) [¬Human(x) V Does(x, m(x))] &
                    [¬Human(x) V Mistake(m(x))]

Clausal form   (d) Does(x, m(x)) <— Human(x)
                    Mistake(m(x)) <— Human(x)

In the clausal form, the same condition Human(x) needs to be repeated for
each separate conclusion. Notice that using the derived conversion rules
for implication, the conversion from (a) to (d) can be done in one step.

Example   One person is an ancestor of another if he is a parent of
                 the other or he is an ancestor of an ancestor of the
                 other.

Standard Form   Anc(x,y) <— Par(x,y) V ∃z [Anc(x,z) & Anc(z,y)]

Conversion   (a) Anc(x,y) V ¬[Par(x,y) V ∃z [Anc(x,z) & Anc(z,y)]]

                (b) Anc(x,y) V [¬Par(x,y) & ¬∃z [Anc(x,z) & Anc(z,y)]]

                (c) [Anc(x,y) V ¬Par(x,y)] &
                    [Anc(x,y) V ¬∃z [Anc(x,z) & Anc(z,y)]]

                (d) [Anc(x,y) V ¬Par(x,y)] &
                    [Anc(x,y) V ∀z [¬Anc(x,z) V ¬Anc(z,y)]]

                (e) [Anc(x,y) V ¬Par(x,y)] &
                    ∀z [Anc(x,y) V ¬Anc(x,z) V ¬Anc(z,y)]

Clausal form   (f) Anc(x,y) <— Par(x,y)
                    Anc(x,y) <— Anc(x,z), Anc(z,y)

In the clausal form, the same conclusion needs to be repeated for each
alternative condition. The conversion from standard form is simplified
if the derived equvalences are used:

                (a') [Anc(x,y) <— Par(x,y)] &
                     [Anc(x,y) <— ∃z [Anc(x,z) & Anc(z,y)]]

                (b') [Anc(x,y) <— Par(x,y)] &
                     ∀z [Anc(x,y) <— Anc(x,z) & Anc(z,y)]

                (c') Anc(x,y) <— Par(x,y)
                     Anc(x,y) <— Anc(x,z), Anc(z,y)

For the sake of simplicity we shall use the derived equivalences in the
rest of the chapter.

Disjunctive conclusions

Standard form is both more economical and more intelligible when the alternatives in a conclusion are conjunctions.

Example	The earth is round and finite or flat and infinite.
Standard form	[Round(E) & Finite(E)] V [Flat(E) & Infinite(E)]
Conversion	(a) [[Round(E) & Finite(E)] V Flat(E)] & [[Round(E) & Finite(E)] V Infinite(E)]
	(b) [Round(E) V Flat(E)] & [Finite(E) V Flat(E)] & [Round(E) V Infinite(E)] & [Finite(E) V Infinite(E)]
Clausal form	Round(E), Flat(E) <— Finite(E), Flat(E) <— Round(E), Infinite(E) <— Finite(E), Infinite(E) <—

Only-if halves of definitions

We shall argue in the next chapter that Horn clauses often express only the if-half of an if-and-only-if definition. The full if-and-only-if definition can be expressed compactly in the standard form by using the sign of equivalence <—>. In the clausal form, the if-half and the only-if half need to be expressed separately. The only-if half generally expresses alternative conclusions and can be both uneconomical and unnatural.

Example	The only-if half of the if-and-only-if definition of ancestor.
Standard form	Anc(x,y) —> Par(x,y) V ∃z[Anc(x,z) & Anc(z,y)]
Conversion	(a) ∃z [Anc(x,y) —> Par(x,y) V [Anc(x,z) & Anc(z,y)]]
	(b) Anc(x,y) —> Par(x,y) V [Anc(x, f(x,y)) & Anc(f(x,y), y)]
	(c) Anc(x,y) —> [Par(x,y) V Anc(x, f(x,y))] & [Par(x,y) V Anc(f(x,y), y)]
Clausal form	Par(x,y), Anc(x, f(x,y)) <— Anc(x,y) Par(x,y), Anc(f(x,y), y) <— Anc(x,y)

Implications as conditions of implications

It is common for sentences of natural language to have conditions which are themselves implications rather than simple atoms. Such sentences can be expressed directly and naturally in standard form, but may be difficult to understand in clausal form.

Example   x⊃y is true if y is true whenever x is true.

Standard form   True(x⊃y) <— [True(y) <— True(x)]

Clausal form   True(x⊃y), True(x) <—
                 True(x⊃y) <— True(y)

Example   Bob is happy if all his students like logic.

Standard form   Happy(Bob) <— ∀x [Studentof(Bob,x) —> Likes(x,logic)]

Conversion   (a) ∃x [Happy(Bob) <— [Studentof(Bob,x) —>
                                           Likes(x,logic)]

                 (b) Happy(Bob) <— [Studentof(Bob,☺) —> Likes(☺,logic)]

Clausal form   Happy(Bob), Studentof(Bob,☺) <—
                 Happy(Bob) <— Likes(☺,logic)

Example   A supplier is preferred if all the parts he supplies
                 arrive on time.

Standard form   Preferred(x) <— Supplier(x) &
                               ∀u [Supplies(x,u) —> Arriveontime(u)]

Clausal form   Preferred(x) <— Supplier(x), Arriveontime(p(x))
                 Preferred(x), Supplies(x, p(x)) <— Supplier(x)

Example   A set is well-ordered if and only if every non-empty
                 subset has a least element. A set is non-empty if and
                 only if it has at least one element. An element of a set
                 is a least element if and only if it is less than or equal
                 to every element of the set.

Standard form   Wellordered(x) <—> ∀z [Hasleastelmt(z) <— z∈x &
                                                       Nonempty(z)]

                 Nonempty(z) <—> ∃u u∈z

                 Hasleastelmt(z) <—> ∃u [u∈z & ∀v [v∈z —> u≤v]]

Clausal form   Wellordered(x), arb(x) ∈ x <—
                 Wellordered(x), Nonempty(arb(x)) <—
                 Wellordered(x) <— Hasleastelmt(arb(x))
                 Hasleastelmt(z) <— Wellordered(x), z∈x, Nonempty(z)
                 Nonempty(z) ∈ <— u∈z
                 select(z) ∈ z <— Nonempty(z)
                 Hasleastelmt(z), el(z,u) ∈ z <— u∈z
                 Hasleastelmt(z) <— u ≤ el(z,u), u∈z
                 smallest(z) ∈ z <— Hasleastelmt(z)
                 smallest(z) ≤ u <— Hasleastelmt(z), u∈z

Derivation of programs from specifications

   Programs can be expressed more naturally in logic if implications are
allowed as conditions. The definition of subset is a simple example:

$$x \subseteq y \;\longleftarrow\; \forall z \; [z \in x \rightarrow z \in y]$$

The condition that "every element of x is an element of y" is neutral
about the manner in which the elements of x are investigated and shown to
be elements of y. In particular, it is consistent with the possibility
that all elements of x are investigated simultaneously, in parallel.
Such high-level specification is not possible in normal programming
languages. It is not even possible with Horn clauses.

   Suppose that sets are represented by finite lists.   Then the notions
of both membership and subset can be defined recursively by means of Horn
clauses:

$$z \in z.v \;\longleftarrow\;$$
$$z \in u.v \;\longleftarrow\; z \in v$$
$$nil \subseteq y \;\longleftarrow\;$$
$$u.v \subseteq y \;\longleftarrow\; u \in y, \; v \subseteq y$$

The Horn clause program is less natural and closer to the level of the
computer than the specification in standard form.   It expresses details
which are left to the initiative of the theorem prover in the standard
form specification. It works, moreover, only for finite sets represented
by means of lists. The standard form specification, on the other hand,
works for both finite and infinite lists. Exercise (6b) demonstrates
this for the notion of ordered list.

   The use of logic is more widely accepted as a specification language
than it is as a programming language. Methods for verifying conventional
programs relative to logic specifications are complicated therefore by
the need to relate two different languages. The methods of Floyd [1967],
Manna [1969], Hoare [1969] and Dijkstra [1976] express specifications in
logic and relate them to programs by defining the semantics of programs
in logic.

   Verification of programs is significantly easier when programs and
specifications are expressed in the same language. This is confirmed by
the results of Boyer and Moore [1975] who use LISP for both programs and
specifications, Manna and Waldinger [1977], who use LISP for programs and
LISP augmented with universally quantified implications for
specifications, and Burstall and Darlington [1977], who use recursion
equations for both programs and specifications. More recently, using the
procedural interpretation of Horn clauses, deduction strategies for
deriving logic programs from logic specifications have been developed by
Clark and Tarnlund [1977], Bibel [1976a, 1976b, 1978], Clark and Sickel
[1977], Hogger [1978a, 1978b, 1979] and Clark and Darlington [1978]. In
addition, Manna and Waldinger [1978] have developed an extension of
resolution for deriving LISP programs from logic specifications.

   The derivation of logic programs from logic specifications has the
special characteristic that deduction is used both to run programs and to
derive programs from specifications.   Programs can be regarded as

computationally useful logical consequences of the specifications.

We shall illustrate the general method by deriving the Horn clause program for subset from the standard form specification The inference steps can be thought of as combining resolution with conversion to clausal form. We start with the if-and-only-if specifications of the subset and membership relations.

S1 $x \subseteq y \longleftrightarrow \forall z \ [\underline{z \in x} \longrightarrow z \in y]$
S2 $\forall z \ \neg[z \in nil]$ (i.e. $\longleftarrow z \in nil$)
S3 $\underline{z \in u.v} \longleftrightarrow z=u \lor z \in v$

The basis of the recursive Horn clause program

> nil $\subseteq$ y $\longleftarrow$

can be obtained directly by resolving the clausal form of S2 with the first of the two clauses

          $x \subseteq y, \ arb(x,y) \in x \longleftarrow$
          $x \subseteq y \longleftarrow arb(x,y) \in y$

obtained by converting S1 into clausal form.

The recursive clause of the program can be derived more naturally by reasoning with the specifications in standard form. By matching the underlined atoms in S1 and S3 we obtain

S4 $u.v \subseteq y \longleftarrow \forall z \ [[z=u \lor z \in v] \longrightarrow z \in y]$.

It suffices, in this case, to use only the if-half of the definition of subset. We can think of S4 as obtained by letting x be u.v in S1 and then using the equivalence S3 to replace $z \in u.v$ by $z=u \lor z \in v$. Next, we begin to convert S4 to clausal form.

S5 $u.v \subseteq y \longleftarrow \forall z \ [z=u \longrightarrow z \in y] \ \&$
                    $\forall z \ [z \in v \longrightarrow z \in y]$

Any further conversion would result in non-Horn clauses. Fortunately the two non-atomic conditions in S5 can be replaced by equivalent atomic ones.

S6 $\forall z \ [z=u \longrightarrow z \in y] \longleftrightarrow u \in y$
S7 $\forall z \ [z \in v \longrightarrow z \in y] \longleftrightarrow v \subseteq y$

Applying the two equivalences to S5 we obtain the rest of the program

> u.v $\subseteq$ y $\longleftarrow$ u $\in$ y, v $\subseteq$ y

It remains to demonstrate the equivalences S6 and S7. The second one S7 is easy; it is an instance of S1. The first equivalence is a special case of a more general equivalence

> $\forall z \ [z=u \longrightarrow X] \longleftrightarrow X'$
> where X' is obtained from X by
> replacing all occurrences of z by u.

which is useful in general.

The derivation of the subset program illustrates the use of inference rules which apply directly to the standard form and which resemble both resolution and the rules for converting from standard to clausal form.

Exercises

1) Express the following sentences in standard form and transform them into clausal form.

- a)   A number is the maximum of a set of numbers if it belongs to the set and is $\geq$ all numbers which belong to the set. (Hint: Define an auxiliary relationship Dominates(x,y) which holds when x $\geq$ all numbers which belong to the set of numbers y.)

- b)   A list of numbers is ordered if it is empty or its first number is $\leq$ all numbers in the rest of the list and the rest of the list is ordered.

- c)   A number is the greatest common divisor of numbers x and y if it divides x and y and is $\geq$ all numbers which divide x and y.

2) The derived equivalences on page 199 can be justified by converting each half of an equivalence to the same formula, by replacing subformulae by equivalent subformulae. For example, both halves of the equivalence

$$X \longrightarrow [Y \ \& \ Z] \longleftrightarrow [X \longrightarrow Y] \ \& \ [X \longrightarrow Z]$$

convert to the same formula

$$[\neg \ X \ V \ Y] \ \& \ [\neg \ X \ V \ Z].$$

Derive the remaining equivalences on page 199.

3)   a) Express the following assumptions in standard form and transform them into clausal form.

A dragon is happy if all its children can fly.
Green dragons can fly.
A dragon is green if at least one of its parents is green and is pink otherwise.

- b)   Use resolution (and factoring if necessary) to show:

- (i) Green dragons are happy.
- (ii) Childless dragons are happy.

You will need to supply some "obvious" missing assumptions.

c)   What should a pink dragon do to be happy?

4) This exercise is an extension of exercise 8 of Chapter 2. Given
data in the Supplier, Part and Supply tables, express the following
queries in standard form. Use both the binary and n-ary representations.

a)   What are the numbers of suppliers who supply all parts?

b)   What are the names of suppliers who do not supply books?

c)   What are the numbers of those suppliers who supply at
least all parts supplied by John?

5)   a) Express the following assumption in standard form and
transform it into clausal form.

A logician is happy if all his arguments are sound.

b)   Use resolution to show that the following conclusions are
implied by the assumption.

(i) A Logician is happy if everyone's arguments are sound.
(ii) A logician is happy if he doesn't argue.

6)   a) Express the following assumptions in standard form and
transform them into clausal form.

(i)   A sequence z is ordered if for every x, y, i and j,
x is the i-th element of z,
y is the j-th element of z and
i ≤ j imply x ≤ y.

(ii) If i ≤ j then u*i ≤ u*j, for all i, j and u.

(iii)The i-th element of sequence S is 3*i for all i.

b)   Use resolution to show that the sequence S is ordered.
Notice that S might have infinitely many elements.

7) Assume that the following relations are already defined:

x ≤ y
x > y
Empty(x)   the tree x contains no nodes.
Split(x,y,u,v)   the tree x has root node labelled by item y,
                  left subtree u and right subtree v.

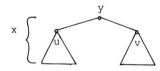

a)   Express the following definition of the relation Ord(x) in
      standard form:

      The tree x is ordered if for every non-empty subtree z of
      x

i)   all items which belong to the left subtree of z are ≤ the
      item at the root of z and

ii)   all items which belong to the right subtree of z are > the
      item at the root of z.

      You should define the following relations for this
      purpose.

      Subtree(z,x)   z is a subtree of x
      Belongs(y,x)   the item y belongs to tree x.

b)   Transform the definition of Ord(x) into clausal form.

8) The relationship Sl(x,y), i.e. x is a sublist of y, can be
specified by:

      Sl(x,y)   <-> ∃u∃v∃w[Append(u,x,v) & Append(v,w,y)]
      Append(x,y,z) <-> [x=nil & y=z] V
                        ∃u∃v∃w[x=u.v & z=u.w & Append(v,y,w)]

Derive a recursive program for Sl(x,y), not involving Append, using the
following assumptions about equality if necessary:

      x.y = u.v <-> x=u & y=v
      ¬ ∃u∃v u.v = nil
      x = x

9) The relationship Fact*(x,y,u,v) can be specified by

      Fact*(x,y,u,v) <-> [Fact(x,y) -> Fact(u,v)]
      Fact(x,y)   <-> [Zero(x) & Succ(x,y)] V
                        ∃u∃v[Succ(u,x) & Fact'(u,v)
                                         & Times(x,v,y)]

      Zero(0) <-
      Succ(x, s(x)) <-

a)   Derive a recursive program for   Fact*(x,y,u,v), not
      involving Fact.

b)   Show that Fact(u,v) <-> Fact*(0,s(0),u,v).

10) Given the specification

      Ord(x) <-> ∀u∀v[Consec(u,v,x) -> u≤v]

derive a Horn clause program for Ord(x), using the following assumptions:

> ¬ Consec(u, v, nil)
> ¬ Consec(u, v, x.nil)
>   Consec(u, v, x.y) <—> Consec(u,v,y) ∨ ∃z[u=x & y=v.z]

CHAPTER 11

If-and-only-if

In classical logic, definitions are expressed by means of "if-and-only-if" (abbreviated "iff"). For example:

G*   Grandparent(x,y) <—> ∃z [Parent(x,z) & Parent(z,y)]

Horn clause programs and databases, however, express only the "if-halves" of iff-definitions:

G   Grandparent(x,y) <— Parent(x,z), Parent(z,y)

We have managed to avoid the full iff-form of definitions because the if-halves alone are adequate for deriving all positive instances of the relations. All variable-free assertions of the form

                Grandparent(s,t) <—

which are implied by G* are already implied by G. It is not possible to compute more factorials with the iff-definition

F*   Fact(x,y) <—> [x=0 & y=1] V
                               ∃x'∃y'[x=x'+1 & Fact(x',y') & y=x*y']

than with the if-half alone:

F1   Fact(x,y) <— x=0, y=1
F2   Fact(x,y) <— x=x'+1, Fact(x',y'), y=x*y'

However, as we shall see in the next section, the full iff-form of definitions is needed for proving properties of programs. It is also needed in databases for answering queries involving universal quantifiers and negation.

In the informal use of natural language, the if-form of definitions is often employed even when the iff-definition is intended. This gives rise to the problem of distinguishing when the missing only-if half of the definition is intended and when it is not.

We shall argue that the problem is complicated by the fact that the only-if halves of definitions are ambiguous.

                A only if B

can be interpreted in the object language

                B <— A

or in the meta-language

"A <— B" expresses the only condition under which A holds.

Consequently, proofs which need to appeal to the only-if halves can be carried out either in the object language or in the meta-language. Despite this difference, however, the structure of the proofs is remarkably similar in both cases.

The need for the only-if halves of definitions

The only-if halves of definitions are needed for proving program properties and for verifying database integrity constraints. Consider, for example, the Horn clause program F1-2 for computing factorials. It is a property of the program that

> The only factorial of 0 is 1,
> i.e. y=1 <— Fact(0,y).

To prove the property, however, requires the only-if half of the definition of factorial as well as the property of equality that

> <— 0 = u+1.

The only-if halves of definitions are also needed for answering queries in logic databases. Consider, for example, the iff-definitions of the Teaches and Professor relations:

T*   Teaches(x,y) <—> [x=A & y=104] V
                            [x=A & y=301] V
                            [x=B & y=221] V
                            [x=C & y=105] V
                            [x=C & y=201] V

P*   Professor(x) <—> x=A V x=B

Given, in addition, the clauses

> Isa(104,programming) <—
> Isa(221,programming) <— ,

the query

> Do all professors teach programming?

> $\forall x \exists y$[Professor(x) —> Teaches(x,y) & Isa(y,programming)]?

can be answered positively. To answer the query, however, requires the only-if half of the definition of the Professor relation. The object language and meta-language proofs of the query are presented and compared later in the chapter.

Terms versus relations as data structures

The relationship between iff-definitions and their if-halves bears
upon the relationship between the use of terms and the use of relations
as data structures in logic programs. The use of terms in Horn clause
programs gives some of the power of the use of relations defined by means
of iff.

Consider, for example, the data depicted in the following scene:

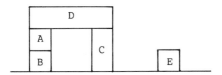

Restricted to the use of Horn clauses, the On and Clear relations have to
be defined independently:

```
On(A,B) <-              Clear(D) <-
On(D,A) <-              Clear(E) <-
On(D,C) <-
```

The connection between the two relations can be expressed only by means
of an integrity constraint.

```
<- On(x,y), Clear(y)
```

By using iff-definitions, however, the Clear relation can be defined
in terms of the On relation.

```
Clear(y) <-> ¬∃x On(x,y)
On(x,y)  <-> [x=A & y=B] ∨
             [x=D & y=A] ∨
             [x=D & y=C] ∨
```

Notice, however, that in this formulation and the next everything is
clear except A, B and C. The Clear relation can be restricted, if
necessary, by adding an extra condition to the definition

```
Clear(y) <-> Block(y) & ¬∃x On(x,y)
```

and appropriately defining the new predicate Block.

Iff-definitions cannot usually be expressed by means of Horn clauses.
However, some of the power of iff-definitions can be captured with Horn
clauses by using terms instead of relations as data structures. If the
data concerning the position of objects in the scene is collected in a
single term, then the Clear relation can be defined in terms of the data
about the scene. Here "On" is a predicate symbol, but "on" is a function
symbol.

```
Scene(on(A,B).on(D,A).on(D,C).nil) <-
On(x,y) <- Scene(z), Member(on(x,y),z,T)
Clear(y)<- Scene(z), Member(on(x,y),z,F)
```

```
Member(x, x.y, T) <-
Member(x, nil, F) <-
Member(x, u.v, w) <- Diff(x,u), Member(x,v,w)
```

The term representation of the data is significantly less natural than the relational representation. However, both the iff-definition and its simulation by means of terms have several advantages over the simple, Horn clause if-half of the definition. Many properties of the scene, such as the number of objects it contains, can be determined from both the iff-definition and the term representation but cannot be determined from the simple if-half of the definition. Moreover, any change in the position of objects (either by altering the iff-definition of the On relation or by altering the assertion which describes the scene) automatically implies the appropriate modification of the Clear relation. However, if the two relations are defined independently, then alteration of the scene is more difficult. Both the On and Clear relations have to be changed explicitly and the new relationship between them needs to be checked against the integrity constraint.

The unstated only-if-assumption

The statement of only the if-halves of definitions is common in natural language, even when the full iff-definition is intended. Even logicians, who normally insist on the explicit statement of all assumptions, tolerate the unstated only-if assumption in the case of recursive definitions. It is common for a logician to state only the if-half of the definition of natural number, for example:

N1   0 is a natural number.
N2   If x is a natural number then x+1 is a natural number.

even when he intends the only-if half

N3   The only natural numbers are
            those defined by statements N1-2.

as well.

Natural language, however, carries the unstated only-if assumption to the extreme. The classical fallacy of logic is probably an example of this. Suppose, for instance,

M1   Mortal(x) <- Human(x).

If we now assert

M2   Mortal(Bob) <-

then we may be tempted to conclude

M3   Human(Bob) <- .

But M3, although it may well be true, is not a logical consequence of the explicitly stated assumptions M1-2. The fallacy would disappear, however, if we could appeal to unstated assumptions - if we could assume, in particular, that the full iff-definition

M*   Mortal(x) <-> Human(x)

was intended when only the if-half was stated explicitly.

   Comparing the two examples, the if-half of the definition of number
and the incomplete characterisation M1 of mortality, we are faced with
the dilemma of distinguishing when the unstated only-if assumption is
justified and when it is not. The same dilemma arises in the field of
databases where ·the problem is to decide whether the definition of the
data has already been closed or whether it is still open.   The problem
has been investigated by Reiter [1978] who calls the assumption that the
database contains all the information there is to know the closed world
assumption and the assumption that it may not, the open world assumption.
Our proposal is to identify the closed world assumption with the
assumption that the missing only-if halves of definitions are intended
and to identify the open world assumption with the assumption that they
are not.

   The problem of distinguishing between intended and unintended
assumptions disappears, of course, if   all intentions are made explicit.
Explicit statement of intentions, moreover, makes it easy to mix closed
and open world assumptions in the same database, applying different
assumptions to different relations or even to different instances of the
same relation. We might decide, for example, to close the instances of
the Teaches relation which describe the courses taught by Bob, but to
leave open the ones taught by John.

T1   Teaches(Bob,x) <-> x=304 V x=323 V x=1.4
T2   Teaches(John,212) <-
T3   Teaches(John,1.13) <-

   It is curious that natural language should be so careless about
specifying whether or not only-if assumptions are intended. This may be a
consequence, in part, of the awkwardness of the iff syntax. In order to
close the definition of the courses taught by John, after adding the
assertion

T4   Teaches(John,103) <-

for example, it is necessary either to replace T2-4 by

T*   Teaches(John,x) <-> x=212 V x=1.13 V x=103

or to add to T2-4 the explicit only-if half of the definition

T5   Teaches(John,x) -> x=212 V x=1.13 V x=103.

A more convenient syntax might be one which leaves T2-4 alone and states
that

T5*   all instances of Teaches(John,x) are defined by T2-4.

Ambiguity of only-if

Our discussion of the relationship between iff-definitions and their
if-halves has been simplified by ignoring the ambiguity of the expression

A only if B.

In some cases we have interpreted it as a statement in the object
language

B <— A.

In other cases we have interpreted it in the meta-language

"A <— B" expresses the only condition under which A holds.

The only-if half of the definition of natural number, which was
previously expressed in the meta-language, can also be expressed in the
object language.

Numb(x) —> x = 0 ∨ ∃x'[x = x'+1 & Numb(x')]

Whether the expression "A only if B" is interpreted in the object
language or the meta-language, it has similar properties. For example,
in both cases the conclusion

B <—

is a consequence of the assumptions

A only if B
A <— .

If "only-if" is interpreted in the object language, the conclusion
follows by one step of bottom-up reasoning. If it is interpreted in the
meta-language, it follows by reasoning about proofs:

If the only way of proving A is by proving B, and
A <— can be proved,
then B <— can be proved as well.

This example illustrates a general phenomenon: The two interpretations
of "only-if" justify similar conclusions in different, but structurally
similar, ways.

Object language and meta-language solutions

The problem of showing that all professors teach programming

Q   ∀x∃y[Professor(x) —> Teaches(x,y) & Isa(y,programming)]

can be solved whether the only-if half of the definition P* of the
Professor relation is expressed in the object language or in the meta-
language.

Suppose the only-if half of P* is expressed as a non-Horn clause

$$x = A, \ x = B \ \leftarrow \ Professor(x)$$

in the object language. The query itself reduces to two clauses:

Q1	Professor(☺) ←
Q2	← Teaches(☺,y), Isa(y,programming)

Bottom-up reasoning from the assertion Q1 derives the non-Horn clause

$$☺ = A, \ ☺ = B \leftarrow .$$

The two goals in Q2 can now be solved by case analysis. In the case ☺ = A, the first goal in Q2 is solved by

$$Teaches(x,y) \ \leftarrow \ x = A, \ y = 104$$
$$x = x \ \leftarrow$$

and the second goal by

$$Isa(104,programming) \ \leftarrow .$$

In the second case ☺ = B, the first goal is solved by

$$Teaches(x,y) \ \leftarrow \ x = B, \ y = 221$$
$$x = x \ \leftarrow$$

and the second goal by

$$Isa(221,programming) \ \leftarrow .$$

Suppose, on the other hand, that the only-if half of P* is expressed in the meta-language:

P1	Professor(x) ← x = A
P2	Professor(x) ← x = B
P3	P1 and P2 express the only conditions under which an individual is a member of the Professor relation.

To solve the problem, the query Q needs to be expressed in the meta-language as well.

	Show that for every x which solves the goal
Q1*	← Professor(x)
	there is a y which solves the goals
Q2*	← Teaches(x,y), Isa(y,programming).

Top-down reasoning from the goal Q1* derives only two solutions

$$x = A \quad and \quad x = B.$$

In the case x = A, the two goals in Q2* are solved by y = 104 using the clauses

```
Teaches(x,y) <- x = A, y = 104
x = x <-
Isa(104,programming) <- .
```

In the case x = B, they are solved by y = 221 using the clauses

```
Teaches(x,y) <- x = B, y = 221
x = x <-
Isa(221,programming) <- .
```

Notice that the object language and meta-language proofs have similar structure. In the meta-language proof, however, equality relates variables to the terms to which they are bound in the components of matching substitutions. In the object language proof, equality relates different names for the same individual. Thus the equality symbol used for expressing the only-if halves of definitions satisfies the axioms E1-3 of Chapter 2, page 43. In the general case, these axioms are extremely redundant. In this case, however, they are not even necessary.

Object language and meta-language interpretations of negation

The only-if halves of definitions are necessary to show that a negative condition

```
<- not-P
```

holds. Depending on the interpretation of "only-if", the proof can be carried out either at the object level or at the meta-level. Clark [1978] has shown that for every meta-language proof of not-P obtained by a Horn clause theorem-prover augmented with negation proved by failure, there exists a structurally similar object language proof of not-P.

Consider the problem of showing that D is clear

```
<- Clear(D)
```

given the if-halves of the definitions of the On and Clear relations:

```
On1        On(A,B)   <-
On2        On(D,A)   <-
On3        On(D,C)   <-
On4        Clear(y)  <- not¬∃x On(x,y)
```

In addition, the only-if half of the definition of the On relation is necessary for a solution. However, the if-half of the definition of the Clear relation is sufficient.

Suppose first that the only-if half of the definition is expressed in the object language:

```
On5        On(x,y) -> [x = A & y = B] V
                       [x = D & y = A] V
                       [x = D & y = C] V
```

The sentence is more natural in the standard form than in the clausal

form. It is also more natural to carry out the proof using standard
form. Moreover, the standard form proof is structurally similar to the
meta-language proof, whereas the clausal form proof is not. It will be
useful to reexpress the only-if half of the definition in the equivalent
form

$$\text{not-On}(x,y) \;\leftarrow\; [x \neq A \;V\; y \neq B] \;\&$$
$$[x \neq D \;V\; y \neq A] \;\&$$
$$[x \neq D \;V\; y \neq C]$$

where s $\neq$ t is just an abbreviation for $^-[s = t]$.

The last step of the proof verifies the three conditions by using the
"negative assertions":

On6   D $\neq$ B $\leftarrow$
On7   D $\neq$ A $\leftarrow$
On8   D $\neq$ C $\leftarrow$

The clausal form, resolution proof is left to exercise (2).

    Suppose now that the only-if half of the definition is expressed in
the meta-language:

            Clauses On1-3 express the only conditions
            under which the On relation holds.

The meta-level proof shows that every way of trying to solve the goal
$\leftarrow$On(x,D) fails. The structure of the proof, however, is similar to that
of the object level argument.

The last step of the proof shows that On1-3 fail to match On(x,D), because D is different from (does not match) A, B and C. The object-level proof, however, needs to reason about equality explicitly. Clark [1978] shows that in general explicit axioms of equality are necessary at the object level in order to simulate failure of the matching algorithm at the meta-level.

Horn clauses augmented with negation interpreted as failure

The meta-language interpretation of "only-if" entails the interpretation of negation as failure:

> not-P holds
> if the if-halves of definitions fail to establish P.

The language of Horn clauses augmented with negation as failure provides a powerful extension of the language of Horn clauses alone. It is easy to implement, efficient to use and has much of the expressive power of the full standard form of logic. It is an important feature of all PROLOG implementations that either they provide the negation operator explicitly or else they provide means for defining it.

The expressive power of Horn clauses with negation is illustrated by the definition of subset

$$x \subseteq y \leftarrow \forall z \ [z \in x \rightarrow z \in y],$$

which can be reexpressed

> $x \subseteq y \leftarrow \text{not-}\exists z \ [z \in x, \text{not-}[z \in y]]$
> x is a subset of y if no z in x fails to belong to y.

The explicit existential quantifier $\exists z$ can be eliminated and the negation sign can be moved in front of atomic formulae if an auxiliary predicate Nosub(x,y), which holds when x is not a subset of y, is employed. The definition of subset becomes

> $x \subseteq y \leftarrow \text{not-Nosub}(x,y)$
> $\text{Nosub}(x,y) \leftarrow z \in x, \text{not-}[z \in y].$

> x is a subset of y if it cannot be shown
> that it is not a subset of y.
> x is not a subset of y if there is a z in x
> which fails to belong to y.

A similar transformation can be applied to the definition of Clear block:

> $\text{Clear}(y) \leftarrow \text{not-Covered}(y)$
> $\text{Covered}(y) \leftarrow \text{On}(x,y)$

Clark's analysis of negation interpreted as failure assumes that negations are so transformed that they stand only in front of atomic formulae.

Clark has shown that Horn clauses with negation interpreted as failure do not have the full power of negation in the standard form of logic. The simplest example of this is the sentence

          P <— not-P

which implies

          P <—

in the standard form of logic, since

          P <— not-P   is equivalent to
          P, P <—   is equivalent to
          P <— .

But the attempt to solve

          <— P   given   P <— not-P

does not succeed because it goes into a loop when negation is interpreted as failure.

A more complicated infinite loop arises during the attempt to solve the goal

          <— A   using   1)   A <— P(x)
                               2)   A <— not-P(x)
                               3)   P(x) <— P(f(x))

with negation interpreted as failure. Both procedures (1) and (2) introduce the procedure call

          <— P(x)

which neither succeeds nor fails in finite time. But in the standard form of logic, A <— is a resolvent of (1) and (2).

These examples suggest that the deductive power of negation as failure can be increased by adding loop detection to the resources of the Horn clause problem-solver. Because of the undecidability of logic [Church 1936] however, no problem-solver can recognise all situations in which a goal is unsolvable. There is no best theorem-prover and no limit to the extent to which a problem-solver can improve its ability to detect loops and to establish negation by failure.

The recognition of failure by detecting loops in the meta-language is equivalent to using proof by induction in the object language. by adding proof by induction to the resources of the problem-solver. Proof by induction is needed, moreover, in many cases when the only-if halves of definitions are used to prove program properties.

Proof of program properties

Consider the Horn clause if-half of the definition of the Append-relation

A1   Append(nil,x,x) <—
A2   Append(x.y, z, x.y') <— Append(y,z,y').

It has the property that

              Append(x,nil,x) holds for all lists x.

Proof of the property requires induction on the structure of lists. We
shall present both the object level and meta-level proofs. Both proofs
have similar structure. But the meta-level proof, because it is informal,
is easier to present first.

   Suppose that A is any list. We need to show that

A3   Append(A,nil,A) <—

can be proved using (A1) and (A2). The proof is by induction on the
structure of A. If A is nil, then there is a one-step proof of (A3) using
(A1) alone. If A is B.A', then by the induction hypothesis there is some
n-step proof of

              Append(A',nil,A') <— .

By adding an extra step to the proof, using (A2), we obtain an n+1 step
proof of

              Append(x.A', nil, x.A') <—

for any x and therefore a proof of (A3) in particular.

   For the object level proof, it is necessary to express an induction
schema for lists in the object language.

A4   F(x) <— List(x) & F(nil) & $\forall y \forall z$ [F(z) —> F(y.z)]

where F(x) is any formula containing free occurrences of only the
variable x, and F(t), for any term t, is obtained by replacing all free
occurrences of x in F by t. The object level proof can be carried out in
clausal form; but a non-clausal proof is more natural. We negate the
theorem to be proved and reason backward from the goal:

A5   List(A) <—
                <— Append(A,nil,A)

By A4, letting F(x) be Append(x,nil,x):

                <— List(A), Append(nil,nil,nil),
                $\forall y \forall z$ [Append(z,nil,z) —> Append(y.z, nil, y.z)]

By A5 and A1:

                <— $\forall y \forall z$ [Append(z,nil,z) —> Append(y.z, nil, y.z)]

This reduces to an assertion and a subgoal:

A6   Append(A',nil,A') <—

```
          <— Append(B.A', nil, B.A')
    A2
          <— Append(A',nil,A')
    A6
             □
```

    The method ' of proving properties of logic programs by means of induction axioms expressed in the object language has been developed by Clark and Tarnlund [1977].

The monotonicity criticism of logical consequence

    Logic has often been the subject of criticism. One of the most recent and influential of these criticisms is that formulated by Minsky [1975] concerning the monotonicity of logical consequence.

    Consider again the blocks world example

```
On1          On(A,B)   <—
On2          On(D,A)   <—
On3          On(D,C)   <—
             Clear(y)  <— not-∃x On(x,y)
```

supplemented by the unstated only-if half of the definition of the On relation. These assumptions imply the conclusion

Clear(D) <— .

The monotonicity of logical consequence entails that the same conclusion continues to hold no matter what new assumptions are added. In particular, if we add the new assumption

On4   On(E,D)   <—

the previous conclusion that D is clear still holds, even though it is obviously inconsistent with the new information.

    The critics argue that the monotonicity of logical consequence contradicts common sense. Given the new assumption On(E,D) <— common sense abandons the previous conclusion Clear(D) <— . Logic, because it requires that the conclusion continues to hold, is unacceptable as a model of human reasoning.

    The argument is mistaken, in our opinion, because it oversimplifies what is involved when a new assumption is added to a logic database. We shall argue in the last chapter that, when a database becomes inconsistent, consistency needs to be restored by rejecting or suitably modifying an assumption in the database. In this example, either we reject the new information or we reject or modify the only-if half of the definition of the On relation. It is probably most natural either to replace the original only-if assumption by the new assumption that only

Onl-4 define the On relation or else to abandon the only-if assumption
altogether. In either case the previous conclusion Clear(D) <— no longer
holds in the new database.

Logic avoids the monotonicity criticism of logical consequence, if
proper account is taken of only-if assumptions and a realistic view is
taken of the way in which databases change in time.

Exercises

1) Use the only-if half of the definition of factorial together with
the assumption
$$<— \emptyset = u+1$$
to show that the only factorial of $\emptyset$ is 1.

2) Show that

not-Append(nil, a.nil, nil)

is a consequence of the iff-definition of the Append relation. Compare
the object language and meta-language proofs and identify the axioms of
equality needed for the object language proof.

3) Transform assumptions On4-8 into clausal form and use resolution to
show that

Clear(D)

is a consequence.

4) Show by means of resolution and factoring that

Append(A,nil,A)

is implied by the iff definition of Append together with the appropriate
induction and equality axioms expresed in clausal form.

5) Using negation as failure, reformulate the definions of arch and
tower given in Chapter 4 so that the problem
$$<— Arch(w)$$
has only two solutions

$$w = a(t(B,A), D, C) \text{ and}$$
$$w = a(C, D, t(B,A))$$

for the scene described by A4-12.

   6) Given the Horn clauses

                Append(nil,x,x) <—
                Appned(x.y, z, x.u) <— Append(y,z,u)
                Member(x, x.y) <—
                Member(x, y.z) <— Member(x,z)

show by means of induction in the meta-language that

                for all x, u, v and w,
                if Append(u,v,w) and Member(x,w)
                then Member(x,u) or Member(x,v).

   7)   a) Given the assumptions

N1   x ⊆ y <— not-Nosub(x,y)
N2   Nosub(x,y) <— z ∈ x, not-[z ∈ y]

                   a ∈ A <—
                   a ∈ B <—
                   b ∈ B <—

show that   A ⊆ B

interpreting negation as failure.

       b)   Let membership in the sets A and B be expressed by means
            of Horn clauses. Discuss the circumstances under which it
            can be shown that

       i)   A ⊆ B

       ii) ∅ ⊆ B
            where there is no clause expressing membership in ∅

       iii) A ⊆ U
            given x ∈ U <—

       iv) A ⊆ A.

CHAPTER 12

Formalisation of Provability

The meta-language interpretation of "only-if" and its combination with the object language can be achieved by formalising the meta-language and amalgamating it with the object language. Such a combination of object language and meta-language produces a system of logic which is closer to natural language than the conventional systems which keep the two languages distinct. In natural language, however, the combination of object language and meta-language leads to such paradoxes as the self-referential sentence:

This sentence is false.

We shall see that the attempt to reconstruct the paradoxes in the amalgamated formal language leads instead to a true but unprovable sentence:

This sentence is unprovable.

The construction and proof of unprovability are based on those in Gödel's proof of the incompleteness of formal arithmetic [Gödel 1931]. Instead of the incompleteness of arithmetic, however, we have the impossibility of any attempt to completely formalise the notion of provability. The proof of incompleteness, moreover, is simpler for provability than it is for arithmetic.

Our purpose in combining the object language and meta-language, however, is primarily a practical one. The amalgamated language is more expressive and has greater problem-solving power than the object language alone. It provides essential facilities for such applications of logic programming as natural language understanding, database management, job control and editing of programs.

The amalgamated language combines object language and meta-language while preserving the normal semantics of logic. Thus all of the theory of problem-solving, formulated in the previous chapters for the object language alone, applies without change to the more powerful combination of object language and meta-language.

The combination of object language and meta-language is a special case of a more general construction. Given any two languages (i.e. systems of logic with their associated proof procedures) it may be possible to simulate the proof procedure of one language L_1 within the other L_2. The simulation is accomplished by defining in L_2 the binary relationship which holds when a conclusion can be derived from assumptions in L_1. Sentences in L_1 need to be named by terms in L_2 and the provability relation needs to be named by a binary predicate symbol, say

"Demonstrate", and defined by means of sentences Pr   in L_2. Provided the definition   Pr   correctly represents the provability relation of L_1, simulation by means of Pr in L_2 is equivalent to direct execution of the proof procedure of L_1. L_2, the language in which   Pr   simulates L_1, is a meta-language for the object language L_1. To serve as meta-language, L_2 needs to possess sufficient expressive power. For any object language, the language of Horn clauses is already adequate.

There are a number of cases of special interest. In the case in which the meta-language is restricted to the Horn clause subset of logic, but the object language encompasses the whole standard form, the meta-language improves its own problem-solving abilities by simulating the more powerful object language. In general, a simple unsophisticated problem-solver can improve itself by using simulation to behave like a more sophisticated one.

In the case in which the object language and meta-language are identical the single language augmented by the definition Pr of its own provability relation is an amalgamation of an object language with its meta-language.

Correct representability

The condition of correct representability is the same in principle for the definition of the provability relation as it is for the definition of the addition of natural numbers.

In order to define addition in logic, it is necessary to name numbers by means of terms. The easiest way to name the non-negative integers, for example, is by means of a constant symbol 0 for zero and a one-place function symbol s for the successor function.

> If t names the integer n
> then s(t) names the integer n+1.

The following Horn clause definition correctly represents the addition relation, named by the predicate symbol "Plus".

Plus1   Plus(0,x,x) <—
Plus2   Plus(s(x),y,s(z)) <— Plus(x,y,z)

Plus1-2 correctly represents the addition relation in the sense that

> whenever l, m and n are non-negative integers named by r,
> s and t respectively, the relationship l+m = n holds if-
> and-only-if Plus1-2 implies Plus(r,s,t) <— .

Notice that correct representability does not require that

> Plus1-2 implies ¬Plus(r,s,t) <— when l+m = n does not
> hold.

In order to define provability it is necessary to name sentences and other expressions by means of terms. This can be accomplished in a variety of ways and we shall not concern ourselves with the details here.

Given a representation of sentences by means of terms, a definition Pr
in a language L_2 correctly represents the provability relation, named
"Demonstrate", of a language L_1 if-and-only-if

> whenever X and Y are sentences of L_1 named by terms X' and
> Y' of L_2 respectively, conclusion Y can be derived from
> assumptions   X   in L_1 if-and-only-if   conclusion
> Demonstrate(X',Y') can be derived from assumptions Pr   in
> L_2.

Correct representability, however, does not require that   Pr   implies
¬Demonstrate(X',Y') in L_2 when X does not imply Y in L_1.

  Given a language L_1, the construction of a definition which correctly
represents its proof procedure is not a particularly difficult matter.
Since proof procedures can be implemented by means of computer programs,
they can be implemented by means of Horn clause programs in particular.
Moreover, any Horn clause program which correctly implements a proof
procedure correctly represents its provability relation.

A simple definition of a provability relation

  We shall present the top-level of a Horn clause definition of the
provability relation for a Horn clause language in which assumptions are
regarded as programs and conclusions as collections of goals. In order to
increase readability, we use lower case character strings, such as

>   prog, goals, sub,

as variables and ones beginning with an upper case character, such as

>   NIL, Zeus, A,

as constants.

  The first clause of the program states that

> any program demonstrates the solvability of an
> empty collection of goals.

The second clause, interpreted top-down, says that

> to demonstrate the solvability of a collection of goals:
> select a goal;
> find an appropriate procedure in the program;
> rename the variables in the procedure so that they are
> distinct from the variables in the collection of goals;
> match the selected goal with the head of the procedure;
> add the body of the procedure to the rest of the goals;
> apply the matching substitution to obtain a new collection
> of goals; and
> demonstrate that the program solves the new collection of
> goals.

```
D1              Demonstrate(prog,goals) <- Empty(goals)
D2              Demonstrate(prog,goals) <- Select(goals,goal,rest),
                                           Member(procedure,prog),
                                           Renamevars(procedure,goals,
                                                      procedure'),
                                           Parts(procedure',head,body),
                                           Match(goal,head,sub),
                                           Add(body,rest,intergoals),
                                           Apply(intergoals,sub,newgoals),
                                           Demonstrate(prog,newgoals)
```

To complete the definition it is necessary to define the lower-level relations and to settle upon data structures for naming programs, goals, collections of goals and substitutions. Rather than define these in general, we shall present only an interface for the top-level with a simple data structure for the problem of the fallible Greek.

We shall name an atomic formula whose predicate symbol is named P and list of arguments is named t by the term

                    atom(P,t).

Bodies of procedures and collections of goals are named by lists of the names of the atomic formulae they contain. Programs and procedures are named by constants. The following clauses define the interface between the top-level of the definition of Demonstrate and the data structures for the problem of the fallible Greek.

```
              Member(F1, F) <-
              Member(F2, F) <-
              Member(F3, F) <-
              Member(F4, F) <-
              Parts(F1, atom(Fallible,X.NIL), atom(Human,X.NIL).NIL) <-
              Parts(F2, atom(Human,Turing.NIL), NIL) <-
              Parts(F3, atom(Human,Socrates.NIL), NIL) <-
              Parts(F4, atom(Greek,Socrates.NIL), NIL) <-
```

The top-level goal is described by the clause

        <- Demonstrate(F, atom(Fallible,X.NIL).atom(Greek,X.NIL).NIL).

The constant symbol X names the variable x.

Direct execution versus simulation

Let Pr consist of the clauses D1-2 together with whatever lower-level clauses are needed to complete the definition of Demonstrate. Suppose that Pr correctly represents the provability relation of a language L_1 and is expressed in a language L_2 (which may be identical to L_1). Correct representability guarantees that direct execution in L_1 and simulation in L_2 are equivalent and interchangable:

Given sentences X and Y of L_1 named by terms X' and Y'
respectively of L_2, direct execution of   the proof
procedure of L_1 to determine whether Y can be derived from
X in L_1 is equivalent to simulation of L_1 by showing that
Demonstrate(X',Y') can be derived from Pr in L_2.

The equivalence of direct execution and simulation is identical to the
reflection principles investigated by Weyhrauch [1978].

  Correct representability of the provability relation means that the
object language and meta-language can cooperate to solve problems. A
problem in the object language can be solved by simulation in the meta-
language. Conversely, a problem of the form

          Demonstrate(X',Y')

in the meta-language can be solved by showing that

          Y can be derived from X

in the object language. This has the advantage that direct execution is
generally more efficient than simulation in the meta-language.

  Simulation in the meta-language, however, can be more powerful than
direct execution. It may be possible, in particular, to replace several
proofs of different, but similar, theorems in the object language by a
single proof in the meta-language. As a trivial example, all of the
problems below need to be solved separately in the object language, but
can be solved once and for all in the meta-language.

          Mortal(Socrates) <—   can be derived from
          Human(Socrates) <—   and
          Mortal(x) <— Human(x)

          Poisonous(♄) <—   can be derived from
          Boletus(♄) <—   and
          Poisonous(x) <— Boletus(x)

          Animal(Puff) <—   can be derived from
          Dragon(Puff) <—   and
          Animal(x) <— Dragon(x)

In the meta-language it is possible with a single proof to show that

          for any variable x, predicate symbols P and Q,
          and term t of the object language,

          Q(t) <—   can be derived from
          P(t) <—   and
          Q(x) <— P(x).

  The meta-language is more powerful than the object language in another
sense. The object-level proof procedure can only show that

          X can be derived from Y

when both X and Y are given as input. The meta-level proof procedure, however, can solve Demonstrate goals of any pattern of input and output.

Given, for example, an appropriate definition of what constitutes an interesting sentence, the meta-level goal statement

$$\leftarrow \text{Demonstrate}(X',y), \text{Interesting}(y)$$

can be used, in theory at least, to generate interesting consequences of a given set of assumptions X. Moreover, by solving the two problems cooperatively rather than sequentially, it is possible for the criteria characterising interesting sentences to guide the generation of consequences of X.

The goal statement

$$\leftarrow \text{Demonstrate}(t,Y'),$$

where Y' names a given consequence and t is a partially instantiated term which names a given collection of assumptions X together with unknown additional assumptions x, can be used to find the missing assumptions x. The goal statement

$$\leftarrow \text{Demonstrate}(t,Y_1'),\text{Demonstrate}(t,Y_2'),...,\text{Demonstrate}(t,Y_m')$$

moreover, can be used to find missing assumptions which together with the given assumptions X imply all of the conclusions $Y_1,Y_2,...,Y_m$. In the simplest case, if the conclusions are sufficiently similar, the missing assumptions may be an inductive generalisation of the conclusions. Provided the proof procedure is sufficiently constrained it will avoid generating useless assumptions such as $Y_1\&Y_2\&...\&Y_m$, which trivially imply the conclusions.

Addition and suppression of assumptions

Languages in the PLANNER family and most versions of PROLOG achieve some of the power of the Demonstrate relation by providing facilities for adding and suppressing statements during the course of a demonstration. Instead of explicitly trying to solve a goal of the form

$$\text{Demonstrate}(X',Y')$$

in these languages it is necessary to

> add the statements X to the program,
> try to show Y, and then
> suppress X afterwards.

Since assumptions change dynamically during the course of a single demonstration, such programs can be exceedingly dangerous.

Addition and suppression of assumptions can be accomplished more safely by means of the Demonstrate relation. Moreover, efficiency can be achieved by directly executing the proof procedure recursively on the same machine or cooperatively on another machine instead of simulating it with the definition. On the other hand, Demonstrate goals of other

input-output patterns, which can not be solved by addition and
suppression of assumptions, can be solved by using the definition.
Addition and suppression of assumptions can only be used when the object
language and meta-language are the same. But, provided the meta-language
is sufficiently powerful, the Demonstrate relation can be used to connect
any two languages.

Bootstrapping

The meta-language L_2 may differ in sophistication from the object
language L_1. If it is less sophisticated to start with, then it can use
its definition Pr of provability in L_1 to simulate L_1 and to increase
its own sophistication. This is bootstrapping: the language L_2 pulling
itself up by its own bootstraps, using the definition Pr to solve
problems more intelligently than it would otherwise, acting the way it
thinks a more intelligent proof procedure would behave.

Bootstrapping can be effective even if the more sophisticated language
L_1 does not have an independent existence of its own. The definition, if
it is consistent, can serve as a construction which causes the language
L_1 to come into existence.

Bootstrapping, and more generally, defining an implementation of one
language within another is a common technique in computing. An
implementation of a language is created by writing a program which
functions as a translator or interpreter for it in another existing
language.

The clauses D1-2, which define the top-level of a Horn clause proof
procedure L_1 can be used to bootstrap a simple top-down Horn clause proof
procedure L_2 which executes procedure calls sequentially in the order in
which they are are written. By means of appropriate definitions of the
rest of the program and of the procedure Select in particular, it is
possible to define a proof procedure which executes procedure calls
cooperatively. Although L_2 executes procedure calls sequentially, the new
proof procedure L_1 executes procedure calls as coroutines according to
the criteria specified in the procedure Select. By appropriate
modification of the definition, other improvements, such as loop
detection, intelligent backtracking and goal transformation, can also be
incorporated in the new proof procedure L_1. More modestly, the definition
of Demonstrate might only enhance the input syntax of L_2, defining infix
notation for predicate symbols and function symbols, for example. More
ambitiously, it might define a proof procedure for a richer version of
logic, full clausal form or standard form, for example.

PROLOG systems and programs have used the bootstrapping technique
since their first implementation in 1972 in Marseille. They have been
used primarily for improving the input syntax and for coroutining. A
variety of Horn clause programs defining Horn clause provability have
also been written at Imperial College. Simple Horn clause programs
typically run about 100 times slower when simulated by using such
definitions than they do when executed directly. PROLOG programs have
also been written for non-Horn clause provability and by Broda for the
standard form of logic. The PROLOG compiler written in PROLOG by
Warren, Pereira, and Pereira [1977] and Colmerauer's [1977] interpreter

for a restricted subset of natural language can also be regarded as applications of bootstrapping.

Combining the object language and meta-language

So far we have assumed an asymmetric relationship between the two languages L_1 and L_2. There is no reason in principle, however, why one language should know more about its companion than the other. Both languages might possess a definition of the other's proof procedure. Each language could serve as the other's meta-language and could simulate its proof procedure.

There is no reason either why the two languages should not be identical in all respects. It is possible therefore to have a single language equipped with a definition Pr which is a correct representation of its own proof procedure. Given a problem of the form

Demonstrate(X',Y')

it can use the definition to simulate itself or equivalently it can show that

Y can be demonstrated from X

directly. Solving the problem by direct execution is equivalent to the proof procedure calling itself recursively.

Such a relationship between object language and meta-language is already familiar in the programming language LISP [McCarthy et al 1962]. The function of a LISP interpreter or compiler is

to evaluate an expression y in an environment x, which defines the values of the symbols occurring in y, producing a result z which is the value of y in the environment x.

In functional notation this can be expressed

eval(x,y) = z,

which is like Demonstrate, except that the additional parameter z names the output. We shall argue later that it is useful to extend Demonstrate to a four argument relation

Demonstrate(x,y,u,z)

which holds when

given the assumptions named x,
the conclusion named y and
the control named u,
the proof procedure generates the output named z.

The function eval can be defined in LISP, like Demonstrate can be defined in logic. In the same way that Demonstrate-goals with appropriate

input can be solved either by using the definition or by direct
execution, eval-function calls can be evaluated in LISP either by using
the definition of eval or by recursive invocation of the LISP evaluation
mechanism. Since LISP functions have fixed input parameters, explicit use
of the definition of eval can always be relaced by recursive invocation.
Indeed, it was a study of the analogue in logic of eval in LISP which led
the author and Ken Bowen to propose the amalgamation of object language
and meta-language presented in this chapter.

Incompleteness of the combined object and meta-language

The combination of object language and meta-language avoids the
paradoxes of self-reference in natural language. The attempt to
reconstruct them leads instead to the construction of a true but
unprovable sentence:

D   ¬ Demonstrate(Pr',D)

which mentions its own name D. The term Pr' names the definition Pr of
Demonstrate.

It is easy to show that, if Pr is consistent and correctly
represents the provability relation, then neither the sentence named D
nor its denial can be derived from Pr.

Proof:
Consider the two cases:

(1) The sentence named D can be derived from Pr.
(2) Its denial Demonstrate(Pr',D) can be derived from Pr.

Case(1) By the assumption of correct representability, (1)
implies that

Demonstrate(Pr',D) can be derived from Pr. But then
both the sentence and its denial can be derived from
Pr, contradicting the assumption that Pr is
consistent.

Case(2) By the assumption of correct representability (2)
implies that

the sentence named D can be derived from Pr.

Again, both the sentence and its denial can be derived from Pr,
contradicting the assumption that Pr is consistent.

Since both cases lead to contradiction, neither the sentence
named D nor its denial can be derived from Pr.

But the proposition

The sentence named D can be derived from Pr.

or equivalently (by correct representability)

> Demonstrate(Pr',D)

is either true or false of the provability relation. We have just shown
(Case 1) it is not true. Therefore its denial

D   ¬ Demonstrate(Pr',D)

is true, though unprovable.

The sentence named D is related to negation interpreted as failure.
Given the problem

> Demonstrate(Pr',D)

the proof procedure neither succeeds nor fails in finite time. (Finite
failure would imply that

D   ¬ Demonstrate(Pr',D)

could be proved from the iff-definition of Pr.) Thus the proof procedure
does not terminate in its attempt to solve the problem, and therefore its
denial

D   ¬ Demonstrate(Pr',D)

truly states that the problem cannot be solved.

The sentence named D can be constructed in a variety of ways including
the one used in Gödel's original incompleteness proof.

More comprehensive form of the Demonstrate relation

To simplify the discussion we have assumed that a proof procedure
determines a two-place relation between assumptions and conclusions. In
reality proof procedures are more complicated. They also accept control
specifications which guide the proof strategy and they return output. It
is more realistic, therefore, to regard a proof procedure as determining
a four-place relation

> Demonstrate(x,y,u,z)

which holds when

> given the assumptions named x,
> the conclusion named y and
> control named u,
> the proof procedure generates the output named z.

The control parameter u might specify, for example,

> (1)   whether one proof method or another should be applied,
> (2)   whether one, all or "best" solutions are required, and
> (3)   whether a proof, trace of the search,

substitution for variables in the conclusion, or
simple Yes-No answer is required for the output z.

The trace of a proof procedure consists of the sequence of sentences
and other expressions generated by the proof procedure during the course
of searching for a solution. Thus the proof procedure may successfully
return as output the trace of an unsuccessful search for a solution. It
may also return a simple No-answer if it can determine that the search
space contains no solutions.

The more comprehensive form of the Demonstrate relation is useful for
obtaining and processing lists of all solutions. This is especially
useful in database applications to count all answers to a query or to
print the list of all answers as a table. Given a Horn clause database S
of suppliers and parts, for example, the Demonstrate relation can be used
both to formulate and answer the question

How many suppliers of stationery are located in London?

<- Demonstrate(S, atom(Supplies,X.Stationery.NIL).
                   atom(Location,X.London.NIL).NIL, all(X),z),
   Count(z,w).

Here all(X) specifies that a list of all distinct answers, consisting of
substitutions for the variable X, is required for the output z.
Count(z,w) can be defined by

Count(NIL, 0) <-
Count(u.v, w) <- Count(v,w'), Plus(w',1,w).

Instead of counting the list of all answers, a procedure

Format(z,w)

could rearrange the list z, inserting new page, new line and space
characters, so that the resulting list w, when printed, has the
appearance of a table.

Exercises

1) The top-level D1-2 of the definition of the Horn clause provability
relation can be tested for the problem of the Fallible Greek without
defining the lower-level procedures in full. It suffices to supply
assertions which solve the sub-problems which arise during the course of
trying to solve the top-level problem. The following assertions are
sufficient for renaming the procedures F1-4 and for finding the parts of
the resulting procedures.

Renamevars(F1, goals, F1') <-
Renamevars(F2, goals, F2) <-
Renamevars(F3, goals, F3) <-
Renamevars(F4, goals, F4) <-
Parts(F1', atom(Fallible,Y), atom(Human,Y).NIL) <-

a)   Supply assertions or simple procedures for the remaining
     conditions in Dl-2.

b)   Using the assertions and simple procedures from (a), test
     Dl-2 for the problem of the Fallible Greek by using top-
     down inference and backtracking to find a solution.

2) Complete the definition Dl-2 of the Demonstrate relation by
defining the lower-level procedures in full.   For this purpose it is
useful to employ a different data structure for naming expressions of the
object language:

a)   Predicate symbols and function symbols can be named by
     constant symbols.

b)   Constant symbols can be named by terms const(t) where t
     names a number, e.g. $\emptyset$, s($\emptyset$), ... etc.

c)   Variables can be named by terms var(t) where t names a
     number.

d)   Composite terms can be named by terms of the form
     term(s,t) where s names a function symbol and t names a
     list of terms.

e)   Atoms and lists of atoms in goal statements and procedure
     bodies can be named as before.

f)   Procedures can be named by terms proc(s,t) where s names
     the head and t the body of the procedure.

g)   Programs can be named by lists of the procedures they
     contain.

h)   Substitutions can be named by lists of substitution
     components of the form sub(s,t) where s names a variable
     and t names a term.

Notice that a simple way to rename the variables in a procedure is to

i)   find T the maximum t such that var(t) occurs in the goals
     and

ii) replace every occurrence of a variable var(s) in the
     procedure by an occurrence of the variable var(r) where
     r = s+T.

The simple definition of the Match relation

          Match(expr1,expr2,sub) $\leftarrow$ Apply(expr1,sub,expr3),
                                   Apply(expr2,sub,expr3)

is liable to go into a loop when the two expressions do not match. A
safer definition is the one which employs two substitution parameters,
one for the current substitution which matches the parts of the two
expressions which have been examined so far and another for the final

matching substitution.

3) Modify   the definition   of the   Demonstrate relation,   defining the
relationship

Demonstrate(prog,goals,sub)

which holds when   the program solves the goals   and generates a
substitution of terms for the variables occurring in the goal as a
solution.

This can be done at the top-level simply by adding extra conditions to
D2. The substitution required in the head of the clause can be obtained
by appropriately combining the substitution obtained by the recursive
call to the Demonstrate procedure in the body of the clause together with
the output component of the substitution which matches the selected goal
with the head of the procedure.

4) Define   the top-level of   a deterministic$_1$ Horn clause interpreter
for Horn clause programs. The interpreter can be made deterministic by
explicitly managing the search through the top-down search space one
branch at a time.

Branches of a search space can be represented by lists of nodes. Each
node consists of

    i)   the list of goals at the node,

    ii) the selected goal, and

    iii) the list of untried procedures which have not yet been
         applied to the goal.

To solve the initial collect of goals, process the branch whose only
node consists of the initial goal statement, selected goal and the
appropriate list of untried procedures.

Any program successfully processes a branch whose tip contains the
empty list of goals.

To process a branch whose tip node contains a non-empty list of
untried procedures for the selected goal try to match the goal with the
head of the first untried procedure.

    i)   If the match fails, remove the procedure from the list of
        untried procedures and process the new branch.

    ii) If the match succeeds, remove the procedure from the list
        of untried procedures, add a new tip containing the new
        goal statement obtained by applying the successful
        procedure, and process the new branch.

To process a branch whose tip node has an empty list of untried
procedures for its selected goal, backtrack by deleting the tip from the
branch and processing the new branch.

5) Show that for any set of clauses S there exists a corresponding set of Horn clauses S* such that S is consistent (or inconsistent) if and only if S* is.   Thus any problem which can be expressed in clausal form can be expressed by means of Horn clauses using the correspondence *.

The correspondence can be established by showing that the provability relation for clauses in general can be defined by means of Horn clauses.

CHAPTER 13

Logic, Change and Contradiction

Logic can be used to represent information and to solve problems. But information changes and its representation needs to change accordingly. In this chapter we consider the processes by means of which an information system needs to change in time. The information systems considered include not only programs and databases but also more complex systems of the kind involved in scientific theories and computer-based natural language understanding. We shall consider in detail the role that contradiction plays in guiding the direction of change.

Information systems

Throughout this chapter the terminology information system, and sometimes belief system, is used to refer to any collection of assumptions (or beliefs) expressed in logic together with a proof procedure and maintenance procedures, which manage the way the information system deals with change.

Information systems include both assumptions which are explicit as well as consequences which are implicit. In practice whether a sentence is an implicit consequence is a matter of degree. The accessibility of a consequence depends upon the complexity of finding a derivation. The more complex the derivation, the more inaccessible its consequence. If a derivation is too complex, its consequence is as inaccessible as if it were not implied at all. Thus different information systems may entail the same logical consequences but differ significantly in their pragmatic value. Useful consequences may be efficiently accessible in one system but practically inaccessible in another.

Databases can be regarded as simple information systems. A database might change as the result of internal reorganisation or in response to incoming data and queries. The proof procedure is used not only to answer queries but also to assimilate new data into the database. There are four possibilities:

> The new data might already be implied by the database,
> imply existing data,
> be independent from it, or
> inconsistent with it.

It is the last case which is most important. It includes both the case in which new data violates integrity constraints as well as the one in which it is an exception to a general rule.

Programs together with their specifications can also be regarded as information systems. A program which is inconsistent with its specification can be made consistent by modifying either the program or the specification. A program which is consistent with its specification can be changed by replacing an inefficient procedure with a more efficient one. It can also be changed by adapting it to a different purpose.

In text comprehension, the information system consists of the reader's understanding of the text which has been read so far. It needs to change when new information needs to be assimilated. The new information might be the reader's interpretation of the next sentence in the text or it might be an hypothesis needed to explain information previously obtained from the text. In both cases the new information might be one among several alternatives. The new sentence might be ambiguous and admit alternative interpretations or the previous information might be explained by alternative hypotheses. If the new information is inconsistent with the current information system an alternative to the new information or to previously assimilated information may need to be considered.

Scientific theories can be interpreted as information systems which organise past experience and predict future ones. A theory may need to change in the light of new experience or as the result of a new hypothesis. An ambiguous experience can be reported in alternative ways, and alternative hypotheses might explain the same phenomena. The alternatives need to be compared by evaluating their effect on the state of the scientific theory as a whole. If an alternative renders the theory inconsistent then consistency can be restored by restricting or suitably modifying any of the premises which contribute to the contradiction. This includes both the case in which the new sentence is rejected and replaced by an alternative as well as the one in which the new sentence is accepted and an old one is rejected instead.

Dynamics of information system change

Both the situation in which an information system records its interaction with the environment and the situation in which it generates its own hypotheses result in the need to assimilate new information. There are four possible deductive relationships between the new information and the current information system. Each possibility suggests different candidates for the new system.

(1) The new information can already be derived from the current information system. The information system successfully anticipates the new information and the new system is the same as the old one. Assumptions which participate in the derivation can be identified and their utility can be evaluated. More generally, assumptions can be evaluated by assessing the extent to which they contribute to the derivation of useful consequences. The evaluation of assumptions according to utility can be used later to help determine which assumptions should be abandoned or modified when a contradiction occurs.

(2) Part of the information in the current system can be derived from the new information together with the information in the rest of the

system. The explicit assumptions of the new system consist of the new information together with the explicit assumptions of the old system without the part that can be derived. The new system subsumes the old one. It implies the same consequences and possibly new ones as well. The assessed utility of the assumptions which participate in the derivations can be increased by an amount which takes into consideration the number of derived consequences, the complexity of the derivations and the utility of the derived consequences themselves.

The simplest example is the one in which the new information is an inductive generalisation of existing information. The situation in which it is an abductive assumption [Peirce 1931] is more complicated. Suppose, for example, that the current system already contains the information

(1)   A & B & C <— D
(2)   A

Then the new information

            D

is an abductive hypothesis. Together with (1) it implies (2). Moreover, it also implies B and C. In order to justify its incorporation into the information system, the hypothesis D may need to prove its utility. It can do so, for example, by showing that B or C is already redundantly contained in the existing database or by predicting them when they are introduced as new information later on. Generation of abductive hypotheses is similar to reasoning by means of defaults [Minsky 1975], [Reiter 1978b]. If A is given, then D is assumed by default unless it leads to contradiction or does not lead to sufficiently many useful consequences.

Notice that cases (1) and (2) might both apply. Whether one case is better than the other depends upon the overall utility of the resulting information system.

(3) The new information is consistent with the information system but is independent of it. The new information can neither be derived from the current system nor be used to derive existing information. This is potentially an undesirable situation which may lead the system to seek an explanatory hypothesis, which together with the information in the rest of the system implies the new information. Of course, the hypothesis itself would also be independent and to justify its acceptance would have to imply other useful consequences in addition to the one which motivated its generation. The preceding example illustrates the situation. Suppose the information system contains the assumption

         A & B & C <— D

and the new information A is independent. If this leads the system to generate the hypothesis D, then D itself is independent and there is no net gain unless at least one of the additional consequences B or C can be independently confirmed.

It is not always possible to determine in a reasonable time whether one or other of the four deductive relationships apply. In such cases,

whether the new information is logically related to the existing
information system or not, it will need to be treated as independent and
added to it.

(4) The new information is inconsistent with the information system.
A contradiction can be derived when the new information is introduced.
The assumptions which contribute to the refutation can be identified, and
consistency can be restored by rejecting or modifying one or more of the
assumptions which lead to the contradiction. The previous record of the
utility of assumptions can be used to help determine which assumptions
should be changed.

It is this last case, in which a contradiction occurs, which is the
most important.

Restoration of consistency

Contradiction and its reconciliation play an important role in
philosophy and in theories of problem-solving. It is the driving force
behind change (thesis, antithesis and synthesis) in the Hegelian
dialectic and the main instrument for advancing knowledge (conjectures
and refutations [Popper 1963] and proofs and counter-examples [Lakatos
1973]) in the Popperian philosophy of science and mathematics. In
problem-solving, it is an advanced form of intelligent backtracking and
an important component of truth maintenance problem-solving systems
[Doyle 1978], [Stallman and Sussman 1977].

It is a major feature of Quine's [1953] argument against the
distinction between necessary and contingent truths that, when a
contradiction arises, consistency can be restored by rejecting or
modifying any assumption which contributes to the derivation of
contradiction. No belief is immune from possible alteration. Even the
laws of mathematics and logic, to the extent that they are included among
the assumptions of information systems, are subject to critical
assessment and change.

This does not mean that any belief can be altered as easily as any
other. Psychological attachment and even computational commitment may
vary from one belief to another. Nor is it pragmatically desirable to
treat different beliefs the same. Some contribute to the derivation of
useful consequences more often than others; and some participate more
often in the derivation of contradictions. It benefits the well-
functioning of the belief system as a whole, therefore, to abandon, among
the beliefs which lead to contradiction, the one which contributes least
to the derivation of useful consequences. In the longer term, if
contradictions continue and the assessed utility of beliefs changes, it
may be necessary to backtrack, reinstate a previously abandoned belief
and abandon an alternative instead.

Thus the derivation of inconsistency contributes to the search space
of alternative information systems. For each assumption which contributes
to the derivation of a contradiction there exists at least one
alternative new belief system obtained by abandoning or suitably
modifying the assumption. The space can be searched in depth-first
fashion, backtracking when a contradiction arises, or several branches

can be investigated in parallel. Parallel exploration of alternatives has the advantage that the consequences of abandoning a belief can be explored before a decision is made. Such parallel exploration of several internally consistent, but mutually inconsistent, belief systems may, of course, give an external observer the illusion of a single inconsistent system.

The derivation of inconsistencies plays an important role in the development of computer programs and databases. Generally, when an inconsistency arises between a program and its specification or between data and integrity constraints, it is the program or the data which is rejected. Indeed, by definition, it is a main function of specifications and integrity constraints to rule out incorrect programs and data. None the less there are frequent occasions when it is necessary to abandon or modify the specification or integrity constraint instead. For example, given the conflict which arises between the integrity constraint

No vehicles are allowed in the park.

and the need for police and other emergency services to have access to the park, it is likely that preference will be given to the police and that the integrity constraint will have to be modified instead:

No unauthorised vehicles are allowed in the park.

Preference is also given to incoming data when it is treated as an exception to general rules. Early versions of a university department's timetable, for example, might be described by ambitiously general rules:

All first year lectures are held in room 144.
All lectures attended by more than
80 students are held in room 145.

Subsequent additions to the database

The first year logic lectures
are attended by 100 students.

might result in contradiction. Consistency can be restored by treating the new data as an exception to a general rule, replacing the original rule by a more restricted one

All first year lectures, except
logic, are held in room 144.

Notice in this last example that the assumption which has been modified is not necessarily the one which has been least useful in the past. What matters in general is not simply the utility of a belief but rather the difference between its utility and that of its replacement. Treating new data as an exception to a general rule when a contradiction arises has the advantage of avoiding the contradiction while preserving most of the useful consequences of the existing information system.

Contradiction also plays an important role in text comprehension. It helps to disambiguate sentences by rejecting interpretations which are inconsistent with the current interpretation of the text-so-far, and it helps to reject inconsistent explanatory hypotheses. If all interpretations of a new sentence lead to contradiction, the system may attempt to restore consistency by altering a previous hypothesis or an interpretation of a previous sentence instead.

Perhaps the classical example in which an information system needs to cope with contradiction is the case in which the report of an empirical observation or experiment contradicts a scientific theory. Whether it is more beneficial to reject the report or a statement of the theory depends on the overall effect on the information system. It is even possible that several alternatives might lead to incomparable, equally viable, but mutually incompatible, theories.

As Lakatos [1974] argues, in a mature theory with a history of useful consequences it is generally more useful to reject an anomalous conflicting report than it is to abandon the theory as a whole.

But it is almost never the case that a whole theory needs to be abandoned anyway. A complex information system is a collection of cooperating individual beliefs, some of which are more useful and more firmly held than others. Propositions which reside in the central core of a theory are more firmly held than those which are located closer to the periphery, where rival hypotheses may coexist as mutually incompatible alternatives. Reports of empirical observations can help to accumulate evidence in favour of one alternative over another.

Even without restoring consistency, an inconsistent system can still organise useful information. Although in theory inconsistent assumptions imply any conclusion, in practice efficient proof procedures derive only relevant conclusions with varying degrees of accessibility. Indeed, it can be argued that practical provability, acheived by efficient resolution-based proof procedures, satisfies all of the criteria necessary for relevant entailment [Anderson and Belnap 1962].

Thus contradiction, far from harming an information system, helps to indicate areas in which it can be improved. It facilitates the development of systems by successive approximation - daring conjectures followed by refutation and reconciliation. It favours bold, easily falsified beliefs, which can be weakened if the need should arise, over safe, timid beliefs, which are difficult to strenthen later on. Better to make mistakes and to correct them than to make no progress at all.

A logic program for natural language

As a test of the theory of information systems outlined in this chapter, a logic program for managing a natural language front-end to a logic database has been designed by the author with Jacqueline Shane and Karen Ritchie. A pilot version is being implemented using a theorem-prover for the standard form of logic written by Krysia Broda.

The top-level of the program

$$Process(x,y,z,x')$$

starting with an initial logic database x, processes a list y of natural language input sentences, producing a correlated list z of output sentences, finishing with a new database x' at the end of the session.

```
Process (db, nil, nil, db) <-
Process (db, input.restin, output.restout, newdb) <-
        Represents (input, logic, control),
        Assimilate (db, logic, control, output, interdb),
        Process (interdb, restin, restout, newdb)
```

Here as in the previous chapter, lower case character strings (e.g. "db", "input", "restin") are variables.

Represents(input, logic, control) holds when the natural language input can be interpreted as consisting of a logic statement together with a control component.

Assimilate(db, logic, control, output, interdb) holds when assimilating the logic statement and associated control into the logic database results in an appropriate output and a new intermediate database.

    At the simplest level, control simply indicates whether a sentence is a declarative statement or a question. Here clause (1) deals with the case that the input is a question. The result of attempting to answer the question may or may not be a proof. (2) deals with the case that the input is a declarative sentence already implicitly contained in the database. In both cases, (1) and (2), assimilation of the new information does not change the database. In the case A3, the next database consists of the new information together with part (stay) of the existing database. The new database implies all the data in the part (go) of the old database which is no longer explicitly contained in the new database. A4 adds the new information to the database if it cannot be derived or be used to derive existing information. A5 deals with the case in which the new information is inconsistent with the current database. The new database results from analysing the proof of contradiction and restoring consistency.

```
A1  Assimilate(db,logic,control,output,db) <- Question(control),
                              Demonstrate(db,logic,control,result),
                              ExtractOutput(result,output)

A2  Assimilate(db,logic,control,output,db) <- Declarative(control),
                              Demonstrate(db,logic,control,result),
                              Proof(result), IAlreadyKnowThat(output)

A3  Assimilate(db,logic,control,output,nextdb) <- Declarative(control),
            db = stay ∪ go,
            nextdb = stay ∪ {logic},
            ∀data[data ∈ go ->
                  ∃result[Demonstrate(nextdb,data,control,result) &
                          Proof(result)]],
            ThanksForTellingMe(output)

A4  Assimilate(db,logic,control,output,nextdb) <- Declarative(control),
                              Independent(db,logic,control),
                              nextdb = db ∪ {logic},
                              Acknowledge(output)
```

A5 Assimilate(db,logic,control,output,nextdb) <− Declarative(control),
                          incon = db ∪ {logic},
                          Demonstrate(incon,□,control,result),
                          Proof(result),
              AnalyseFailureRestoreConsistency(incon,result,output,nextdb)

This is only a top-level sketch of part of the natural language program. Important lower level procedures need to be defined and specifications, such as A3, need to be transformed into efficient procedures.

Our intention has been to deal with a restricted subset of natural language suitable for untrained database users. However we do not insist that input sentences be completely unambiguous. Certain ambiguities can be dealt with by allowing Represents to be non-deterministic$_1$; others, such as those resulting from anaphora ("he","she","it",etc.), by adding extra parameters to the Represents relation in order to deal with the context of the previous natural language input.

For users interacting with a database it can be required that all information included in the database be described explicitly. Implicit assumptions, however, cannot be avoided in normal conversation and text comprehension, where hypothesis generation schemes, such as frames [Minsky 1975] and scripts [Schank 1975] are needed to fit sentences into a coherent framework. The natural language program can be extended, in theory at least, to accommodate the abductive generation of assumptions by adding extra procedures. Here, in the case that the input is independent from the existing database, clause A6 generates and adds to the database a new assumption which together with the rest of the database implies the new information. To be worth the effort, the new information must be sufficiently more useful than the incoming information itself.

A6 Assimilate(db,logic,control,output,nextdb) <− Declarative(control),
                          Independent(db,logic,control),
                          nextdb = db ∪ {newassump},
                          Demonstrate(nextdb,logic,control,result),
                          Proof(result),
                          newassump is more useful in db than logic,
                          Iassume(newassump,output)

Conclusion

The theory of information systems attempts to combine the traditional role which logic plays in epistemology and the philosophy of science with its new role in computing. It attempts to reconcile the use of logic without computational considerations with the use of complex, computer-based computational systems without logical foundations. By exploiting the computational interpretation of logic, it hopes to contribute to a more useful communication of techniques between logic and computing.

References

Amarel, S., [1966], On Machine Representations of Problems of Reasoning about Actions - the Missionaries and Cannibals Problem. Machine Intelligence 3, Edinburgh University Press, New York, (B. Meltzer and D. Michie, Eds.) pp. 131-171.

Anderson, A.R., Belnap, N.D., [1962], The Pure Calculus of Entailment. Journal of Symbolic Logic, Vol. 27, No.1, pp. 19-52.

Anderson, D.B., Hayes, P.J. [1972], An Arraignment of Theorem-proving or the Logicians' Folly. D.C.L. Memo No.54, University of Edinburgh.

Bergman, M., Kanoui, H. [1973], Application of Mechanical Theorem Proving to Symbolic Calculus. Third International Symposium on Advanced Computing Methods in Theoretical Physics, C.N.R.S., Marseilles, June 1973.

Bibel, W., [1976a], Synthesis of Strategic Definitions and their Control. Techn. Univ. München, Abt. Mathem., Bericht Nr. 7610.

[1976b], A Uniform Approach to Programming. Techn. Univ. München, Abtl. Mathem., Bericht Nr. 7633.

[1978], On Strategies for the Synthesis of Algorithms. Proc. AISB/GI Conf. on AI, Hamburg, July 18-20, 1978.

Bledsoe, W.W., [1971], Splitting and Reduction Heuristics in Automatic Theorem proving. Artificial Intelligence 2, pp. 55-77.

[1977], Non-resolution Theorem Proving. Artificial Intelligence, Vol 9. pp. 51-35.

Bobrow, D.G., Raphael, B., [1974], New Programming Languages for Artificial Intelligence Research. ACM Computing Surveys, Vol. 6, No.3. pp. 153-174.

Boyer, R.S., Moore, J.S., [1972], The Sharing of Structure in Theorem Proving Programs. Machine Intelligence 7, Edinburgh University Press, New York, (B. Meltzer and D. Michie, Eds.) pp. 101-116.

[1975], Proving Theorems about LISP Functions. J. ACM, Vol.22, No.1 pp. 129-144.

Brand, D., [1976], Analytic Resolution in Theorem Proving. Artificial Intelligence Vol. 7. pp. 285-318.

Brough, D.B., [1979], Loop Trapping in Logic Programs, Dep. Rep. 79/9 Dep. of Computing and Control, Imperial College, London.

Brown, F.M., [1973] The use of Several Models as a Refinement of Resolution with Sets of Horn Clauses. Department of Computational Logic, University of Edinburgh, Memo No. 63.

[1974], SLM. Dep. of Comp. Logic Memo No. 72, Univ. of Edinburgh.

[1977], A Theorem prover for Elementary Set Theory. International Joint Conference on Artificial Intelligence, 5,

Bruynooghe, M., [1976], An Interpreter for Predicate Logic Programs, Part 1. Report CW 10, Applied Maths and Programming Division, Katholieke Univ., Leuven, Belgium.

[1977], The Inheritance of Links in a Connection Graph and its Relation to Structure Sharing. Applied Mathematics and Programming Division, Katholieke Universiteit, Leuven, Belgium.

[1978], Intelligent Backtracking for an Interpreter of Horn Clause Logic Programs. Report CW 16. Applied Maths and Programming Division, Katholieke University, Louven, Belgium. Also in Proc. Colloqium on Mathematical Logic in Programming, Hungary, Sept. 1978.

Bundy, A., [1971], There Is No Best Proof Procedure. Sigart Newsletter, December 1971. p6.

[1976], My Experiences with Prolog. DAI Working Paper No. 12, University of Edinburgh.

(editor) [1978], Artificial Intelligence, Edinburgh University Press.

Bundy, A., Byrd, L., Luger, G., Mellish, C., Milne, R., Palmer, M., [1979], MECHO: A Program to Solve Mechanics Problems. DAI Working Paper No. 50, Univ. of Edinburgh.

Burstall, R.M., Darlington, J., [1977], Transformation for Developing Recursive Programs. J. ACM Vol.24 No.1. pp. 44-67.

Chang, C.L., [1976], DEDUCE: A Deductive Query Language for Relational Data Bases. Pattern Recognition and Artificial Intelligence (C. H. Chen Ed.), Academic Press, New York, pp. 108-134.

Chang, C.L., Lee, R.C.T., [1973], Symbolic Logic and Mechanical Theorem Proving. Academic Press, New York.

Chomsky, N., [1957], Syntactic Structures, Mouton and Co., The Hague.

Church, A., [1936], A Note on the Entscheidungsproblem. Journal of Symbolic Logic, Vol.1 pp. 40-41, Correction ibid., pp101-102.

Clark, K.L., [1978], Negation as Failure. Logic and Data Bases. (H. Gallaire and J. Minker, Eds.), Plenum Press, New York,, pp. 293-322.

Clark, K.L., Darlington, J., [1978], Algorithm Classification through Synthesis. To appear in Computer Journal.

Clark, K.L., McKeeman, W., Sickel, S., [1978], Logic Programming Applied to Numerical Integration. Technical Rep. 78-8-004, Univ. of

California Santa Cruz.

Clark, K.L., Tarnlund, S-A., [1977] A First Order Theory of Data and Programs. Proceedings IFIP 77, North Holland, pp. 939-944.

Clark, K.L., McCabe, F., [1979], Programmers' Guide to IC-Prolog. CCD Rep. 79/7, Imperial College, London.

Codd, E.F., [1970], A Relational Model for Large Shared Data Bases. CACM Vol. 13, No. 6 (June 1970), pp. 377-387.

[1972], Relational Completeness of Data Base Sublanguages. Data Base Systems (R. Rustin, Ed.), Prentice-Hall, Englewood Cliffs, N.J., pp. 65-98.

Coelho, H., Pereira, L., [1975], The Dialectic Development of GEOM, a PROLOG Geometry Theorem Prover. Dept. of Art. Int., Univ. of Edinburgh.

Colmerauer, A., [1973], Les systemes-Q ou un Formalisme pour Analyser et Synthetiser des Phrases sur Ordinateur. Publication Interne No.43, Dept. d'Informatique, Universite de Montreal.

[1977], An Interesting Natural Language Subset. Proc. Workshop on Logic and Data Bases. Toulouse.

[1978], Metamorphosis Grammars. Natural Language Communication with Computers, (L. Bolc, Ed.), Lecture Notes in Computer Science No. 63, Springer-Verlag, Berlin, Heidelberg, New York. pp. 133-189.

Colmerauer, A., Kanoui, H., Pasero, R., Roussel, P., [1973], Un Systeme de Comunication Homme-machine en Francais. Rapport, Groupe Intelligence Artificielle, Universite d'Aix Marseille, Luminy.

Cox, P., [1978], Locating the Source of Unification Failure. Proc. of 2nd National Conf. Canadian Soc. for Computational Studies of Intelligence, Toronto, pp. 20-29.

Cox., P., Pietrzykowski, T., [1976], A Graphical Deduction System. Department of Computer Science, University of Waterloo, Ontario, Canada.

Dahl, V., Sambuc, R., [1976], Un Systeme de Bases de Donnees en Logique du Premier Ordre, en Vue de sa Consultation en Langue Naturelle. Rapport, Groupe d' Intelligence Artificielle, Universite Marseille-Luminy.

Darlington, J., [1975], Application of Transformation to Program Synthesis. Proc. IRIA Symp. on Proving and Improving Programs, Arc-et-Senans, France, pp. 133-144.

Darlington, J., Burstall, R.M., [1976], A System that Automaticaly Improves Programs. Acta Informatica, Vol.6, pp. 41-60.

Darlington, J.L., [1969], Theorem Proving and Information Retrieval. Machine Intelligence 4, (B. Meltzer and D. Michie, Eds.), American Elsevier Co., New York.

Davies, J., [1973], Popler 1.5 Reference Manual. T.P.U. Report No. 1, University of Edinburgh, May 1973.

Dawson, C., Siklossy, L., [1977], The Role of Preprocessing in Problem -solving Systems. International Joint Conference on Artificial Intelligence, 5, pp. 465-471.

Deliyanni, A., Kowalski, R.A., [1979], Logic and Semantic Networks. Comm. ACM. Vol. 22, No. 3, pp. 184-192..

Derkson, J., Rulifson, J.F., Waldinger, R.J., [1972], QA4 Language Applied to Robot Planning. AFIPS Fall Joint Computer Conference, pp. 1181-1192.

Dijkstra, E.W., [1976], A Discipline of Programming. Prentice-Hall, Englewood Cliffs, New Jersey.

Doran, J.E., Michie, D., [1966], Experiments with the Graph Traverser Program. Proc.R. Soc.A., Vol.294. pp. 235-259.

Doyle, J., [1978], Truth Maintenance Systems for Problem Solving. TR-419, MIT AI Lab., Also IJCAI 5 pp. 247.

Earley, J., [1970], An Efficient Context-free Parsing Algorithm. CACM, pp. 94-102.

Elcock, E.W., Foster, J.M., Gray, P.M.D., McGregor, J.J., Murray, A. M., [1971], ABSET, a Programming Language Based on Sets: Motivation and Examples. Machine Intelligence 6, Edinburgh University Press, New York, (B. Meltzer and D. Michie, Eds.), pp. 467-492.

Ernst, G.W., [1971], The Utility of Independent Subgoals in Theorem Proving. Information and Control, April 1971.

Feldman, J.A., Low, J.R., Swinehart, D.C., Taylor, R.H., [1972], Recent Developments in SAIL - an Algol-based Language for Artificial Intelligence. IJCAI 5 pp. 235-246.

Fikes, R.E., Hendrix, G.G., [1975], A Network-based Knowledge Representation and its Natural Deduction System. SRI Memo.

Fikes, R.E., Nilsson, N.J., [1971], STRIPS: A New Approach to the Application of Theorem-proving to Problem Solving. Artificial Intelligence Vol 2., pp. 189-208.

Fillmore, C.J., [1968], The Case for Case. Universals in Linguistic Theory, (Bach and Harms, Eds.), Holt, Rinehart and Winston, Chicago.

Fishman, D.H., Minker, J., [1975], Pi - Representation. A Clause Representation for Parallel Search. Artificial Intelligence, Vol. 6, No.2, pp. 103-127.

Floyd, R.W., [1967], Assigning Meanings to Programs. Proc. Symposia in Applied Mathematics, Vol.19, American Maths Society, pp. 19-32.

Foster, J.M., [1970], Automatic Syntactic Analysis. Macdonald / Elsevier.

Foster, J.M., Elcock, E.W., [1969], ABSYS 1: An Incremental Compiler for Assertions. Machine Intelligence 4, Edinburgh University Press, New York, (B. Meltzer and D. Michie, Eds.). pp. 423-439.

Friedman, D.P., Wise, D.S., [1978], Aspects of Applicative Programming for parallel processing. IEEE Trans Comp. C-27 (April 78), pp. 289-296.

Futo, I, Darvas, F., Cholnoky, E., [1977], Practical Application of an AI Language 2. Proceedings of the Hungarian Conference on Computing, Budapest. pp. 385-400.

Futo, I, Darvas, F., Szeredi, P., [1978], The Application of PROLOG to the Development of QA and DBM Systems. Logic and Data Bases. (H. Gallaire and J. Minker, Eds.), Plenum Press, New York, pp. 347-375.

Gallaire, H., Minker, J., (Editors), [1978], Logic and Data Bases. Plenum Press, New York,

Gallaire, H., Minker, J., Nicholas, J.M., [1978], An Overview and Introduction to Logic and Data Bases. Logic and Data Bases (H. Gallaire and J. Minker, Eds.), Plenum Press, New York 1978. pp. 3-30.

Gelernter, H., [1963], Realization of a Geometry-Theorem Proving Machine. Reproduced in Computers and Thought, (Feigenbaum and Feldman, Eds.),McGraw Hill, New York. pp. 134-152.

Gilmore, P.G., [1977], Defining and Computing Many-valued Functions. Parallel Computers - Parallel Mathematics. (M. Feilmeier, ed.) pp. 17-23.

Gödel, K., [1931], Über Formal Unentscheidbare Sätze der Principia Mathematica und verwandter System 1. Monatshefte für Mathematik und Physik 38. pp. 173-198. English translation in From Frege to Gödel: A Sourcebook in Mathematical Logic 1879-1931. (Ed. by van Heijenoort), Harvard University Press, Cambridge, Mass., pp. 596-616.

Golomb, S., Baumert, L., [1965], Backtrack Programming. J. ACM Vol.12, pp. 516-524.

Green, C.C., [1969a], Theorem Proving by Resolution as a Basis for Question-Answering Systems. Machine Intelligence 4, Edinburgh University Press, New York, (B. Meltzer and D. Michie, Eds.) pp. 183-205.

[1969b], Application of Theorem-Proving to Problem Solving. Proc. Int. Joint Conf. on AI, Washington, DC. (D.E. Walker,and L.M. Norton, Eds.), pp. 219-240.

Hayes, P.J., [1973], Computation and Deduction. Proc. 2nd MFCS Symp. Czechoslovak Academy of Sciences, pp. 105-118.

[1977], In Defense of Logic. International Joint Conference on Artificial Intelligence, 5, pp. 559-565.

Henderson, P., Morris, J., [1976], A Lazy Evaluator. 3rd. Symp. on principles of programming languages. Atlanta. pp. 95-103.

Hendrix, G.G., [1975], Expanding the Utility of Semantic Networks through Partitioning. IJCAI 4, Tiblisi, Georgia. pp. 115-121.

Herbrand, J., [1930], Recherches sur la Theorie de la Demonstration. Travaux de la Societe des Sciences et des Letters de Varsovie, Classe III, Science Mathematique et Physique, No. 33.

Hewitt, C., [1969], PLANNER: A Language for Proving Theorems in Robots. Proc. IJCAI, Washington, D.C., pp. 295-301.

[1975], How to use what you know. Proc. IJCAI, Tbilisi, Georgia, pp. 189-198.

Hill, R., [1974], LUSH Resolution and its Completeness. DCL Memo No. 78, University of Edinburgh, School of Artificial Intelligence, August 1974.

Hoare, C.A.R., [1961], Algorithm 64. CACM, Vol. 4, pp. 321.

[1969], An Axiomatic Basis for Computer Programming. CACM, Vol. 12, No.10 pp. 576-583.

[1972], Proof of Correctness of Data Representation. Acta Informatica 1. pp. 271-281.

Hodges, W., [1977], Logic. Penguin Books, Middlesex, England.

Hogger, C.J., [1978a], Goal Oriented Derivation of Logic Programs. Proc. MFCS Conf., Polish Academy of Sciences, Zakopane.

[1978b], Program Synthesis in Predicate Logic. Proc. AISB/GI Conf. on AI, Hamburg, July, 18-20.

[1979], Derivation of Logic Programs. Ph.D. Thesis, Imperial College.

Horn, A., [1951], On Sentences which are True of Direct Unions of Algebras. Journal of Symbolic Logic, 16, pp. 14-21.

Kellogg, C., Klahr, P., Travis, L., [1978], Deductive Planning and Pathfinding for Relational Data Bases. Logic and Data Bases, (H. Gallaire and J. Minker, Eds.), Plenum Press, New York, pp. 179-200.

Kowalski, R.A., [1969], Search Strategies for Theorem-proving. Machine Intelligence 5, Edinburgh University Press, New York, (B. Meltzer and D. Michie, Eds.), pp. 181-201.

[1972], And-or Graphs, Theorem Proving Graphs and Bi-directional Search. Machine Intelligence 7, Edinburgh University Press, New York, (B. Meltzer and D. Michie, Eds.) pp. 167-194.

[1974a], A Proof Procedure Using Connection Graphs. J. ACM 22, pp. 572-595.

[1974b], Logic for Problem Solving. Memo No. 75, Dept. of

Computational Logic, University of Edinburgh.

[1974c], Predicate Logic as Programming Language.   Proc. IFIP 74,
North Holland Publishing Co., Amsterdam. pp. 569-574.

[1978], Logic for Data Description.   Logic and Data Bases.   (H.
Gallaire and J. Minker, Eds.), Plenum Press, New York, pp. 77-102.

[1979], Algorithm = Logic + Control. CACM, August 1979.

Kowalski, R.A., Hayes, P.J., [1968], Semantic Trees in Automatic Theorem-
    proving. Machine Intelligence 4, (B. Meltzer and D. Michie, Eds.),
    Edinburgh University Press, pp. 87-101.

Kowalski, R.A., Kuehner, D., [1971], Linear Resolution with Selection
    Function. Artificial Intelligence Vol 2, pp. 227-260.

Kuehner, D., [1972], Some Special Purpose Resolution Systems. Machine
    Intelligence 7, Edinburgh University Press, New York, (B. Meltzer and
    D. Michie, Eds.) pp. 117-128.

Lakatos, I., [1963], Proofs and Refutations.   British Journal for the
    Philosophy of Science,Vol. 14, pp. 1-25,120-139, 221-243, 296-342.

    [1974], History of Science and its Rational Reconstructions.   The
    Interaction between Science and Philosophy.   (Y. Elkana, Ed.),
    Humanities Press, Atlantic Heights, N.J., pp. 195-241.

Lawler, E., Wood, D. Branch and Bound Methods: A Survey. Oper. Res. Vol
    14, No 4, pp. 699-719

Lee, R.C.T., Waldinger, R.J., [1969], PROW: A Step Toward Automatic
    Program Writing. Proc. IJCAI, Washington D.C.

Loveland, D.W., [1968], Mechanical Theorem Proving by Model Elimination.
    JACM 15, April 1968, pp. 236-251.

    [1969], A Simplified Format for the Model Elimination Procedure. J.
    ACM, July 1969, pp. 349-363.

    [1970], A Linear Format for Resolution. Symposium on Automatic
    Demonstration, Lecture Notes in Math 125, Springer-Verlag, Berlin,
    pp. 147-162.

    [1972], A Unifying View of Some Linear Herbrand Procedures. JACM 19,
    (April 1972). pp. 366-384.

    [1978], Automated Theorem Proving: A Logical Basis.   North Holland
    Publishing Co., Amsterdam, New York and Oxford.

Loveland, D.W., Stickel, M.E., [1973], A Hole in Goal Trees: Some
    Guidance from Resolution Theory.   Reproduced in IEEE Trans on
    Computers, C-25, April 1976, pp. 335-341.

Luckham, D., [1970], Refinement Theorems in Resolution Theory. Symp. on
    Automatic Demonstration, Lecture Notes in Math 125, Springer-Verlag,
    Berlin, pp. 163-190.

Manna, Z., [1969], The Correctness of Programs. J. Computing and System Science, Vol. 3, pp. 119-127.

Manna, Z., Waldinger, R.J., [1975], Knowledge and Reasoning in Program Synthesis. Artificial Intelligence Journal, Vol. 6, No.2., pp. 175-208.

[1977], The Automatic Synthesis of Systems of Recursive Programs. Proc. IJCAI Conf. pp. 405-411.

[1978], A Framework for Deductive Programming. Computer Science Dept, Stanford Univ, and SRI International.

Markusz, Z., [1977], How to design variants of flats using the programming language PROLOG based on mathematical logic. Proc. IFIP 77 North Holland, Amsterdam, pp. 885-889.

Martelli, A., Montanari, U., [1977], Theorem Proving with Structure Sharing and Efficient Unification. International Joint Conference on Artificial Intelligence, 5, pp. 543.

McCarthy, J., [1963], A Basis for a Mathematical Theory of Computation. Computer Programming and Formal Systems, (P. Brafford and D. Hirschberg, Eds.), North Holland, Amsterdam. pp. 33-70.

[1968a], Programs with Common Sense. Semantic Information Processing, (Minsky,M., Ed), MIT Press, Cambridge, Mass., pp. 403-418.

[1968b], Situations, Actions and Causal Laws. Semantic Information Processing, (M. Minsky, Ed.) MIT Press, Cambridge, Mass. pp. 410-417.

McCarthy, J., Abrahams, P.W., Edwards, D.J., Hart, T.P., Levin, M.I., [1962], LISP Programmers Manual. MIT Press. Cambridge, Mass.

McCarthy, J., Hayes, P.J., [1969], Some Philosophical Problems from the Standpoint of Artificial Intelligence. Machine Intelligence 4, Edinburgh University Press, New York, (B. Meltzer and D. Michie, Eds.), pp. 463-502.

McDermott, D., Doyle, J., [1978], Non-monotonic Logic I. AI Memo 486, August 1978, AI Lab., MIT.

McDermott, D.V., Sussman, G.J., [1972], The Conniver Reference Manual. AI Memo No.259, MIT, Project MAC.

McSkimin, J.R., Minker, J., [1977], The Use of a Semantic Network in a Deductive Question-answering System. International Joint Conference on Artificial Intelligence, 5, pp. 50-58.

Meltzer, B., [1966], Theorem Proving for Computers: Some Results on Resolution and Renaming. Computing Journal 8, (January 1966), pp. 341-343.

[1972], The Impossibility of Perfect Proof Procedures. AISB European Newsletter, Issue 15, Nov. 1973. pp. 28-29.

Michie, D., Ross, R., Shannan, G.J., [1972], G-Deduction. Machine Intelligence 7, Edinburgh University Press, New York, (B. Meltzer and D. Michie, Eds.) pp. 141-165.

Minker, J., [1975], Performing Inferences over Relational Data Bases. Proceedings of 1975 ACM SIGMOD International Connference on Management of Data, pp. 79-91.

Minker, J., Fishman, D.H., and McSkimin, J.R., [1973], The Q* Algorithm – a Search Strategy for a Deductive Question-answering system. Artificial Intelligence, Vol 4. pp. 225-243.

Minsky, M.L., [1968], Descriptive Languages and Problem Solving. Semantic Information Processing, (M. Minsky, Ed.), MIT Press. Cambridge, Mass., pp. 413-424.

[1975], A Framework for the Representation of Knowledge. The Psychology of Computer Vision, (P. Winston, Ed.), McGraw Hill, New York, pp. 211-280.

Moore, R.C., [1975], Reasoning from Incomplete Knowledge in a Procedural Deduction System. Memo Al-TR-347, Artificial Intelligence Lab., MIT.

Moss, C.D.S., [1977], A Comparison of Hoare's Axiomatic Approach to Semantics and Plan Formation Studies. Imperial College, Dept. of Computing and Control, M.Sc.Thesis.

[1979], A New Grammar for Algol 68. Dep. Rep. 79/6, Imperial College, London.

Murray, N., [1978], A Proof Procedure for Non-Clausal First Order Logic. Research Report, University of Syracuse, New York.

Mylopoulos, J., Cohen, P., Borgida, A., and Sugar, L., [1975], Semantic Networks and the Generation of Context, 4th IJCAI, Tiblisi, Georgia. pp. 134-142.

Nevins, A.J., [1974], A Human-Oriented Logic for Automatic Theorem Proving. JACM, Vol 21, pp. 606-621.

Newell, a., Shaw, J.C. and Simon, H.A., [1963], Empirical Explorations with the Logic Theory Machine: A Case Study in Heuristics. Reproduced in Computers and Thought, (Feigenbaum and Feldman, Eds.), McGraw Hill, New York, pp. 109-133.

Newell, A., Simon, H., [1963], GPS, A Program that Simulates Human Thought. Reproduced in Computers and Thought, (Feigenbaum and Feldman, Eds.), McGraw Hill, New York, pp. 279-296.

Nicholas, J.M., Gallaire, H., [1978], Data Base: Theory vs. Interpretation. Logic and Data Bases, (H. Gallaire and J. Minker Eds.), Plenum Press, New York, pp. 33-54.

Nicholas, J.M., Syre, J.C., [1974], Natural Question-answering and Automatic Deduction in the System SYNTEX. Proceedings IFIP Congress 1974, North Holland, Amsterdam. pp. 595-599.

Nilsson, N.J., [1971], Problem Solving Methods in Artificial
    Intelligence. McGraw Hill, New York.

Paterson, M.S., Wegman, M.N., [1976], Linear Unification. Proc. 8th
    Annual ACM Symp. on Theory of Computing. pp. 181-186.

Peirce, C.S., [1931], Collected Papers of Charles Saunders Peirce.
    Vol.2, 1931 -1958, (C. Hartshorn et al, Eds.), Harvard University
    Press, Cambridge, Mass.

Pereira, F., Warren, D.H.D., [1978], Definite Clause Grammars Compared
    with Augmented Transition Networks. Research Report, Dept. of AI,
    Edinburgh.

Pereira, L.M., Monteiro, L.F., [1978], The Semantics of Parallelism and
    Coroutining in Logic Programming. Colloquium on Mathematical Logic
    in Programming, Salgo'tarjan, Hungary.

Pirotte, A., [1978], High Level Data Base Query Languages. Logic and
    Data Bases, (H. Gallaire and J. Minker, Eds.), Plenum Press, New
    York, pp. 409-436.

Pohl, I., [1970], Heuristic Search Viewed as Pathfinding in a Graph.
    Artificial Intelligence Vol.1, pp. 193-204.

    [1972], Bi-directional search. Machine Intelligence 7, Edinburgh
    University Press, New York, (B. Meltzer and D. Michie, Eds.), pp.
    127-140.

Pople, H., [1973], On the Mechanisation of Abductive Logic, Proc. IJCAI
    3, pp. 387-419.

Popper, K.R., [1963], Conjectures and Refutations; The Growth of
    Scientific Knowledge. Rouledge and Kegan Paul, London.

Pratt, V.R., [1977], The Competence/ Performance Dichotomy in
    Programming. 4th ACM SIGACT / SIGPLAN Symp. on Principles of
    Programming Languages, Santa Monica, California, pp. 194-200.

Prawitz, D., [1960], An Improved Proof Procedure. Theoria 26, pp.
    102-139.

Quillian, M.R., [1968], Semantic Memory. Semantic Information
    Processing, (Minsky, M., Ed.), MIT Press, Cambridge, Mass., pp.
    227-270.

Quine, W.V.O., [1941, Revised 1965], Elementary Logic. Harper and Row,
    New York.

    [1953], Two Dogmas of Empiricism. In "From a Logical Point of View".
    Hutchinson, London.

Quine, W.V.O., Ullian, J.S., [1978], The Web of Belief, 2nd Edition,
    Random House, New York.

Raphael, B., [1971], The Frame Problem in Problem Solving Systems.
    Artificial Intelligence and Heuristic Programming. (Findler, N. V.,

Meltzer, B., Eds.), Edinburgh University Press, Edinburgh, pp. 159-169.

Reboh, R., Sacerdoti, E., [1973], A Preliminary Qlisp Manual. Technical Note 81. SRI Project 8721.

Reiter, R., [1971], Two Results on Ordering for Resolution with Merging and Linear Format. J. ACM 18 (October 1971), pp. 630-646.

[1972], The Use of Models in Automatic Theorem Proving. Technical Report 72-09, Dept.of Computer Science, University of British Columbia.

[1978a], Deductive Questioning-Answering on Relational Data Bases. Logic and Data Bases, (H. Gallaire and J. Minker, Eds.) Plenum Press, New York, pp. 149-177.

[1978b], On Reasoning by Default. Proc. 2nd Symp. on Theoretical Issues in Natural Language Processing. Urbana, Illinois.

[1978c], On Closed World Data Bases. Logic and Data Bases, (H. Gallaire and J. Minker, Eds.), Plenum Press, New York, pp. 55-76.

Robinson, J.A., [1965a], A Machine Oriented Logic Based on the Resolution Principle. J. ACM 12 (January 1965), pp. 23-41.

[1965b], Automatic Deduction with Hyper-Resolution. Intern. Journal of Computer Math. 1, pp. 227-234.

[1967], A Review of Automatic Theorem-Proving. Annual Symposia in Applied Math. XIX, American Math. Society, Providence, pp. 1-18.

[1968], The Generalised Resolution Principle. Machine Intelligence 3, (Dale and Michie, Eds.), Oliver and Boyd, Edinburgh 1968, pp. 77-93.

[1971], Computational Logic: The Unification Computation. Machine Intelligence 6, Edinburgh University Press, New York, (B. Meltzer and D. Michie, Eds.). pp. 63-72.

[1979], Logic: Form and Function. Edinburgh University Press.

Robinson, J.A., Sibert, E.E., [1978], Logic Programming in LISP: A Progress Report. School of Computer and Information Science, Syracuse University.

Roussel, P., [1975], PROLOG: Manuel de Reference et d'Utilisation. Groupe d'Intelligence Artificielle, Universite d'Aix-Marseille, Luminy, Sept. 1975.

Rulifson, J.F., Derekson, J.A.C., Waldinger, R.J., [1973], QA 4: A Procedural Calculus for Intuitive Reasoning. Technical Note 73, Artificial Intelligence Center, SRI.

Sacerdoti, E.D., [1975], The Non-linear Nature of Plans. Proc. IJCAI 4, Tiblisi, Georgia, USSR. pp. 206-214.

[1977], A Structure for Plans and Behaviour. Elsevier North Holland,
New York.

Schank, R.C., [1973], Identification of Conceptualizations Underlying
Natural Language. Computer Models of Thought and Language.
(R.C.Schank and K. Colby, Eds.) W.H.Freeman and Co., San Francisco.
pp. 187-247.

[1975], Conceptual Information Processing. North Holland Publishing
Co., Amsterdam. American Elsevier Publishing Co., New York.

Schmidt, C.F., Sridharan, N.S., Goodson, J.L., [1978], The Plan
Recognition Problem: An Intersection of Psychology and Artificial
Intelligence. Artificial Intelligence, Vol. 11, Nos. 1,2. Aug. 1978,
pp. 45-83.

Schubert, L.K., [1976], Extending the Expressive Power of Semantic
Networks. Artificial Intelligence, Vol 7. pp. 163-198.

[1977], Inferences on Quantified Semantic Networks. Tech. Rep. NL32,
University of Texas, February 1977.

Schwartz, J., [1977], Using Annotations to Make Recursion Equations
Behave. Research Memo, Dept. of Artificial Intelligence, University
of Edinburgh.

Shapiro, S.C., [1971], A Net Structure for Semantic Information Storage,
Deduction and Retrieval. Proc. IJCAI, The British Computer Society,
London. pp. 512-523.

[1977], Representing and Locating Deduction Rules in a Semantic
Network. Proc. of the Workshop on Pattern-directed Inference
Systems. ACM/SIGART Newsletter No.63. pp. 14-18.

Sickel, S., [1976], A Search Technique for Clause Interconnectivity
Graphs. IEEE Transactions on Computers, Special Issue on Automatic
Theorem Proving, C-25, 8, August 1978. pp. 823-835.

[1978], Invertibility of Logic Programs. Technical Rep. 78-8-005,
Univ. of California, Santa Cruz.

Siekmann, J., Stephan, W., [1976], Completeness and Soundness of the
Connection Graph Proof Procedure. Interner Bericht Nr. 7/76, Inst.
für Informatik I, Universität Karlsruhe.

Simmons, R.F., [1973], Semantic Networks: Their Computation and Use for
Understanding English Sentences. Computer Models of Thought and
Language, (Schank R. C., and Colby, K., Eds.), W. H. Freeman and Co.,
San Francisco, pp. 63-113.

Simmons, R.F., Chester, D., [1977], Inferences in Quantified Semantic
Networks. International Joint Conference on Artificial Intelligence,
5, p267.

Stallman, R.M., Sussman, G.J., [1977], Forward Reasoning and Dependency-
directed Backtracking in a System for Computer-aided Circuit
Analysis. Artificial Intelligence, Vol.9, No.2, pp. 135-196.

Sussman, G.J., [1975], A Computer Model of Skill Acquisition. American Elsevier Publishing Co., Amsterdam.

Sussman, G.J., McDermott, D.V., [1972a], Why Conniving is Better than Planning. AI Memo No. 255, MIT Project Mac, April 1972.

[1972b], From PLANNER to CONNIVER - a Genetic Approach. AFIPS Fall Joint Computer Conf. pp. 1171-1179.

Sussman, G.J., Winograd, T., Charniak, E., [1971], MICRO-PLANNER Reference Manual. AI Memo 203a, AI Lab, MIT.

Tarnlund, S-A., [1975a], An Interpreter for the Programming Language Predicate Logic. Proc. IJCAI, Tiblisi, pp. 601-608.

[1975b], Logic Information Processing. TRITA-IBADB 1034, Department of Information Processing and Computer Science, The Royal Institute of Technology and The University of Stockholm, Sweden.

[1976], A Logical Basis for Data Bases. TRITA -IBADB 1029, Dept. of Computer Science, Royal Institute of Technology, Stockholm.

[1977], Horn Clause Computability. BIT 17, 2, pp. 215-226.

Tate, A., [1974], INTERPLAN: A Plan Generation System that Can Deal with Interactions between Goals. Memo MIP-R-109, Machine Intelligence Research Unit, University of Edinburgh.

Van der Brug, G.J., Minker, J., [1975], State Space, Problem Reduction and Theorem Proving - Some Relationships. C. ACM 18, (February 1975), pp. 107-115.

Van Emden, M.H., [1976], Verification Conditions as Representations for Programs. Proc. Third Int. Col. on Automata, Languages and Programming, Edinburgh University Press. pp. 99-119.

[1977], Programming in Resolution Logic. Machine Intelligence 8, pp. 266-299.

[1978], Computation and Deductive Information Retrieval. Formal Description of Programming Concepts, (E. Neuhold, Ed.), North Holland, pp. 421-440.

Van Emden, M.H., Kowalski, R.A., [1976], The Semantics of Predicate Logic as a Programming Language. J. ACM, Vol 23, No 4, pp. 733-742.

Waldinger, R., [1977], Achieving Several Goals Simultaneously. Machine Intelligence 8, (Elcock, E. W., Michie, D, Eds.), Ellis Horwood Ltd. and John Wiley. pp. 94-136.

Warren, D.H.D., [1974], WARPLAN: A System for Generating Plans. DCL Memo 76, Dept. of Artificial Intelligence, University of Edinburgh.

[1976], Generating Conditional Plans and Programs. Proc. AISB Summer Conference, Edinburgh. pp. 344-354.

[1977a], Implementing Prolog. Res. Rep. 39, 40. Dept. of A.I., Univ.

of Edinburgh.

[1977b], Logic Programming and compiler writing. Research Rep. 44, Dep. of A.I., Univ. of Edinburgh.

Warren, D.H.D., Pereira, L.M., Pereira, F., [1977], PROLOG- The Language and its Implementation Compared with LISP. Proc. Symp. on AI and Programming Languages, SIGPLAN Notices, Vol. 12, No.8, and SIGART Newsletters No. 64, August 1977. pp. 109-115.

Welham, R., [1976], Geometry Problem Solving. DAI Research Report No.14. University of Edinburgh.

Weyhrauch, P., [1978], Prolegomena to a Theory of Formal Reasoning. Report AIM-315, Computer Science Department, Stanford University.

Winograd, T., [1972], Understanding Natural Language. Academic Press.

[1975], Frame Representation and the Declarative-procedural Controversy. Representation and Understanding, (Bobrow and Collins, Eds.), Academic Press.

Winston, P.H., [1977], Artificial Intelligence. Addison-Wesley, Reading, Mass.

Wong, H.K.T., Mylopoulos, J., [1977], Two Views of Data Semantics: A Survey of Data Models in Artificial Intelligence and Database Management. INFOR, Vol. 15, No.3

Woods, W.A., [1975], What's in a link - Foundations for Semantic Networks. Representation and Understanding, (D. Bobrow and A. Collins, Eds.), Academic Press, New York. pp. 35-582.

Yates, R., Raphael, B., Hart, T., [1970], Resolution Graphs. Artificial Intelligence 1, (Winter 1970), pp. 257-289.

Zloof, M.M., [1975], Query-by-Example. Proceedings AFIPS 1975 NCC, Vol 44, AFIPS Press, Montvale, N. J., pp. 431-348.

Zloof, M.M., de Long, S.P., [1977], The System for Business Automation (SBA): Programming Language. CACM Vol 20, No. 6 (June 1977), pp. 385-396.

Index